WILLIAM K. DURR • **VIVIAN O. WINDLEY** • **MILDRED C. YATES**

CONSULTANT • **PAUL McKEE**

LINGUISTIC ADVISOR • **JACK E. KITTELL**

IMAGES

HOUGHTON MIFFLIN COMPANY • **BOSTON**

ATLANTA · DALLAS · GENEVA, ILLINOIS · HOPEWELL, NEW JERSEY · PALO ALTO

Acknowledgments

For each of the selections listed below, grateful acknowledgment is made for permission to adapt and/or reprint original or copyrighted material, as follows:

"Albert Schweitzer: Jungle Doctor," condensed from *The Story of Albert Schweitzer,* by Anita Daniel. Copyright 1957 by Anita Daniel. Reprinted by permission of Random House, Inc. and W. H. Allen and Co., London.

"Ben and Me," adapted from *Ben and Me,* by Robert Lawson. Copyright 1939 by Robert Lawson, by permission of Little, Brown and Co.

"Call It Courage," reprinted with the permission of The Macmillan Company from *Call It Courage* by Armstrong Sperry. Copyright 1940 by The Macmillan Company, renewed 1968 by Armstrong Sperry.

"City," by Langston Hughes. Copyright 1958 by Langston Hughes. Reprinted by permission of Harold Ober Associates Inc.

"Computers—Giant Brains?" by Malcolm Weiss and Anita Soucie. © 1968 by Scholastic Magazines, Inc., reprinted by permission from *Young Citizen.*

"The Computer Triumphs Again," from *Ollie's Team and the Baseball Computer* by Clem Philbrook. Copyright © 1967, Hastings House Publishers.

"Crossing," from *Letter from a Distant Land* by Philip Booth. Copyright 1953 by Philip Booth. Originally appeared in The New Yorker Magazine; reprinted by permission of The Viking Press.

"A Day in the Life of Henry Reed," from *Henry Reed, Inc.* by Keith Robertson. Copyright © 1958 by Keith Robertson. All rights reserved. Reprinted by permission of The Viking Press, Inc.

"Doublets," reprinted from *The Language Book,* by Franklin Folsom. Copyright © 1963 by Franklin Folsom. Published by Grosset and Dunlap, Inc.

"The Earned Name," from *Crazy Horse,* by Shannon Garst. Copyright 1950 by Doris Shannon Garst. Reprinted by permission of Houghton Mifflin Company.

"Expedition from Arreol," by Michael C. Slaughter. © 1968 The Curtis Publishing Company, by special permission from *Jack and Jill* Magazine.

"From Supercold to Superheat," from *Numbers and Discoveries,* by Arthur J. Snider. Copyright 1968, The Southwestern Company.

"Frozen Victory," slightly adapted from "Frozen Victory" by Charles Coombs, from *Young Readers Sports Treasury,* published by The Lantern Press, Inc.

"The Fun They Had," from *Earth Is Room Enough,* by Isaac Asimov. Copyright 1957 by Doubleday and Co., Inc. Used by permission of the author.

"The Ghost of Black John," adapted from "The Ghost of Black John" by William MacKellar, from *Ghost Stories,* published by The Lantern Press, Inc.

"The Grasshopper," from *Every Time I Climb a Tree* by David McCord, copyright 1952 by David McCord. Used by permission of Little, Brown and Co.

Haiku: "In the falling snow . . ." and "Make up your mind, snail!" copyright © by Richard Wright. Reprinted by permission of Paul R. Reynolds, Inc., 599 Fifth Avenue, New York, N.Y. 10017.

"Henry and the Garbage," from *Henry and Ribsy,* by Beverly Cleary. Copyright © 1954 by Beverly Cleary. Reprinted by permission of William Morrow and Company, Inc., Publishers.

"Herbert's Chemistry Set," from *Herbert,* by Hazel Wilson. Copyright 1948 by Hazel Wilson. Reprinted by permission of Alfred A. Knopf, Inc.

"A Horse for Reg," from *Trust a City Kid* by Anne Huston and Jane Yolen. Copyright © 1966 by Anne Huston and Jane Yolen. Reprinted by permission of Lothrop, Lee and Shepard Company.

"How to Catch a Thief," from *By The Great Horn Spoon!* by Sid Fleischman. Copyright © 1963 by Albert S. Fleischman. Reprinted by permission of Atlantic-Little, Brown and Co.

"In Time of Silver Rain," from *Fields of Wonder,* by Langston Hughes. Copyright 1938 and renewed 1966 by Langston Hughes. Reprinted by permission of Alfred A. Knopf, Inc.

Japanese Haiku: "I must go begging . . . ," "If things were better . . . ," and "O, moon, why must you . . . ," from *Cricket Songs: Japanese Haiku,* translated and © 1964 by Harry Behn. Reprinted by permission of Harcourt, Brace and World, Inc.

"Jeremiah, a thrifty young fox . . . ," from *Animal Limericks,* by Edward S. Mullins, Copyright © 1966, by Edward S. Mullins. Reprinted by permission of Follett Publishing Company.

"The King of the Frogs," adapted from *Tales Told Near a Crocodile,* by Humphrey Harman. Copyright © 1962 by Humphrey Harman. All rights reserved. Reprinted by permission of The Viking Press, Inc. and Hutchinson and Co., Ltd.

"Miranda's Cat," from *Miranda and the Cat,* by

1973 IMPRESSION
Copyright © 1971 by Houghton Mifflin Company

PRINTED IN THE U.S.A.
ISBN: 0-395-10853-5

Contents

LIFTOFF *(pages 9–112)*

CORNUCOPIA *(pages 113–208)*

PATTERNS

PATTERNS *(pages 209–318)*

MOSAICS *(pages 319–422)*

PAGEANT *(pages 423–520)*

LIFTOFF

Contents

LIFTOFF

Henry Huggins and his dog Ribsy have a great talent for getting into trouble. In this story from Beverly Cleary's book HENRY AND RIBSY, *Henry once again gets into trouble. This time it's a very messy problem — garbage — and it's all Ribsy's fault.*

HENRY AND THE GARBAGE

by Beverly Cleary

Two weeks before school started, Henry Huggins was in the kitchen one evening feeding Ribsy, while Mr. Huggins washed the dinner dishes and Mrs. Huggins wiped them. Henry took some horse meat and half a can of Woofies Dog Food out of the refrigerator. Thump, thump, thump went Ribsy's tail on the floor as he watched Henry.

Henry cut up the horse meat and put it on Ribsy's dish. "Why don't you chew it?" he asked, when Ribsy began to gulp down the pieces of meat.

Henry spooned the last of the can of Woofies into the plastic dish with D O G printed on it. Ribsy sniffed at the food. Then he wagged his tail and looked hopefully at Henry, who knew this meant that Ribsy would eat the dog food only when he was sure he was not going to get any more horse meat.

"That's all," said Henry. "Eat your Woofies like a good dog. A Woofies dog is a happy dog. See, it says so right here on the can."

"Wuf," said Ribsy, and went to the refrigerator to show that what he really wanted was another piece of horse meat.

"All right, just one more piece," said Henry, opening the refrigerator door. "You've stayed out of trouble for nearly two weeks so I guess you deserve it."

Mrs. Huggins hung up the dish towel. Henry started to put the empty Woofies can in the step-on garbage can his mother kept under the sink. Mr. Huggins stepped aside to let Henry pull it out. Henry did not have to step on the pedal to raise the lid. The lid was already up, because the can was so full of garbage it would not close.

Ribsy came over to sniff just in case someone had thrown away a bone by mistake. Henry carefully balanced the Woofies can on top of some potato peelings. He was about to push the garbage can back under the sink when his mother spoke. "I am tired of taking out the garbage," she announced firmly.

Henry and his father looked at each other. Then Mr. Huggins said, "Henry, your mother is tired of taking out the garbage."

Henry didn't say anything. He didn't want to get mixed up with garbage.

"I have taken out the garbage every day for eleven years," said Henry's mother.

"Eleven years," said Mr. Huggins. "Think of it!"

"Day in and day out," said Mrs. Huggins, and laughed.

"Year after year," Mr. Huggins went on.

Henry did not see why his mother and father thought this was so funny. He couldn't say he was tired of taking out the garbage, because he had never taken it out. Instead he said, "Well, so long. I'm supposed to go over to Robert's house to work on his electric train."

"Just a minute, Henry," said his father. "It's just as much your garbage as ours."

Henry didn't think this was very amusing. "Aw . . ." he muttered. He didn't want to have anything to do with smelly old garbage. None of the other kids on Klickitat Street took out garbage, at least not every day.

"I'll tell you what I'll do," said Mr. Huggins. "I'll raise your allowance fifteen cents a week if you'll take out the garbage."

"You mean take it out every day?" asked Henry, in case his father might mean every other day. He eyed the heaped-up can. Garbage, ugh! He could understand his mother's being tired of it, all right.

"Every day," said Mr. Huggins firmly.

"Maybe there's something else I could do to earn fifteen cents," Henry suggested hopefully. "Something like . . . like . . ."

"No," said his father, "just garbage."

Henry thought. His allowance was now twenty-five cents a week. That plus ten cents made thirty-five cents, plus another nickel made forty cents. He could find lots of uses for the extra money. Most fathers would just say, "Take out the garbage," without offering to pay for the job. And there prob-

ably were worse things than garbage, although right now Henry couldn't think what. Besides, if he didn't say yes, his father might tell him he had to take it out anyway.

"O.K., it's a deal," said Henry without any enthusiasm. He held his nose with one hand and lifted the garbage container out of the step-on can with the other.

"Oh, it's not as bad as all that," said Mrs. Huggins cheerfully. "It's nice fresh garbage."

Ribsy followed Henry out the back door, sniffing as he went, and watched Henry lift the lid off the thirty-gallon galvanized metal can that was just like the can standing by the back door of every other house on Klickitat Street.

Henry peered into the can, which was half full of garbage. Ribsy put his paws on the edge of the can and peered in too. Most of the garbage was wrapped in newspapers so it was not as bad as Henry had expected. However, some of the juicier garbage had soaked through the paper, and the whole thing was pretty smelly, especially a couple of old tuna-fish cans. Henry emptied the container and took it back into the kitchen. Then he and Ribsy went over to Robert's house.

That week, Henry took out the garbage every day. His mother never had to remind him more than twice. By the end of the week, the can was full of soggy newspapers, old dog-food cans, pea pods, grass clippings, chicken bones which Ribsy was not allowed to chew, used tea bags, and dabs of this and that, all blended into a tangled smelly mess. Henry could not keep from peering into the can to see how awful it all was. Ugh, thought Henry, and hoped he wouldn't have to take the garbage out for eleven years. He wondered how much one of those electric garbage chopper-uppers cost that some people had installed in their sinks.

Henry had never thought much about Monday before, but now it was an important day—the day the garbage man emptied the can and hauled away the garbage. Then Henry could start all over with a new set of smells.

Monday morning, Robert and Scooter came over to Henry's house to see what they could find to do. Scooter tinkered with the chain on his bicycle, Henry held one end of a rope while Ribsy tugged at the other end, and Robert sat on the front steps and thought. In the distance Henry could hear the rattle and thump of garbage cans as the garbage men emptied them.

Robert spoke first. "There was a girl in my room at school last year who was double-jointed."

"That's nothing. So am I," boasted Scooter. "See how far back I can pull my thumb."

"I can pull my thumb back farther than that," said Henry, jerking the rope to make the game of tug-of-war more interesting for Ribsy. The rattles and thumps of the garbage cans were growing louder, Henry thought, and the garbage men must be almost at his house.

"Aw, you guys aren't really double-jointed," said Robert. "This girl in my room could bend her fingers backwards without pushing them with her other hand."

The garbage truck had stopped between the Huggins's and the Grumbie's houses. The boys watched two big men get out of the truck and balance their barrels on their shoulders. One went across the street to pick up the garbage. The other walked up the driveway between Henry's house and the house next door.

The boys forgot about double joints. "Gee, I hope I have muscles like that someday," said Robert.

Henry did not answer. He noticed that Ribsy had dropped his end of the rope and was looking anxiously toward the back of the house. He heard the thump of the Grumbie's garbage can. The man came down the driveway with his barrel full of the Grumbie's garbage, emptied it into the truck, and walked up the driveway with the barrel once more. Ribsy watched every move he made. Then Henry heard the man take the lid off the Huggins's can.

Ribsy growled deep in his throat. Henry looked at him anxiously. It was the first time he had ever heard him growl anything but a pretend growl. Suddenly Ribsy flew into a frenzy of barking and tore down the driveway toward the back of the house. Henry was too shocked to move. He sat listening to Ribsy snarl and bark. Ribsy! He couldn't believe it— not good old Ribsy. Now he really was in trouble.

Scooter was the first to move. "Boy, is he mad about something!" he exclaimed, and ran over to the driveway.

Then Henry got into action. He started down the driveway, but what he saw made him stop. Ribsy was growling and jumping at the garbage man, who was using his empty barrel to protect himself.

"Ribsy!" wailed Henry. "Cut that out!"

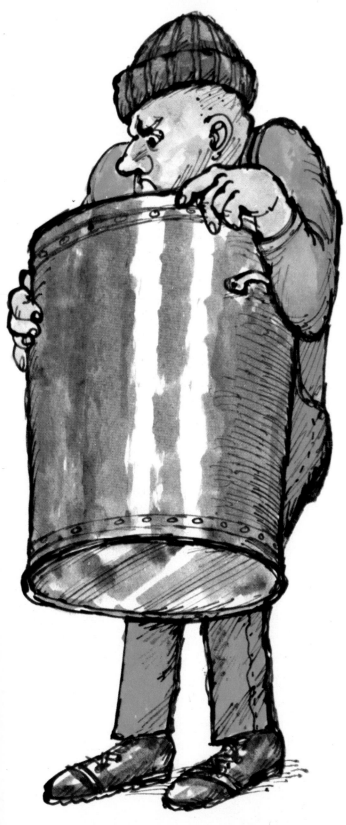

Ribsy continued to snarl and advance while the garbage man retreated down the driveway behind his barrel. When Henry tried to grab Ribsy, the garbage man picked up his barrel and ran toward the truck. He threw the barrel up onto the garbage in the back of his truck and jumped inside the cab. Ribsy had his front paws on the running board before Henry could grab him by the collar.

"You keep that dog shut up or you keep your garbage. Understand?" The garbage man glared at Ribsy, who was still growling deep in his throat.

"But he's not really a fierce dog," protested Henry, while Ribsy strained so hard at his collar that he choked and coughed.

"Not much he isn't," said the garbage man. "You keep him shut up when I come around. See?"

"Yes, sir." Henry knew he couldn't explain that Ribsy wasn't a fierce dog—not after the way he had just behaved.

As soon as the garbage men drove on, Ribsy stopped growling. He looked at Henry and wagged his tail as if he expected to be praised for what he had done. Henry was too stunned to say anything for a minute. Then he said crossly, "Now look what you've done. You've got us both in trouble, that's what." Henry scowled at his dog. His father had told him he must keep Ribsy out of trouble if he wanted to go salmon fishing and now, for no reason he could see, Ribsy had attacked the garbage man. And if he had bitten the garbage man . . . Well, Henry could not bring himself to think about it, because he knew that biting dogs were sent to the pound.

Scooter was careful to stay a few feet away from Ribsy. "I wouldn't get too close to him if I were you," he said. "He looks pretty ferocious."

Henry looked sadly at Ribsy, who rolled over on his back with

his four feet in the air to show that he wanted his stomach scratched. "See, he isn't a bit ferocious." Henry was anxious to defend his dog, even though he knew he couldn't convince Scooter.

"You just saw him, didn't you?" asked Scooter.

"But that wasn't like Ribsy," protested Robert. "He's a good dog." Henry noticed that even though Robert defended Ribsy he was careful to stay away from him, too.

"Oh, I don't know," said Scooter. "You never can tell about dogs. Sometimes they get mean."

"Not my dog," said Henry, trying frantically to think of an explanation for Ribsy's behavior. "Maybe he just doesn't like garbage men." That gave him a better idea. "Say, maybe the garbage man reminds Ribsy of the vet," he said excitedly. "Once when Ribsy got foxtails in his ears from running through some tall grass, we had to take him to the vet to have them taken out. The vet had to hurt Ribsy to get the foxtails out of his ears, and for a long time afterwards, every time I got a haircut, Ribsy would sit outside the barber shop and bark at the barber because he wore a white coat like the vet."

"I suppose Ribsy thought you went to the barber to have foxtails taken out of your ears," jeered Scooter. "Besides, the garbage man doesn't wear a white coat. He wears blue overalls."

Leave it to old Scooter to spoil an explanation. "Yeah, I guess that's right," Henry answered dejectedly. How did he get mixed up in these things anyway? He had been sitting on the front steps, just minding his own business, and now all of a sudden he was in trouble. And the worst of it was, Scooter had seen the whole thing. Now everyone on Klickitat Street would know about Ribsy.

And then Henry realized he had another problem—the garbage. A whole week's collection was still in the can in the backyard. What was worse, it was going to stay there for seven days until the garbage man came around again. What was he going to do with the garbage he had to take out until then?

That evening Henry put off telling his mother and father what had happened until they were washing dishes and he was cutting up horse meat for Ribsy.

They both looked serious. "I can't understand it," said Mrs. Huggins. "He's always been such a good-natured animal. If he really is getting to be ferocious, maybe we should keep him tied up."

"Oh, Mom, no," protested Henry. "He hates to be tied up, and anyway he always chews through the rope." Henry hoped his mother wouldn't mention buying a chain. Why, he wouldn't have any fun with Ribsy chained in the yard—not even riding his bike. It wouldn't be the same without Ribsy riding in the box tied to the back fender or loping along beside him.

"There must be some reason for his not liking the garbage man," said Mr. Huggins. "I wonder if the garbage man ever kicked him."

"Gee, Dad, do you think so?" Henry asked eagerly.

"Oh, I'm sure he wouldn't do that," said Mrs. Huggins.

Henry was anxious to change the subject before anything more was said about tying Ribsy in the backyard. He lifted the container out of the step-on garbage can and started to go out. Then, with a groan, he remembered that the can outside was already full. "Jeepers, Mom, what'll I do with the garbage?" he asked.

"You'll just have to manage the best you can. Push it down in the can somehow." Mrs. Huggins wiped

a cup and sighed. "Henry, I don't know how you get mixed up in things the way you do."

Henry emptied the container on top of the garbage in the big can and tried to put the lid on again. He pushed it down as hard as he could, but it would not close. The can was extra full because Mr. Huggins had mowed the lawn again and emptied the grass clippings into it. "You old dog, you," Henry said crossly to Ribsy, who was sniffing the can. "It'll be all your fault if I don't get to go fishing."

Ribsy sat down and scratched a flea while Henry stared gloomily at the garbage can. There was one thing he was sure of. When he grew up and had a boy of his own, he would never ask him to take out the garbage.

Unfortunately, the week turned out to be unusually warm. Tuesday evening when Henry and his mother and father were eating dinner, a breeze moved the curtains at the dining-room window. "Pee-yew," said Henry, catching a whiff of overripe garbage from the can below.

"Never mind the sound effects," said Mr. Huggins, as he got up from the table to close the window. This made it very warm in the dining room.

It was even warmer in the kitchen when Henry's mother and father were washing and wiping dishes. Mrs. Huggins had to put down the dish towel several times to swat flies.

Henry fed Ribsy in silence. He dreaded the trip to the garbage can. When he could put it off no longer, he picked up the container and started out, followed closely by Ribsy. This time he arranged the day's refuse a handful at a time around the pile. Then he balanced the lid on top. The whole thing looked and smelled terrible.

On Wednesday, when Henry walked reluctantly down the back steps with the garbage, he saw Mr. Grumbie standing on his back porch.

As Henry took the lid off the can, Mr. Grumbie looked across the driveway. "So that's where the smell is coming from," he said.

"I'm afraid it is, Mr. Grumbie," answered Henry.

"I heard about Ribsy tearing the seat out of the garbage man's overalls," said Mr. Grumbie.

Jeepers, thought Henry miserably, the story's not only going around the neighborhood, it's getting worse than it really was. Next thing, people would be saying Ribsy bit the garbage man. He explained what had really happened, and then Mr. Grumbie went in and closed all the windows that faced the Huggins's house.

Henry grew more and more discouraged. On Thursday, after he had piled the garbage on top of the can and replaced the lid as well as he could, he got an apple box out of the garage, climbed up on it, and stepped carefully onto the lid. He stamped his feet a few times to work the garbage down into the can and then jumped up and down. It helped some but not much.

On Friday Henry suggested to his mother that they buy a second garbage can, but she did not think this was a good idea. Then Henry decided to take the garbage out before dinner when the container was not so full. He distributed the milk cartons and carrot tops as well as he could on the heap and was jumping up and down on the lid when Robert and Scooter came up the driveway looking for him.

"What are you doing up there?" Robert demanded, with one eye on Ribsy. "Look at it, Scooter! Did you ever see so much garbage?"

"Pee-yew," said Scooter, staying on the driveway well away from Ribsy, who was rolling on the grass to scratch his back.

"Never mind the sound effects." Henry jumped to the ground. It

was all right for him to criticize his own garbage, but he didn't want anyone else to do it. "Come on, let's go out in front."

"Yes, let's," agreed Scooter. "Pee-yew."

Henry was about to suggest they all go over to the park. Then he decided he had better not take a chance on Ribsy's behavior toward strangers. "Come on, let's see who can walk farthest on his hands," he said, to keep Scooter and Robert from talking about his troubles.

While the three boys were busy trying to walk across the lawn on their hands, they heard a sudden clatter and crash from the backyard and promptly got on their feet.

"Sounds like a garbage can to me," said Scooter.

Henry, who had known instantly what made the noise, was already on his way around the house with Ribsy at his heels. Scooter and Robert were close behind. Henry

found the garbage can tipped on its side. The lid had rolled halfway across the backyard, and garbage was strewn all the way from the steps to the cherry tree. In the midst of the litter stood a collie and another big dog. A crust of bread hung from the collie's mouth.

The dogs started to run when they saw the boys. Ribsy chased them while Henry grabbed an old Woofies can and threw it after them. "You beat it," he yelled. Then he looked at the mess and groaned. Garbage! He was sick and tired of it. He kicked at an eggshell and groaned again. It wasn't worth fifteen cents a week. It wasn't worth a hundred, or a thousand, or even a million dollars.

Scooter and Robert held their noses. Then Scooter made a gagging noise and Robert copied him.

"Aw, hey, fellows, cut it out." Henry glared at his friends and pulled the can, still half full, upright. He looked around and sighed.

"Well, I guess I'd better be going," said Scooter. "I just remembered I'm supposed to go to the store for my mother."

"Me, too," said Robert. "So long, Henry."

Some friends, thought Henry, and set to work. He was busy scooping up coffee grounds and mildewed pea pods when he heard his father's car turn into the driveway.

Mr. Huggins looked around the backyard. "Dogs?" he asked.

"That collie and that other big dog down the street," answered Henry.

Mr. Huggins did not say anything. He found a shovel in the garage and went to work.

"Uh . . . Dad," began Henry. "The garbage man isn't exactly a *neighbor*. Does his complaining about Ribsy mean I don't get to go fishing with you?"

"We'll see what happens Monday before we decide," answered his father. "Perhaps we can find out what made him act the way he did."

On Saturday Henry did not take the garbage out at all. When neither his mother nor his father reminded him, he guessed they must be as tired of garbage as he was.

Sunday afternoon Robert and Scooter came over to see if anything new had happened to the garbage or to Ribsy.

"Aw, fellows, forget it," said Henry. Then he saw Beezus and her little sister Ramona coming down the street. Beezus's real name was Beatrice, but Ramona called her Beezus and everyone else did too. "Hi!" Henry was glad to be interrupted.

"Hello, Henry. Did the garbage man ever take away your garbage?" Beezus asked.

"He'll take it tomorrow," said Henry coldly. The way things got around on Klickitat Street!

"Ramona, look out!" screamed Beezus. She rushed over to her little sister, who had a firm hold on Ribsy's tail and was pulling as hard as she could. "He bites!" said Beezus. "He bit the garbage man."

"He did *not* bite the garbage man." yelled Henry. "Don't you dare say he did!"

Ribsy looked around at Ramona. "Wuf," he said mildly, and waited patiently while Beezus frantically pried Ramona's fingers loose from his tail.

"He didn't bite when Ramona pulled his tail, did he?" Henry asked angrily.

"No." Beezus looked doubtfully at Ribsy. "But somebody told Mother he bit the garbage man."

"Oh, for Pete's sake!" Henry was thoroughly disgusted. This was too much.

"Of course, you don't know what Ribsy would have done if he had

got at the garbage man," observed Scooter.

"You keep quiet." Henry glared at Scooter. "The garbage man must have kicked him or something. Look at him. Does he look the least bit cross?"

Beezus and the boys looked at Ribsy, who lay on the grass with a patient look on his face. Ramona was sitting on top of him. When she grabbed his ear, Ribsy looked at Henry as if to say, "Get her off me, won't you?"

"No, he doesn't look a bit cross," admitted Beezus, pulling her little

sister away. "He seems to understand she's little and doesn't know
any better."

Thinking secretly that Ramona
did know better, Henry turned to
Scooter. "Now are you satisfied?"
he demanded.

"Well . . ." Scooter was not easy
to satisfy.

Henry tried to think of something, anything, to change the
subject. "Say, Scooter," he said,
"I wish you'd take a look at the horn
on my bike. It's been sounding
funny lately."

"Sure," said Scooter eagerly.
If there was one thing he enjoyed,
it was tinkering with a bicycle.
"Where is it?"

"In the garage," answered Henry,
and they all started down the driveway toward the open garage doors.

As Scooter took hold of the

handle bars and started to wheel
the bicycle out of the garage, Ribsy
began to growl deep in his throat.
The hair stood up on his neck and
he moved toward Scooter.

Everyone stared at Ribsy. Scooter
hastily dropped the bicycle on the
driveway, and Ribsy stopped growling at once. He went to Henry and
wagged his tail, waiting to be
praised.

"Hey, did you see that?" Henry
shouted.

"I sure did," said Scooter. "He's
a vicious dog!"

"He is not vicious. He was protecting my bike!" Henry was growing more excited. "He isn't cross
at all. He was just protecting my
bike."

Scooter did not look convinced.
"Don't you see?" Henry went on.
"That explains about the garbage
man. Ribsy was protecting the garbage from the garbage man because he thought it was mine!"

"He's a watchdog," agreed
Beezus.

"Sure," said Henry eagerly.
"It takes a smart dog to be a watchdog."

At this Robert and Scooter began
to shout with laughter. "What a
watchdog!" hooted Scooter.

"Whoever heard of a dog guard-

ing the garbage?" Robert doubled up with laughter.

"Your *valuable* garbage," shouted Scooter.

"Your *precious* garbage," howled Robert.

"Aw, cut it out," said Henry sheepishly and began to laugh, partly because he thought it was funny but mostly from relief at proving that Ribsy was not a vicious dog. His fishing trip was still safe!

Robert and Scooter whooped and pounded each other on the back. Ribsy, sensing that they were laughing at him, hung his head and slunk over to Henry, who hugged him and went on laughing.

"Boy, oh, boy," gasped Scooter. "I can just see the Huggins's back yard a year from now when it's ten feet deep——"

"In Henry's very own valuable precious garbage," finished Robert, and the boys whooped some more.

Henry stopped laughing. The picture of his back yard ten feet deep in garbage was too terrible to think about.

Mr. Huggins appeared in the kitchen door. "What's all this about?" he asked, as he joined the group on the driveway. When he heard the story, he laughed too. He snapped his fingers at Ribsy

and when the dog bounded over to him, he slapped his side and said, "You're a pretty good dog, aren't you?" Ribsy wriggled with delight.

Henry's friends, knowing it must be nearly dinner time, started to leave. "I'll look at your horn tomorrow if you'll get your bike out of the garage yourself," promised Scooter.

"Take good care of your garbage," said Robert.

"Aw, keep quiet," answered Henry, and grinned. When the others were gone, he turned to his father. "Say, Dad, about this garbage . . . ."

"What about it?" asked his father.

"Well, we didn't have any trouble with Ribsy protecting it from the garbage man when Mom took it out and I was wondering . . . ."

Henry paused and looked at his father.

Mr. Huggins smiled. "Wondering what?"

"Well, I was wondering if there wasn't something else you would rather have me do for the extra fifteen cents than take out the garbage."

Mr. Huggins thought it over. "All right," he said, "I'll take out the garbage if you'll clip around the edge of the lawn after I mow it each week."

It was Henry's turn to think it over. Clipping the edge of the lawn was harder than taking out the garbage. It meant crawling around on his hands and knees for about an hour. Still, as far as Henry knew now, there was no possible way either he or Ribsy could get into trouble doing it. "O.K., Dad," he said. "It's a deal!"

"O.K.," said Mr. Huggins. "But just to make sure, we'd better put Ribsy in the basement when we hear the garbage man coming."

"He won't mind for a little while," said Henry, giving the garbage can a good hard whack as he and his father went into the house.

AUTHOR

When Beverly Cleary was in elementary school in Portland, Oregon, she lived in Henry Huggins's neighborhood. She says that there really is a Klickitat Street. In those days she wanted more than anything to read funny stories about everyday American boys and girls who really had adventures. It seemed to her that the children in all the books she read either had adventures that could never happen in real life, or they didn't have any adventures at all. When she grew up, she decided to write the sort of books she had always wanted to read.

Beverly Cleary says that her first attempt at writing was *Henry Huggins,* unless you count an essay she wrote when she was ten years old. "I won two dollars," she says, "because no one else entered the contest."

Mrs. Cleary, who was born in McMinnville, Oregon, attended schools in Oregon and college in California and Washington. She now lives in Carmel, California, with her husband, and their twins, Marianne and Malcolm. The other family member is a cat named George.

Some other books she has written for young readers are *Beezus and Ramona, Mitch and Amy, The Mouse and the Motorcycle,* and *Ellen Tebbits.*

UNITS OF MEASURE – HOW THEY WERE NAMED

by Barry Thompson

When you use a ruler to find out that the fish you just caught is eight inches long, you are using a unit of measure. The names for most of the units of measure came to us from ancient Rome by the way of England.

The Angles and the Saxons were people from northwest Germany who invaded and settled in England from about 400 to 600 A.D. Our word *inch* comes to us from the Anglo-Saxon, or Old English, word *ince*. This in turn came from the Latin word *uncia*, meaning one twelfth. As you know, an inch is one twelfth of a foot.

Those early Englishmen used three barleycorns placed end to end to show how big an *ince* was. It usually came out to about what we know as an inch.

Foot, coming from another Anglo-Saxon word *fot*, tells its origin in its name. But some people have big feet, and some people have little feet. To determine the length of an average foot, it is said that the first twelve men coming out of a church stood with their left feet one behind the other, each man's toes touching the heel in front of him. The distance covered by the twelve men's feet was marked on a long stick, then carefully divided into twelve equal parts. Each part was a measure of one foot.

Yard comes from another Anglo-Saxon word, *gerd* or *gierd*, which originally meant a stick, twig, or measuring rod. *Girth*, the distance around one's body, may have come from the same origin as *yard*. There are several stories about the origin of the length of a yard. The distance around a man's chest in the Anglo-Saxon times might have averaged about 36 inches, or our present yard. In the early 1100's King Henry I of England was said to have proclaimed that a yard was to be measured as the distance from his nose to the end of his thumb. This was supposed to have been about 36 inches.

The origin of the word *mile* is Latin, the language spoken in ancient Rome. A Roman mile was a *mille passuum*, meaning a thousand paces, or steps. A Roman pace was the distance between the heel mark of one foot and the spot where that same foot came down again in walking. Since that distance was equal to about five feet, a thousand paces was about 5,000 feet. The present-day definition of a mile has stretched that distance a bit since the English mile today is 5,280 feet.

CITY

In the morning the city
Spreads its wings
Making a song
In stone that sings.

In the evening the city
Goes to bed
Hanging lights
About its head.

Langston Hughes

USING A DICTIONARY

Do you know how to use a dictionary to find the meaning and to check the pronunciation of a strange word you meet in your reading? Here are some things you should remember to do when you use a dictionary.

First, you must find the word in the dictionary list. To do that, you must use alphabetical order, because all the words in that list are arranged in alphabetical order.

On the next page is a page from a dictionary. The two words *belt* and *berry* above the columns on the dictionary page are called **guide words.** Notice that *belt* is the first word and that *berry* is the last word in the dictionary list on that page. The other words listed on that page belong alphabetically between *belt* and *berry. Begin* is not listed on the page because it comes before *belt* in an alphabetical list. *Berth* is not there because it comes after *berry.*

Suppose that you opened a dictionary to a page on which the guide words are *moat* and *modern.* Why or why not would you expect to find on that page each of the following words? *Moan, mob, module, model?*

When you start to look up a word in a dictionary, you will save time by opening the book near the page on which the word is listed. If the word you are looking for begins with *c,* open the dictionary near the front because *c* comes near the beginning of the alphabet. A word beginning with *n* would

belt (bĕlt). 1. A strip of leather or cloth, etc. worn around a person's body for holding up a piece of clothing, for decoration, or for carrying something; as, a money *belt*. 2. Anything looking like a belt; a band; a circle; as, a *belt* of trees. 3. An area famous for one certain thing; as, the cotton *belt* of the United States. 4. In machinery, an endless band that moves the wheels, pulleys, etc. that it passes over. 5. To fasten on with a belt. 6. To hit.

be • mire (bĭ-mīr′). 1. To make dirty with mud. 2. To sink in mud.

be • moan (bĭ-mōn′). To express sorrow for; as, the man will *bemoan* the loss of his coat.

bend (bĕnd). 1. A turn or curve from a straight line. 2. To cause a curve in; as, he can *bend* the metal into a ring. 3. To bow or stoop. 4. To force to give in or give away.

be • neath (bĭ-nēth′). 1. Under; below; as, the cat crawled *beneath* the house. 2. Lower than in place or rank; as, a private is *beneath* a sergeant. 3. Unworthy of; as, that rude remark was *beneath* you.

ben • e • fac • tor (bĕn′ə-făk′tər). A person who does a kind thing, such as giving money or help to someone in need.

be • nef • i • cence (bə-nĕf′ə-səns). 1. The act of doing good. 2. A charitable act or gift.

ben • e • fi • cial (bĕn′ə-fĭsh′əl). Useful; helpful; producing good results.

ben • e • fit (bĕn′ə-fĭt). 1. A help; an advantage; something that does good to a person or thing; as, the *benefit* of fresh air. 2. A performance or entertainment to raise money for a charitable cause; as, the movie was a *benefit* for the orphanage. 3. To improve or to help. 4. To receive good from something; as, they *benefited* from their vacation.

be • nev • o • lence (bə-nĕv′ə-ləns). 1. The desire to do good. 2. A kindly act; a charitable gift.

be • nev • o • lent (bə-nĕv′ə-lənt). Having the desire to do good; kindly.

be • nign (bĭ-nīn′). 1. Friendly or pleasant; mild; as, a *benign* smile. 2. Favorable to health; as, a *benign* climate.

be • nig • nant (bĭ-nĭg′nənt). 1. Gracious and kind. 2. Favorable.

bent (bĕnt). 1. A natural gift or talent; as, John has a *bent* for music. 2. Past tense and past participle of **bend.** 3. Crooked; no longer straight. 4. Determined; as, a man *bent* on going his own way.

be • quest (bĭ-kwest′). A possession or anything which has been given or left by a person in his will.

be • ret (bə-rā′). A round, flat cap of wool or some other soft cloth.

ber • ry (bĕr′ē). 1. A small, pulpy fruit, such as the strawberry. 2. To gather berries.

ă pat/ ā pay/ âr care/ ä father/ ĕ pet/ ē be/ ĭ pit/ ī pie/ îr fierce/ ŏ pot/ ō toe/ ô paw, for/ oi noise/ ou out/ ŏŏ took/ ōō boot/ th thin/ *th* this/ ŭ cut/ ûr turn/ yōō use/ ə about/ zh pleasure

come near the middle of the dictionary; a word beginning with *s*, near the end. By thinking where the first letter of the word comes in the alphabet, you can tell just about where to open the dictionary.

A second thing you need to know is how to decide which meaning of a word that you look up is the one you should use. Choose the meaning which makes the best sense in the reading you are doing. Which meaning given on page 32 for the word *bend* fits best in each of the following sentences?

1. Since Ted hurt his back, he cannot bend over to tie his shoelaces.
2. The road made a sharp right bend to the north.
3. The strong wind began to bend the tree.

The third thing you need to know is how to get the correct pronunciation of a word that you look up. That pronunciation is shown in a **special spelling** that is given right after the word. For example, in one dictionary the pronunciation of *acrimony* is shown in this way:

ac • ri • mo • ny (ăk′rə-mō′nē)

Do you know how to use the special spelling to get the correct pronunciation of a word? Somewhere in any good dictionary or glossary, usually at the bottom of each page or every other page, is a **pronunciation key.** The pronunciation key contains rows of words called **key words.** These words are common words that you already know how to pronounce, and they show what sounds to give to vowels and certain other letters in the special spelling. Here is the pronunciation key from one dictionary and it is the one used in the glossary at the back of this book:

ă pat/ ā pay/ âr care/ ä father/ ĕ pet/ ē be/ ĭ pit/ ī pie/ îr fierce/ ŏ pot/ ō toe/ ô paw, for/ oi noise/ ou out/ ŏŏ took/ o͞o boot/ th thin/ *th* this/ ŭ cut/ ûr turn/ yo͞o use/ ə about/ zh pleasure

Look again at the special spelling ăk′rə-mō′nē. The first syllable is ăk. Notice the little mark above *a* in that syllable. Now find the letter *a* with that mark above it in the pronunciation key. What key word comes after it? Yes *pat*. Notice that the **a** in p**a**t is printed in heavy black print. This means that the ă in the first syllable of ăc′rə-mō′nē is pronounced like the *a* in *pat*.

Do you see the mark (ə) in the second syllable rə? Find that mark and the key word that comes right after it in the pronunciation key. The key word tells you that ə stands for a sound you often use for vowels in different words. That sound is the sound you hear at the beginning of *about*, and it is the sound *i* stands for in *acrimony*.

The third syllable is mō. Notice the mark above the *o*. Find the letter *o* with that mark above it in the pronunciation key. You can see the key word *toe* coming right after it with oe in heavy black type. It tells you that ō in the special spelling stands for the vowel sound you hear at the end of *toe*.

Look at the last syllable nē. The key word in the pronunciation key shows that the *e* in that syllable is pronounced like the *e* in *be*.

The mark (′) after the first syllable in ăk′rə-mō′nē is called a **primary stress mark.** It tells you that the syllable just before it should be said with more force, or stress than the other syllables.

In some longer words, more than one syllable needs to be stressed. In such words, usually one syllable has a stronger stress than the other stressed syllable. The syllable with the weaker stress is marked with a **secondary stress mark** which looks like this: (′). Notice that it is a lighter mark than the primary stress mark. A secondary stress mark is used after the third syllable of ăc′rə-mō′nē. That syllable should be stressed, but not as strongly as the first syllable. You should be able to pronounce *acrimony* correctly now. Try it.

Most dictionaries have the stress mark coming right after the syllable that should be stressed. Some dictionaries, however, place the stress mark *before* the syllable that should be stressed. Just inside the front cover or within the first few pages of every dictionary is a full explanation of all the marks used by the dictionary to show correct pronunciations. Before you look up the pronunciation of any word in a dictionary, check that explanation to find out how that dictionary shows which syllable should be stressed.

35

Discussion

Help your class answer these questions:

1. In what order are the words in a dictionary list placed? Would the word *mask* be listed near the beginning, near the middle, or near the end of a dictionary? In what part of a dictionary would *beetle* be listed? *tablet? office? lark?*

2. How can guide words help you find a word that you are looking for in a dictionary? When the guide words on a dictionary page are *lamp* and *lane* would you expect to find the word *lame* on that page? Why? Would you expect to find *lantern?* Why?

3. If more than one meaning is given for a word you look up in a dictionary, how can you tell which meaning to choose?

4. What does the word *bend* mean in each of the three numbered sentences on page 33?

5. What does a primary stress mark (′) tell you? A secondary stress mark (′)?

6. Below are four words. What is the correct pronunciation of each of them as shown by the dictionary page on page 32?

    bemire   beret
    beneficence   benignant

On Your Own

As you read the paragraphs that follow, you may find that the words in heavy black type may be strange to you in meaning or pronunciation, or both. Try using the context to figure out the meaning of any of those words you do not know. If the context does not give you the help you need, use the glossary at the back of this book. If you are not sure you know how to pronounce one or more of those words, use the glossary to check the pronunciations.

The art of making statues by carving in stone is called **sculpture.** It is a very old art and was practiced thousands of years ago in ancient **Egypt.**

Most of the stone statues made in the past were made to **commemorate** important persons. Perhaps you have seen a statue of George Washington or Abraham Lincoln.

Some **sculptors** before they begin to carve a statue in stone will first **fashion** a small model of the statue in clay. Doing this helps the sculptor to **visualize** what the finished **work** will look like.

A large, rough block of stone, usually marble, is what the sculptor begins to work on. Using a **mallet** and a **chisel** to cut the stone away, he carefully shapes the stone into the form he wants. When this is done, the statue is ready to have a **finish** put on it.

Checking your work

If you are asked to do so, give the pronunciation and the meaning for one of the words in heavy black print. If you pronounce incorrectly any word that you looked up in the glossary, find out what mistake you made when you checked the pronunciation. If the meaning you chose is not correct, find out what meaning is correct and why the one you chose is not correct.

Isaac Asimov writes about life in the year 2157 when books
are seen only on television screens.

The FUN They Had

Margie even wrote about it that night in her diary. On the page headed May 17, 2157, she wrote, "Today Tommy found a real book!"

It was a very old book. Margie's grandfather once said that when he was a little boy *his* grandfather told him that there was a time when all stories were printed on paper.

They turned the pages, which were yellow and crinkly, and it was awfully funny to read words that stood still instead of moving the way they were supposed to — on a screen, you know. And then, when they turned back to the page before, it had the same words on it that it had had when they read it the first time.

"Gee," said Tommy, "what a waste. When you're through with the book, you just throw it away, I guess. Our television screen must have had a million books on it, and it's good for plenty more. I wouldn't throw *it* away."

"Same with mine," said Margie. She was eleven and hadn't seen as many telebooks as Tommy had. He was thirteen.

She said, "Where did you find it?"

"In my house." He pointed without looking, because he was busy reading. "In the attic."

"What's it about?"

"School."

Margie was scornful. "School? What's there to write about school? I hate school."

Margie always hated school, but now she hated it more than ever. The mechanical teacher had been giving her test after test in geography. She had been doing worse and worse, until her mother had shaken her head sorrowfully and sent for the County Inspector.

He was a round little man with a red face and a whole box of tools with dials and wires. He smiled at Margie, gave her an apple, and then took the teacher apart. Margie had hoped he wouldn't know how to put it together again, but he knew how, all right. After an hour or so, there it was again, large and square and ugly, with a big screen on which all the lessons were shown and the questions were asked. That wasn't so bad. The part Margie hated most was the slot where she had to put homework and test papers. She always had to write them out in a punch code they had made her learn when she was six years old, and the mechanical teacher calculated the mark in no time.

The Inspector had smiled after he was finished and patted Margie's head. He said to her mother, "It's not the little girl's fault, Mrs. Jones. I think the geography sector was geared a little too quick. Those things happen sometimes. I've slowed it up to an average ten-year level. Actually, the over-all pattern of her progress is quite satisfactory." And he patted Margie's head again.

Margie was disappointed. She had been hoping they would take the teacher away altogether. They had once taken Tommy's teacher away for nearly a month because the history sector had blanked out completely.

So she said to Tommy, "Why would anyone write about school?"

Tommy looked at her with very superior eyes. "Because it's not our kind of school, stupid. This is the old kind of school that they had hundreds and hundreds of years ago." He added loftily, pronouncing the word carefully, "*Centuries* ago."

Margie was hurt. "I don't know what kind of school they had all that time ago." She read the book over his shoulder for a while. Then she said, "Anyway, they had a teacher."

"Sure they had a teacher, but it wasn't a *regular* teacher. It was a man."

"A man? How could a man be a teacher?"

"Well, he just told the boys and girls things and gave them homework and asked them questions."

"A man isn't smart enough."

"Sure he is. My father knows as much as my teacher."

"He can't. A man can't know as much as a teacher."

"He knows almost as much, I betcha."

Margie wasn't prepared to dispute that. She said, "I wouldn't want a strange man in my house to teach me."

Tommy screamed with laughter. "You don't know much, Margie. The teachers didn't live in the house. They had a special building, and all the kids went there."

"And all the kids learned the same thing?"

"Sure, if they were the same age."

"But my mother says a teacher has to be adjusted to fit the mind of each boy and girl it teaches and that each kid has to be taught differently."

"Just the same, they didn't do it that way then. If you don't like it, you don't have to read the book."

"I didn't say I didn't like it," Margie said quickly. She wanted to read about those funny schools.

They weren't even half finished when Margie's mother called, "Margie! School!"

Margie looked up. "Not yet, Mamma."

"Now!" said Mrs. Jones. "And it's probably time for Tommy, too."

Margie said to Tommy, "Can I read the book some more with you after school?"

"Maybe," he said nonchalantly. He walked away whistling, the dusty old book tucked beneath his arm.

Margie went into the classroom. It was right next to her bedroom, and the mechanical teacher was on and waiting for her. It was always on at the same time every day except Saturday and Sunday, because her mother said little girls learned better if they learned at regular hours.

The screen was lit up, and it said: "Today's arithmetic lesson is on the addition of fractions. Please insert yesterday's homework in the proper slot."

Margie did so with a sigh. She was thinking about the old schools they had when her grandfather's grandfather was a little boy. All the kids from the whole neighborhood came, laughing and shouting in the schoolyard, sitting together in the schoolroom, going home together at the end of the day. They learned the same things, so they could help one another on the homework and talk about it.

And the teachers were people. . . .

The mechanical teacher was flashing on the screen: "When we add the fractions $\frac{1}{2}$ and $\frac{1}{4}$ —"

Margie was thinking about how the kids must have loved it in the old days. She was thinking about the fun they had.

AUTHOR

By the time he was twelve years old, Isaac Asimov was writing stories. When he was eighteen, he completed a story and took it to a publisher who rejected the story at once. Four months later, after receiving eight more rejections, he finally had a science fiction story accepted and printed. Since that time he has written over ninety books mostly about science for adults and young people.

Dr. Asimov was born in the Soviet Union and moved to the United States when he was three years old. While he went to college and studied chemistry, he worked after school hours in his father's candy store. After serving in the armed forces during World War II, he went back to college and received a doctor's degree. Now along with his writing, he teaches at the Boston University School of Medicine and lives with his wife and two children in Newton, Massachusetts.

JOKES

One morning during the week that the baseball World Series was being played, a father failed to hear his alarm clock ring. His daughter went in and shook her dad, trying to rouse him. "Daddy, it's ten to seven." The father sleepily mumbled, **"In whose favor?"**

Harry was boasting to his friend Larry. "Did you see the fish I almost caught? It was three feet long and must have weighed twenty pounds. I never saw such a fish!"
"I believe it!" Larry retorted.

Fred was getting tired of his know-it-all cousin from the city. At last he said, pointing, "I bet you don't even know whether that's a Jersey cow."
"Of course I don't. I can't see its license."

The fifth grade was studying about foods. When Frank turned in his homework, the teacher said, "Frank, you were supposed to write a five-page report about milk, but you only wrote one page."
"I know," Frank answered. "I was writing about condensed milk."

A boy walked into a restaurant carrying an alligator and asked, "Do you serve young boys here?" The waiter logically replied, "Of course!"
"Okay, then," the boy answered, "get a hot dog for me and a young boy for my alligator."

EXPEDITION FROM ARREOL

BY MICHAEL C. SLAUGHTER

A low rumble of thunder rolled out of the foothills, and then the rain came down fast. Everybody took off in different directions. Rob Jacoby grabbed his mitt and bat, and ran home across the park. The warmth of the big old house felt good as he got out of his wet clothes. He thought tonight would be a good time to get started on his history term project.

Since his father was working late at NISI, he and his mother had dinner alone. Afterward Rob went back up to his room to study, but his mind wandered. He just sat with his papers spread out, listening to the rain against the window.

Later, Rob went to the window and stared out at the lights of the NISI installation on the ridge. The National Interplanetary Study Institute was a division of Blakemore Chemical Industries.

Rob's father had been a researcher at NISI since it had started four years ago. Sometimes his work kept him at the laboratory for days at a time. He didn't say much about his research, but he had told Rob that the United States would probably be traveling to other planets sooner than most people expected.

After the rain had almost stopped, Rob opened the window. There was a peculiar odor in the air, almost like the ozone smell made when electric sparks pass through the air. But, somehow, it reminded Rob of almonds. He leaned farther out the window to see if he could tell where it was coming from.

Suddenly his whole body jerked, and he heard a terrible crackling sound. He felt himself pulled off his feet and out through the window. He tried to yell but no sound came. He was suspended in air, a few feet from his upstairs window. The whole house was bathed in an eerie, blue glow. He had a sensation of numbness, of a slow falling. Then he was unconscious.

When he regained consciousness, Rob smelled that same odd odor. He tried to move his arms and legs, but he was enclosed in a plastic capsule, from which a heavy blue gas was being slowly exhausted.

Gradually the cover of the capsule was lifted away. Rob rubbed his eyes and stared into the face of the strangest man he had ever seen. The man's rubbery skin was bright orange, and his head was completely hairless. His large, shiny, green eyes looked back at Rob.

The orange man placed his big hand on Rob's head. "How do you feel, Robert?"

"How do you know my name?" Rob blurted out.

"We have been studying your family for some time. You were transported here by our special force. We had meant to take your father, but unfortunately you triggered the mechanism before we were ready."

"I don't understand."

"We created a force field about your house. We intended to draw your father into it and transport him to us, but you leaned out of the window and entered the field, activating it. At once you were transported into our receiver here in the spacecraft."

"Spacecraft!"

"We are from Arreol, a planet in the solar system beyond yours. Our expedition is composed of three ships. I am the captain."

Rob saw other strange men behind the captain. "Why do you want my father?" he asked.

"We have developed interplanetary travel to a high degree, but our efforts to explore the vastness of the universe are primitive," the captain said. "Your government's space program *seems* to be based on rocket propellants. But actually they've made grants to a private company, Blakemore Chemicals, which has discovered a method for isolating and reproducing energy in a pure form. Your father is the scientist who perfected the process. Because of

this, the United States will, in only a few months, be able to span this galaxy in days."

Rob stared with amazement. "What do you mean to do with my father?"

"We'll take him to Arreol to work in our laboratories."

"You can't do that!" Rob cried. "You can't take him away. My father wouldn't work for you, even if you did take him to Arreol!"

"We were afraid that might be true," the stranger answered coolly. "But since you are now in our possession, he cannot refuse. Harm might come to you. I'm sorry, but that is the way it must be."

Another orange man burst into the room, waving his arms. He was shouting wildly, but his sounds were not words. "Put on your sensor disc so the boy can understand you," the captain said.

Rob realized that all the Arreol men had small discs strapped to their foreheads. The man attached his and spoke again. "We've been discovered! A patrol has been sent out to intercept us."

"Lower the monitor screen!" said the captain. "Are they government soldiers or a NISI patrol?"

A large screen descended from a port just above Rob's head. It flickered and then showed a view of the edge of the woods behind the NISI installation. An odd doughnut-shaped object stood on angled legs like an enormous grasshopper.

The captain saw Rob's puzzled look. "That is our supply ship, but no one is on board. It carries provisions and equipment and is manned by remote control."

Rob looked back at the screen. A faint orange glow was becoming stronger.

"It's a NISI patrol," an Arreol man shouted. "Look at that light! They've already activated their weapons! We must prepare—"

"We can't defend ourselves against NISI weaponry!" the captain exclaimed. "Establish contact with them at once and tell them we have the boy. They won't fire at us if they think he might be hurt."

Just then the screen flared up with a brilliant white light, and Rob heard a rushing noise. The cabin shuddered so violently that he was thrown to the floor.

"It's too late," the captain cried. "We're being attacked!"

Rob covered his head with his hands as the spaceship was rocked by a violent explosion. He looked at the screen in time to see the supply craft swallowed in a bright ball of flame.

"Activate the engines," the captain yelled.

Men leaped to the instrument panel, and Rob felt the floor begin to hum and vibrate beneath him. "Where are we going?" he cried.

"To Arreol."

"We can't! You can't take me away with you."

The captain looked squarely at Rob. "You will be lucky if we get away, boy!"

The cabin rolled under another explosion, and Rob was thrown against the instrument panel. He could see most of the Arreol men sprawled on the floor. One pulled himself painfully to a control panel and moved a large lever forward. Rob felt as if an enormous weight were crushing him and pushing him down. Then, quite quickly, the weight was released. Everyone stood up with some effort.

"What happened?" Rob asked.

"We had to make an emergency takeoff," said the captain. "That last shot was much too close. The ship may have received some structural damage." He turned to the men at the controls. "Give me our course."

"It doesn't look good, sir. We are not accelerating at a proper rate. We have only barely broken the Earth's gravitational field, and now we are rapidly losing forward speed. I think we are operating on our suborbital cruising engines alone."

"Make contact with our sister ship." the captain ordered. "Have it rendezvous with us and survey our external damage."

"We can't, sir. Our radio has been knocked out."

"Fix it. Unless we can call the other ship to come to our aid," the captain said gravely, "it is going to take us a long, long time to travel through space to Arreol."

"How long?" Rob asked.

The captain said, "Oh, we'll be able to live. We have synthetic provisions and a water reclaiming plant on board."

"How long?" Rob repeated.

"About two thousand earth days," the captain answered sharply.

"Over five years!" gasped Rob.

"That's right. Five years at the speed we're traveling to navigate the billions of miles to Arreol." The captain sat down, quite dejected. "We've lost the race to develop interstellar travel. "We've kidnapped you for no purpose, boy."

Rob ran from the cabin. He didn't stop until he found himself in a part of the craft at the farthest point from the control room. He sat down, breathing heavily and shaking.

"Five years!" he said. "I can't spend five years out here in nowhere." A burning sensation spread through his throat.

Suddenly Rob saw a slim figure dart from behind a tall stack of crates toward another stack. Instinctively he leaped. They collided and fell together to the floor. Rob stared at the figure bewildered. It was a boy, an Arreol boy, about his own age. Rob noted that he was wearing a sensor translating disc.

"What are you doing on this

ship?" Rob asked. "You're a stowaway, aren't you?"

"I'm not a stowaway," the orange boy flashed back. "My father is the captain of the craft."

"The captain!"

"That's right. I know almost all there is to know about this ship."

"Then why are you sneaking around?" Rob persisted.

The boy stood silently and then said, "I know all about you, Rob. I've been listening."

"Why are you hiding here if your father is the captain?" Rob asked, growing more puzzled.

"I hardly know my father," the boy said. "On Arreol I'm enrolled in advanced technical classes and I study day and night. My father is always away on ex-

peditions. I decided to leave school and travel with him. It was easy to get aboard and hide, but I haven't the courage to tell my father what I've done." He paused for a moment. "My father will make me go back to school, but I don't want to learn to be a scientist. I want to go on expeditions, and I want to be with him."

He reached back under a cover and withdrew a glass tube with several wire filaments running its length. "I decided to prolong this trip for as long as possible," he said at last, "so I took this part out of the engine."

"What is it?" Rob asked excitedly.

"It's a 'revilator.' The engines can't run well without it."

Rob was astounded. "So that's

why we can't travel fast. You've sabotaged the spacecraft!"

"Yes. That was just after we landed, before I realized what the purpose of the expedition was and that you would be with us."

"What are you going to do now? You must return that part."

"I know. But I don't know how to put it back."

Rob was too excited to be angry. "Come on," he said. "Let's go find your father."

Suddenly the spacecraft veered off course. The boy tripped, and the revilator fell from his hands and smashed on the floor.

Rob stared at the shattered glass. "Five years! How could you have dropped the revilator?" Rob cried in desperation.

"I—I don't know. I just lost my balance," the Arreol boy answered. He tried vainly to piece together the shattered tube.

"Forget it. It's impossible," Rob said. He was disgusted. "Five years stranded in space," he repeated bitterly to himself. He grabbed the boy. "Come on. We're going to tell your father what's happened."

The boy nodded and they walked toward the control room.

The captain turned around sharply as they entered and stared at his son with amazement. The boy hesitated and then ran to his father's arms.

"What is this?" the captain asked, holding his son. "What are you doing here, and why are you with that boy?"

The Arreol boy hung his head. "I was not meant to be a scientist," he answered. "I want to be with you." He looked into his father's face and then slowly began to tell him about the revilator.

The captain stepped back and

held his son at arm's length. His face was pale. Finally he spoke with great difficulty. "Do you mean that you jeopardized this entire expedition just to be at my side?"

"I didn't think of the expedition," the boy answered. "I just thought of you."

The captain gestured to an aide and the man came over. After the captain spoke to him very softly, the aide hurried from the room. When he returned, Rob and the Arreol boy stared at him, disbelieving. He was holding a revilator in his hands.

The captain laughed. "Did you imagine that we didn't carry spare parts aboard the spacecraft? I thought that the engines were damaged from the outside attack. Now that we know what the real problem is, it can be repaired easily." He turned to the aide. "How long will it take to replace the revilator?"

"No more than twenty minutes, sir," the man answered. "However, we can't do it while the ship is in flight. The engines must be turned off."

The captain frowned. "Very well, then. We will have to return to Earth." He appeared thoughtful. "Perhaps there is another reason to land on Earth."

He looked at his son and at Rob. "It seems that I have forgotten what a son can mean to a father. Do you want to go home, Robert?"

"Oh, yes, sir," Rob answered quickly.

"I think that is the best place for you. It was a mistake to have taken you at all."

The captain turned aside to the communications desk. "Is the radio operating yet?"

"Negative, sir. We can't send word out. However, we have been able to receive a few weak signals from our sister ship. They discovered our absence and have made contact with us."

The captain appeared troubled. "If we can't send radio messages, we won't be able to let the NISI ground patrols know of our peaceful intention. They are certain to detect us before the engines are completely repaired. We can't prevent them from firing on us."

Rob spoke up. "Sir, if you can land near NISI, maybe I can get inside to tell them what has happened. I know the guards, and I'll try to reach someone who can stop the attack!"

"We can't do that," answered the captain. "It would be too dangerous for you."

"It's your—our—only chance," Rob protested. Maybe I can stop an attack and allow you time for repairs."

The captain stood considering Rob's idea. He called the navigator to him and discussed their chances. Then he turned back to Rob. "The navigator says that we can get within a mile of NISI before their high energy equipment will interfere with our engines. Can you run that far in time?"

"I will have to," Rob answered.

In a short while, the spacecraft and its cover ship settled silently in a meadow behind the installation. Rob stepped from the door of the craft. The lights of the NISI project burned intensely through the dark night and created strange shadow patterns in the tall meadow grass. There was a light rain. It seemed odd to Rob that it should still be raining. It seemed like such a very long time ago that he had

been standing at the window of his room feeling the rain blow against his face. He stepped away from the spacecraft quickly, but stopped for a moment to look back at the captain and his son standing in the doorway. He felt a twinge within him which he didn't quite understand. Finally he waved, then turned, and ran as fast as he could across the meadow. The mile seemed farther than he thought. He was gasping for breath.

Suddenly he heard a rushing sound overhead, and the sky lighted up in a brilliant white glare. Rob was thrown to the ground, stunned.

"They're attacking the spacecraft!" he exclaimed numbly.

His heart pounded as he saw a bright ball of fire roll into the sky. But it seemed to be several hundred yards beyond where the two sister ships had landed. "There's still time," he said to himself. "They haven't found the range yet."

He picked himself up and began running desperately toward the buildings on the ridge. His sides ached as he ran, and the cuffs of his trousers were soaked from splashing through puddles. The firing continued. Each time it seemed closer to the spacecraft.

At last Rob reached the guard booth at the gate. "Halt!" the guard called. He lowered his rifle as he recognized the figure emerging from the darkness. "What are you doing out here?"

"Get me to the defense officer," Rob panted. "I know what's going on. I've been in the spaceship, and I've got to stop the attack."

The guard looked doubtful.

"Please, it's urgent!"

"I'll call your father. He's in the defense command center right now," the guard said finally, wondering how Rob even knew that the spacecraft existed.

Rob waited anxiously. The distant explosions became more frequent. At last the guard handed the phone to Rob. He blurted out the story to his father and pleaded with him to stop the attack.

"Stay there," his father ordered and hung up.

Very shortly the firing ceased. Rob sat down on an old wooden chair in a corner of the guard booth. At last his father appeared in the doorway. Rob ran over to him. His father put an arm on Rob's shoulder and spoke quietly. "What were they like, son?"

"Like us."

His father was quiet. At last he said, "We can't be sure, but one of the ships may have been destroyed in the attack."

Rob looked up at him in horror. "Which one?"

"We don't know. There's no way of knowing, but it's possible that only one of the two craft escaped."

Rob looked out of the windows of the booth. The dull glow of daybreak was on the horizon beyond the great meadow. He pictured the orange-skinned boy and his father standing in the doorway of their craft. There was an ache in his throat.

Suddenly his father pointed excitedly at the sky just above the woods. "Look, it's the spacecraft! Wait, wait, there's another. Two ships! They both made it."

Rob smiled and moved closer to his father. "The strangers are gone," he said. "My friends are flying toward home."

MIRANDA'S CAT

by Linell Smith

For some time Miranda had been feeding a cat in the alley next to her apartment. Although the food was always eaten, she usually did not see the cat. He was independent to the point of being unfriendly. Still Miranda hoped that one day he would trust her and be her friend. This story, taken from MIRANDA AND THE CAT *by Linell Smith, tells about how Miranda became acquainted with the cat.*

One evening, late in July, something happened. Miranda stayed awhile after she brought the food. She wanted to see the Cat eat if she could. So she was there when the Cat dragged his torn and bleeding body over the fence. He fell with a soft thud at her feet. Miranda looked at the motionless bundle of fur in horror. She could hardly recognize the Cat because there was so much blood. But just then he opened one eye. He looked at her very much the way he had when they first met.

"Impudence!" said the look. "How dare you stare at me! Look to your manners, or I'll claw you!"

So Miranda knew it was the Cat. She gave a little sob and knelt down beside him. She quickly wrapped him in her old torn sweater. Then, carrying him as gently as she could, she hurried home.

When she arrived, her mother and brothers were watching television in the living room. They all looked up when she appeared in the doorway. Her mother asked swiftly, "What is it, darling? What's wrong?"

55

Miranda walked slowly over to the table and put her burden down. "It's the Cat," she said in a small, strained voice. "I think he's almost dead."

They all crowded around then. Her mother pulled back a corner of the bloody sweater. The Cat lay there before their curious eyes. He could do nothing about it. He was too weak.

"Whew!" whistled Tim. "He's *had* it!"

"You're not kidding," said Joey, the oldest brother.

"Don't look at him," begged Miranda. "He doesn't like it."

"Well, for Pete's sake, who do you think he is, the King of England?" drawled Tim.

"No, honestly, I mean it," pleaded Miranda. "He doesn't like people at all, and I think it's horrid to stand so close to him and stare when he's helpless. I just brought him here because—oh, I don't really know. I guess it was because it was so dark out and it seemed sad for me to let him die in the dark."

She began to cry miserably.

"Gee, Sis," said Tim awkwardly, "I didn't know you cared specially about that old cat. Don't cry. I'll stay away from him. Just stop crying, will you?"

"Oh, come on, Rannie," said Joey. "Tim and I won't bother the Cat any more. Cheer up."

Miranda's mother looked quietly at the Cat. He looked back at her with the proud gaze that Miranda knew so well.

"Miranda," she said slowly, "I don't think that this cat is going to die. He looks to me as if he had a lot of will to live. If we help him a little, he may be all right."

"Oh, Mother!" said Miranda breathlessly. "I'll help him. Just tell me what to do."

Her mother went to the cookie jar that stood on the mantel. Out of it she took four dollar bills. She put them in Miranda's pocket.

"Here, Rannie," she said, "I've been saving this for a rainy day. Take the money and the Cat down to Dr. Barton, the vet. I don't know if it's enough, but it's all we can spare. Maybe he'll help."

"Can we go too?" asked the boys.

"Yes," said their mother. "I don't want Rannie to be out by herself this late at night."

So Miranda gathered the Cat up in her arms, and she and her brothers hurried down the dark streets in silence. At last, they came to the veterinarian's office. The lights were still on. Through the window, they could see Dr. Barton in his white coat. They scurried up the steps and rang the bell.

Dr. Barton answered the door himself. "I'm sorry," he began, "I'm afraid office hours are—" But he never finished what he was going to say. He looked down at three pairs of pleading eyes and said instead, "Won't you come in?"

They did. Joe and Tim looked at magazines while Miranda followed Dr. Barton into the examining room. Dr. Barton looked very solemn as he examined the Cat. The Cat was no help at all because he spat and scratched whenever he could. At last Dr. Barton looked at Miranda and said, "Is this your pet, young lady?"

"Not exactly," faltered Miranda. She suddenly found herself telling the veterinarian all about herself and the Cat.

When she had finished, Dr. Barton said, "I see. That's a very interesting story, young lady. I'll try my best to help you out, but this cat is pretty badly cut up. I think he must have been hit by a car."

Miranda reached in her pocket and pulled out the money her mother had given her. "Mother took this from the savings jar," she said timidly. "Will it be enough?"

The vet looked at her over his glasses. "That won't be necessary at all," he said in a gruff voice. "I will handle this case free of charge. Now if you'll take a seat in the waiting room, I'll get to work."

Miranda went back to the boys. They looked up expectantly when she came in. "What did he say?" Tim asked.

"He wouldn't take the money," she said. "He's working on the Cat now, trying to save him."

"Gee," said Joey, "that's a good deal."

They sat in silence for a while. Then Tim said, "How long do you think he'll take, Rannie?"

"I don't know," said Miranda. "He did say that the Cat was hurt pretty badly, so I guess he'll take a good while."

Finally, after what seemed forever, the door of the examining room opened. Dr. Barton appeared, carrying the Cat. The animal was wrapped in bandages and looked furious.

"I've given him something to help the pain and to keep him quiet, so I think you can take him home now," he said to Miranda. "I've done all I can for him. I can't give you much hope, though. He's been badly hurt, and from what I know of this kind of cat, being penned up with people is just as bad for him as his injuries. However, I wish you luck."

Miranda gently took the cat from the vet. "Is there anything special I should do for him?" she asked.

"Yes," said Dr. Barton. "I have some ointment here. It should be put on the wounds every day, and his bandages should be changed when they become soiled. Those are two things that you can do. But the third thing is really the most important. You should leave him alone as much as possible. Try to make him feel that he hasn't lost his freedom."

"Thank you very much," said Miranda gratefully. "I'll try to do everything you said." She slipped the tube of ointment into her pocket. Then she and the boys started towards the door.

"Thanks again," they all said as they went out.

"You're welcome" answered Dr. Barton with a smile. "Don't forget to come again if you need help."

"We won't," promised Miranda.

The next day when Miranda had finished the breakfast dishes, she fixed a dish of scraps and a saucer of milk for the Cat. She carried them into her room and set them on the chest of drawers. She had made a bed for the cat in a box and had put the box in her closet. She opened the closet door quietly and looked in. The milk from last night was gone, she noticed, but the Cat was looking up at her fiercely.

"I'm sorry, Cat," she said, "but I have to put this ointment on now. I'll try not to hurt you, and I'll be as quick as I can."

When she picked him up, the Cat spat at her, but he didn't claw her. Perhaps he couldn't because he was so weak. At any rate, Miranda was encouraged. She began to unwrap his bandages very carefully. She gave a little gasp when she saw his wounds, but she went ahead firmly with the ointment. The Cat did not protest at all. Miranda bandaged him up again and put him back in his box. Then she placed the dishes of food and milk before him and said, "There you are, Cat. Thank you for being so good."

The Cat looked at her coldly and then lowered his eyelids in disdain. Miranda sighed as she closed the door.

Outside her room, her brothers were waiting for her. "How is he?" asked Tim eagerly.

"He's all right, I guess," said Miranda. "I can't quite understand him, though. I expected him to make a fuss when I put the ointment on and he didn't at all. And yet he hates me as much as ever. I can see it in his eyes."

"Maybe he's just smart," offered Joey. "Maybe he knows that you're helping him and that he'll just have to put up with you till he's well. But putting up with someone doesn't mean liking them."

"I think you're right," said Miranda slowly. "You know, I think that's just what he's doing."

And in the days that followed, she was sure of it. The Cat let himself be bandaged and rebandaged with no complaint. He ate the food that was given him. He did not object when Miranda rubbed his wounds with the healing ointment. But he showed no signs of wanting to become friends.

Finally a day came when Miranda knew that the Cat didn't need bandages any more. His wounds had almost healed and he was beginning to prowl back and forth in the closet. After much thought, she decided to let him out in her room for a while.

When she opened the closet door, the Cat glanced up at her briefly and then stalked out into the room. He walked stiff-legged from one piece of furniture to another, sniffing— his tail a bottle brush of suspicion. At last, satisfied that there was nothing dangerous about, he sauntered back to Miranda and sat down.

"Meow," he said, fixing her with his stern green eyes.

"What do you want, Cat?" asked Miranda. She tried to keep the excitement out of her voice, but it was hard. She had never dreamed that he would come near her of his own free will.

The Cat twitched his tail lazily. "Prraouw," he remarked.

"I'll get you something to eat," said Miranda happily. "We're having fish for dinner and you can have the head."

She ran off to the kitchen and found her mother cleaning the fish.

"Can I have the head for the Cat?" she asked.

"Of course," said her mother. "How is he?"

"Fine," said Miranda. "Oh, Mother," she added joyfully, "he came over to me all on his own and spoke to me! He really did!"

"Why, Rannie, how wonderful!" exclaimed her mother. "I know how happy that makes you."

When Miranda returned to her room, the Cat was still sitting where she had left him. He looked up when she came in, and Miranda thought, "Why, he almost looks as if he had accepted me. Not as a real friend, maybe, but at least I'm not an enemy anymore."

She walked over and put the plate with the fish head on it down beside him on some old newspapers. "There, Cat," she said, "I think you'll like that."

The Cat did like it. He growled and snarled to himself as he ate the fish head. He dared anyone to try to take the tasty morsel away from him. When he had finished, he licked his paws and washed his face carefully. Then he returned to his box in the closet and lay down for a snooze.

For the next few days, Miranda was very happy. Although the Cat was by no means affectionate, he behaved politely towards the girl. Once or twice he was almost friendly.

But then he became very restless. He prowled back and forth endlessly. Often he would look at Miranda and give a harsh cry. It was more of a demand than anything else, and Miranda knew it. She also knew what it was that he wanted. For a while, she pretended to herself that she didn't. Finally one evening she gave up. She sat down on the bed and watched him as he paced back and forth.

"Cat," she said in a small voice, "I'll do what you want, I promise. Only—are you sure? Please, won't you change your mind? After all, we're friends now and I love you very much."

The Cat turned and gazed at her with such longing in his eyes that Miranda sighed. "All right," she said. "You're my very best friend and I want you to be happy."

She got up from the bed and walked slowly to the window. Then, squaring her shoulders, she firmly opened it.

Instantly, the Cat sprang to the sill. He stood there a moment, almost as if he were thinking. Then with a "Prraouw" he leaped to the ground. He was soon out of sight, lost among the dim dark shapes of trash cans and rubbish.

A few minutes later, Tim found his sister stretched out on her bed, crying as if her heart would break. Then he saw the open window. Immediately he ran for his mother. "Oh, come quick," he begged. "I think the Cat's gone out the window, and Rannie's crying like anything!"

Together they went back to Miranda's room. They found her sitting up, wiping her tear-stained face on the hem of her dress.

"Rannie," said her mother softly, "Tim says that the Cat's run away—that he got out the window."

Miranda looked up at them slowly. "He *is* gone," she said, "but he didn't run away. I let him go."

"You *let* him go?" gasped Tim. "What in the world did you do that for?"

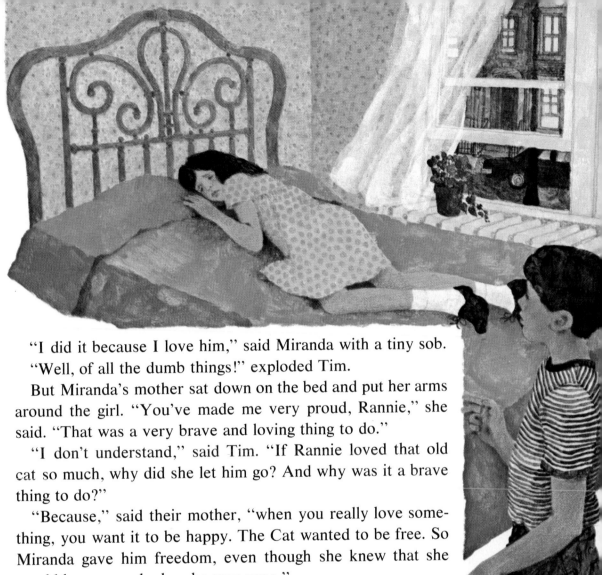

"I did it because I love him," said Miranda with a tiny sob.

"Well, of all the dumb things!" exploded Tim.

But Miranda's mother sat down on the bed and put her arms around the girl. "You've made me very proud, Rannie," she said. "That was a very brave and loving thing to do."

"I don't understand," said Tim. "If Rannie loved that old cat so much, why did she let him go? And why was it a brave thing to do?"

"Because," said their mother, "when you really love something, you want it to be happy. The Cat wanted to be free. So Miranda gave him freedom, even though she knew that she would be very sad when he was gone."

AUTHOR

Linell Smith was born in New York City. She is the daughter of Ogden Nash, who is well known for his many humorous poems.

Today Mrs. Smith, who lives in Sparks, Maryland, is married and has three children. Besides *Miranda and the Cat,* she has written *The Auction Pony* and several other children's books.

Catalogue

Cats sleep **fat** and walk thin.
Cats, when they sleep, **slump**;
When they wake, pull in —
And where the **plump's** been
There's skin.
Cats walk thin.

Cats wait in a **lump**,
Jump in a *streak*.
Cats, when they jump, are sleek
As a grape slipping its skin —
They have technique.
Oh, cats don't creak;
They *sneak*.

Cats sleep **fat**.
They spread out comfort underneath them
Like a good mat,
As if they picked the place
And then sat.
You walk around one
As if he were the City Hall
After that.

If male,
A cat is apt to sing on a major scale;
This concert is for everybody — this
Is wholesale.
For a baton, he wields a tail.

(He is also found,
When happy, to resound
With an inclosed and private sound.)

A cat condenses.
He pulls in his tail to go under bridges,
And himself to go under fences.
Cats fit
In any size box or kit;
And if a large pumpkin grew under one,
He could arch over it.

When everyone else is just ready to go out,
The cat is just ready to come in.
He's not where he's been.
Cats sleep **fat** and walk thin.

Rosalie Moore

DECIDING ON PARAGRAPH TOPICS

The paragraph that follows talks about the clothing which Eskimos wore years ago. Notice that each sentence in the paragraph tells something about that Eskimo clothing.

Clothing made of fur kept Eskimos warm in temperatures that were sometimes as low as sixty degrees below zero. Men, women, and children, all dressed alike in trousers, boots, mittens, and hooded coats called parkas. In coldest weather, Eskimos wore two complete sets of clothing, the inner set with the fur inside and the outer set with the fur outside. Most of the clothing was made from light but warm skins of caribou, a kind of reindeer, although tough walrus hide and sealskin were often used for boots. Eskimo women cut the skins and shaped the garments, sewing the pieces together with thread made from animal tendons.

A good paragraph, like the one above, talks about only one thing. That one thing is called *the topic of the paragraph*. Every sentence in the paragraph tells or asks something about that one topic.

If you are not sure what the topic of a paragraph is, read each sentence of the paragraph again and then try to figure out what one thing all the sentences are talking about. Usually that will show you what the topic of the paragraph is. The following statements tell what the five sentences in the paragraph on

Eskimo clothing talk about. Notice that each sentence listed contains the words *clothing Eskimos wore.*

Sentence one tells about the warmth of *clothing Eskimos wore.*

Sentence two lists the articles of *clothing Eskimos wore.*

Sentence three tells the amount of *clothing Eskimos wore.*

Sentence four tells the materials used for *clothing Eskimos wore.*

Sentence five tells about the making of *clothing Eskimos wore.*

Being able to tell what the topic of a paragraph is will often help you to understand what you are studying, and paragraph topics are good points to use in making notes. Sometimes your first reading of the paragraph will tell you quickly what the topic is. But if you are not sure what the topic is, make a list like the one made for the paragraph about the clothing Eskimos wore. Put into your list statements that tell what the sentences of the paragraph are talking about. If there is one topic that you can use in every statement, as the topic *clothing Eskimos wore* is used, that is the topic of the paragraph.

Now and then in your studies you may come across a paragraph in which all the sentences do not tell something about the same topic. Usually in such a paragraph, most of the sentences talk about only one topic, but the other sentences talk about one or more other topics.

An Eskimo igloo is one topic that the following paragraph tells about. As you read the paragraph, think what each sentence is talking about. Does every sentence in the paragraph tell about *an Eskimo igloo?*

An igloo provided temporary shelter for an Eskimo family while on a hunting trip or traveling in winter. In summer, most Eskimos lived in tents. An Eskimo igloo was a round snowhouse which could be built in only about an hour. It was made from fairly large blocks of wind-packed snow that had been cut with a long knife. The dome-shaped hut was formed by fitting the blocks together in circular rows that became smaller toward the top. The entrance to the igloo was a long tunnel dug out under the snow or built of snow blocks. Inside the igloo was a single room that was ten feet or more from wall to wall. In New England, where there are often heavy snowfalls in winter, children have always enjoyed building playhouses out of snow.

Here is a list that shows what is told by each sentence in the paragraph you have just read:

Sentence one tells the purpose of *an Eskimo igloo*.

Sentence two tells that in summer Eskimos lived in *tents*.

Sentence three tells how long it took to build *an Eskimo igloo*.

Sentence four tells the materials used in making *an Eskimo igloo*.

Sentence five tells how *an Eskimo igloo* was built.

Sentence six tells about the entrance of *an Eskimo igloo*.

Sentence seven tells about the inside of *an Eskimo igloo*.

Sentence eight tells about *children's playhouses* built from snow in New England.

You can see that the first sentence and sentences three through seven tell something about *an Eskimo igloo*. But what do the other two sentences tell about? Sentence two tells about *tents*, and sentence eight tells about *children's playhouses*.

You can understand that if a paragraph talks about several topics, none of those topics can be *the* topic of the paragraph. But usually such a paragraph contains one topic which most of the sentences talk about. We can call that topic the *main* topic *in* the paragraph. The main topic in the paragraph on the opposite page is *an Eskimo igloo*.

When a paragraph talks about more than one topic, try to figure out what the *main* topic in the paragraph is. This will help you to understand what you are reading.

Now read Paragraph A that follows. Think what each sentence in the paragraph is talking about and decide what the *main* topic in the paragraph is. If you need to, make a list of statements that tell what each sentence in the paragraph is talking about.

Paragraph A:

Most of the food Eskimos eat comes from the sea, but land animals like the caribou and polar bear are also a source of food. The flesh of seals, walruses, fishes, and whales provides most of the Eskimo's meat. Some meat is boiled, but often it is served raw and frozen because fuel is so scarce. Most Eskimos have powerful jaws and strong teeth, the result of chewing raw, tough meat and eating foods that contain very little sugar. Heads of small fish are sometimes swallowed whole. Since no fruits or vegetables grow in this frozen land, such parts of an animal as the liver, heart, and stomach are eaten because they provide necessary vitamins and minerals. A special treat is Eskimo "ice cream" which is not ice cream at all but caribou fat shaved fine and mixed with oil to form a cream.

Which of the following is the main topic in Paragraph A?
   1. Why Eskimos eat raw meat
   2. Eskimos' skill in hunting
   3. The food of Eskimos
   4. Why Eskimos have strong teeth

Discussion

Help your class decide on answers to these questions:
1. What is meant by the topic of a paragraph? If you need to figure out the topic of a paragraph, how can you do it?
2. What is meant by the main topic in a paragraph? How can you decide what the main topic of a paragraph is?
3. What is the main topic in Paragraph A? Why is each of the three other topics listed not the main topic in that paragraph?

On your own

In which of the following two paragraphs do all the sentences talk about only one topic? What is the topic of that paragraph? What is the main topic in the other paragraph?

Paragraph B:

Eskimo dogs are a very useful animal in the Arctic regions. They are very strong and can withstand the extremely cold weather of the Arctic. These beautiful animals are used by many Eskimo families for pulling sleds and for hunting. Because of their great strength and endurance, they can pull heavy loads for many miles without tiring. The sleds that they pull are made of wood and bone fastened together with rawhide. The Eskimo dogs are particularly useful in hunting seals. They help the Eskimo hunters find the seals by locating air holes in the ice through which the seals breathe. Eskimos do most of their hunting on the ice, but sometimes they hunt from boats.

Paragraph C:

The one-man boat which some Eskimos use for hunting in open waters is called a kayak. A kayak is usually less than two feet wide but might be twenty feet long. The frame of the kayak, like that of a dog sled, is made of pieces of wood tied together with strips of walrus hide. Except for a round cockpit near the center of the deck top, the entire frame of the boat is covered with wet seal or walrus skin which shrinks as it dries and thus stretches tightly over the frame. The floor of the cockpit is the place where the Eskimo paddler sits. A kayak is a light but seaworthy boat which one man can easily paddle and control.

Checking your work

If you are asked to do so, tell which paragraph talks about only one topic and what that topic is. Tell also what the main topic in the other paragraph is. If a topic you decided on was incorrect, find out why it was incorrect.

A Horse for Reg

by Anne Huston and Jane Yolen

Reg, who lived in New York City, was spending the summer on Jim and Dee Bradshaw's farm. He had hoped that they would have a horse he could take care of, but unfortunately their only horse had died. Reg wasn't too happy on the farm and after a while wondered if he would be able to finish out the summer. Then something happened that caused Reg to change his mind. A truck that was carrying several horses to a farm, where they were to be killed for horsemeat, ran off the road into a ditch. The horses escaped, but soon all except one were recaptured. Reg discovered the one escapee up in the hills near the Bradshaw's farm. Reg befriended the poor animal and hid him in an old deserted cabin. Every night he would secretly slip away from the farm to be with his horse, Roachy.

For the next few days, Reg kept his self-imposed schedule. He got up early and helped on the farm whenever he could. Sometimes he worked in the fields with Jim and Frank. When he did, he was always careful not to say or do anything that might make either one suspicious.

More often, however, Reg stayed around the farmhouse with Dee. He found her more comfortable to work with, for she never questioned anything he did. And he could always manage to hide a few things to take to Roachy at night.

He wrote three postcards home, too, careful to say what a good time he was having. He asked Dee how to spell a few words and gave the cards to Jim to mail. Then they both could read what he had written. He felt like a secret agent fooling the enemy.

Reg didn't like to admit it, but he was getting pretty tired. Still, he kept going. All the Bradshaws were behaving as he hoped they would. No one suspected he was making midnight journeys up the mountain, he felt sure.

And no one seemed to be missing any of the things he was borrowing for Roachy. They were all pleased that he was adjusting to farm life so well.

But Reg was not completely happy with his midnight visits. It wasn't just that he had to lie and sneak in order to be with his horse; that was only part of it. Mainly, Reg was unhappy because he never got to see Roachy in the daylight. It wasn't enough just to feel the horse's sides in the dark and guess if he were filling out. It wasn't enough just to touch the horse's soft muzzle in the blackness. Reg wanted, more than anything, to be with Roachy during the day.

Besides, he thought, a horse shouldn't be cooped up all day. Jim's cows aren't. It's not healthy. Roachy should be out in the sun, like humans. He shouldn't only be a night horse—a nightmare! Reg giggled at the last thought, though Roachy was really a male.

But, try as he might, he couldn't figure out a solution.

It was Dee who found the answer. Toward the end of the

week, Reg was in the kitchen with her, canning cherries. Dee called him the best helper she had ever had. "Though I must admit," she had added, "I never had a helper before."

They both laughed at that.

Reg was sitting at the table with a big bowl of cherries in front of him. His job was to pit them, and it was a simple task. All he had to do was stick a fork in the cherry and pull out the hard little seed. But his eyes kept closing, and he had to jerk himself awake constantly.

"Reg? Reg, did you hear me?"

Reg quickly jerked awake again. "What? Did you say something?"

Dee laughed. "Why, you are a sleepyhead. I said it to you four times. I'm ready for more cherries. You really must be tired."

"No, I'm all right. Honest, I am." Reg sat up straighter and forced his eyes wide open.

Dee came to the table and sat down beside him. "Reg, Jim and I have noticed how hard you have been working this week. We think it's wonderful. But we've also noticed that you've begun to look very, very tired. That's not so good. We don't want you to work so hard that you fall over from exhaustion. You're really a city boy, not used to the hard physical labor on a farm."

"I'm all right. Honest," Reg repeated. He sensed something coming and he couldn't tell what it was.

"Maybe so, but we thought you might like a change, a little recreation. A little more fun." She paused. "Frank is taking this afternoon off and riding his bike over to the Warshams'. They live down the road, and they're twins, a boy and a girl—maybe Frank has told you about them already. Well, I have an old bike you could ride, and you could go along with Frank. It's a girl's bike, but

I don't think that should matter. We want you to have fun, not spend your whole summer working."

"But I *like* working," Reg said guardedly. He still wasn't sure what Dee wanted. "I mean, working on a farm is something new to me. You know, kind of fun."

"And you're doing it very well, too. But, Reg, promise me that you will take a few hours off each afternoon to rest, or to relax. Or if you like, you can join Frank and his friends. Promise?"

With great effort, Reg managed to keep from shouting. He only nodded. Here was the answer to his problem. Dee had handed him the solution without even knowing it.

"That's a swell idea," he said politely. "Maybe I'll take a couple of hours off each day to explore — you know, get to see the country more." Reg measured his words carefully. "Maybe I could wander up on the mountain, or something

like that. But I'd be back in time to get the cows in."

"Of course, Reg. Do whatever you like. Wander. Explore. Discover. My! I think you look better already," Dee said, smiling at him.

Reg grinned back. He *felt* better already.

That afternoon Reg was free, and no one saw him leave. Dee was in the basement, Jim was in the field, and Frank was at the Warshams'. With a bucket of feed, a cow brush, and a horse blanket he had borrowed, Reg headed toward the cabin. He had debated between the blanket and a shovel, because the cabin needed to be cleaned out. Horses, he discovered, weren't the neatest animals in the world. But he could always make a kind of shovel out of branches up there, and the blanket would look so good on Roachy. Besides, the blanket was easier to carry.

Since it was daylight, he had

75

decided to mark a short cut with a kitchen paring knife that he had slipped into his pocket while he was doing the cherries. On the way down the mountain, he would come the short way and notch the trees. That way he would never have to make the roundabout road trip in the dark again.

"It's my last long road trip," he sang softly to himself. He followed the road, staying as close to the trees as possible. He hadn't realized it in the dark, but it seemed to be more than a mile to the cabin by way of the road. Several cars passed him, but he managed to hide behind a tree each time, and no one saw him.

When he got near the cabin, he went very quietly. He wanted to see what Roachy did while he was away. He crept to the window and peeked in. Roachy was standing there asleep.

"Roachy," Reg called softly. "Roachy."

The horse's big ears perked up; he opened his eyes and looked around. When he saw Reg, he whinnied and came to the window. Poking his head out, he nuzzled Reg's face. Reg grinned and ran inside to set down the things he was carrying so he could try the blanket on Roachy. It was a little dirty but it fitted the horse just fine!

For Reg, that afternoon was just about the most beautiful one he

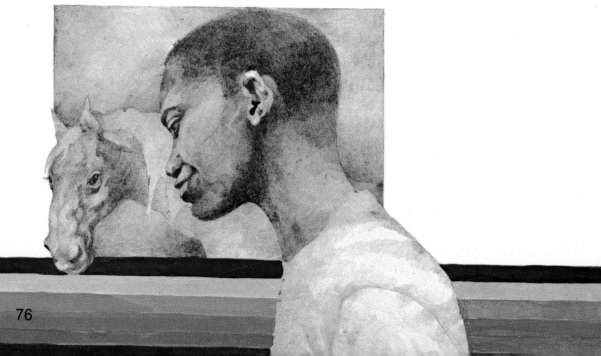

had ever spent. It was cool and peaceful, and a light wind rustled the trees that surrounded the clearing. First, Reg made a branch broom and cleaned out the cabin. It was smelly, messy work, but he kept singing, "It's for Roachy. Old horse Roachy," and the work went quickly.

Then he started talking to the horse—sweet-talking—and getting the horse really used to him. At last, he led Roachy from the cabin and took out the cow brush.

"It's time you got cleaned up, old horse," he said. He brushed and brushed until this time the old horse's coat really did shine. "Boy! You sure don't look like the scarecrow horse I saw that first day," Reg said. "You're beautiful now. Really beautiful . . . in a funny sort of way," he added honestly.

Roachy almost looked like a different horse. His lip still hung down in a pout, but the sharp angles of his body were mostly gone. In their place were the beginnings of nice, round curves.

"Just round enough to ride," Reg said. Then he added softly, "Will you let me get on your back? I just want to sit there a little while. It'll be your first time with me, and my first time ever on a horse. Please, Roachy?"

He stood looking at the broad brown back. Then he stretched his arms up and put his hands on Roachy's withers. The horse didn't move away; he only bent his neck to eat the grass that grew in the clearing. Reg tried to boost himself up. He jumped several times. Once, he got his chest across the horse's back, but he couldn't hang on long enough to swing his legs over. Roachy turned his head and watched the proceedings with interest. He nibbled at Reg's pants, looking for some more sugar.

Reg slid to the ground, discouraged. "At least you stood still for me," he said to Roachy, "even if I couldn't get on."

Reg then looked all around for something to stand on, but there wasn't even a tree stump. Then he had an idea. He led Roachy back to the cabin and placed him alongside the wall, under the window.

"Don't move," he said to the horse, and ran inside. He then

scrambled up onto the window sill. Clinging to the window with one hand, he put his leg out and over the horse. Then he pushed off with his other foot and landed squarely on Roachy's back.

Reg held his breath anxiously. Would Roachy try to buck him off?

The horse only turned his head and nibbled at Reg's leg again.

"You *are* my pal," Reg said joyfully. "You want me to be here." He leaned over and stroked Roachy's neck. Then he straightened up. He felt like an Indian brave; he felt like a soldier; like a knight. No, he felt like a king, a king on his faithful charger.

Reg became aware of Roachy's warmth underneath him. He tightened his grip with his legs and felt the horse's sides swell with breath.

Suddenly the old horse threw his head up as if he had heard a call. He swiveled his ears forward and whinnied loudly, for he had caught the feeling, too.

"Let's take a walk," Reg said proudly as he touched his heels to Roachy's sides. "Let's take a walk around our kingdom!"

AUTHOR

The two authors who wrote *Trust a City Kid,* the book from which the story you just read was taken, are Anne Huston and Jane Yolen.

Miss Huston was born in Lyndhurst, Ohio. After graduation from an Ohio college, she moved to New York to become an actress. Since that time, she has appeared on television, in movies, and in the theater. Another of her activities was organizing a company of actors to perform children's plays in the New York City area. Besides *Trust a City Kid,* Miss Huston has written another book called *The Cat Across the Way.*

Jane Yolen, whose married name is Jane Stemple, enjoys skiing, camping, dancing, and folk-singing. She and her husband spent eight months camping in Europe and in the Middle East. Before returning to the United States, Mr. and Mrs. Stemple worked in Israel on a kibbutz — a kind of farm.

Mrs. Stemple was born in New York City, but she was raised in Westport, Connecticut. Besides writing books for boys and girls, she also writes musical plays for children's theater.

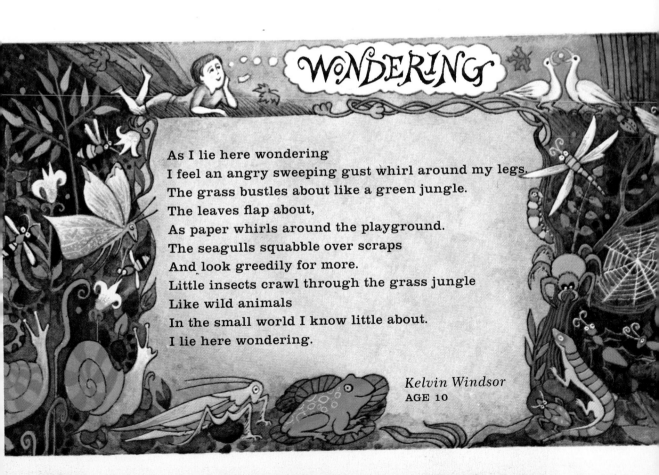

WONDERING

As I lie here wondering
I feel an angry sweeping gust whirl around my legs.
The grass bustles about like a green jungle.
The leaves flap about,
As paper whirls around the playground.
The seagulls squabble over scraps
And look greedily for more.
Little insects crawl through the grass jungle
Like wild animals
In the small world I know little about.
I lie here wondering.

Kelvin Windsor
AGE 10

The King of the Frogs

This fable from Humphrey Harman's book TALES
TOLD NEAR A CROCODILE *tells how the frogs learned
a lesson—the hard way.*

Have you ever been beside a lake in Africa at night and listened to the frogs? You haven't? Then you cannot imagine what the noise is like. And it's not just one kind of noise; it's several. Over there, for instance, are a thousand creaking doors that have never had their hinges oiled, and someone opens and shuts them—and keeps on doing just that. Over there are a thousand fat men snoring, and no one wakes them up. Then there are a thousand carpenters sawing planks, and all the saws need a touch of grease, and a thousand little bells are being struck, and a thousand corks are being pulled out of bottles.

Noise! You can hardly hear yourself think.

Then you go a little closer until you can just see the edge of the water and perhaps a reed or two, and there is silence. Just the splash of a frog jumping into the water late because he was asleep and didn't hear you coming. Then nothing, and you can hear the whole world breathe. There's a story about this.

Long ago the frogs did as they pleased, and the result was dreadful. Not one of them would listen to what another said, and they all shouted at once. Children wouldn't obey their parents, and even wives wouldn't listen to their husbands, which is, indeed, something hardly to be understood. It was all noisy and untidy beyond bearing, and nothing ever got done.

At last a wise, wise old frog called everyone to a meeting. Since he had a very fine voice and went on shouting for long enough, he managed to get them all there at once, for, to tell you the truth, they were pretty sick of living the way they did.

"Frogs!" said the old frog, puffing himself up. "We cannot go on like this. It's no sort of life for anyone and, anyway, when you see how all the other creatures live, it makes one ashamed of being a frog. There is only one thing to do. We must get a king. When people have kings, there is peace and order and everyone does as he is told."

"Agreed!" they all shouted, and they stayed long enough to commission the old frog to see what he could do about getting them one, before everybody fell to quarreling and pushing and splashing. The meeting—as usual—broke up in disorder.

Then the wise, wise old frog went to see the great god Mmumi (you will say the two m's correctly if you hum a little before you begin the word). Mmumi happened to be in charge of that part of the world.

Mmumi is a very slow god and usually gives people more than they bargain for. He agreed drowsily that the frogs needed a king and promised to do something about it. Then he went to sleep again.

So the frogs went on as usual, which was badly, until one day Mmumi woke up, remembered his promise, took a great green mossy boulder which had the rough shape of a gigantic frog, and threw it into the water.

splash

"There you are!" he shouted (it sounded like thunder). "There's your king. His name's Gogo and, like me, he doesn't want to be disturbed. Respect him and be satisfied."

The whole lake was shaken by Gogo's fall. The waves washed through the reeds and tore up the shore, and in the middle of a great cloud of mud Gogo settled on the bottom, and the fat green waterweeds curled round and over him. He looked shocking.

The frogs were terrified and fled under stones and into dark corners and holes under the bank. Their long white legs streaked behind them as they swam. Parents found their children, and husbands found their wives, and then they settled down to explaining what had happened.

"This is our king," they said, "and a fine, terrible one he seems, and from the splash he made, not the sort to fool about with. Now all will be well and this scandalous behavior will stop." And so it did, for a while.

But although Gogo had made such a wonderful first impression, as time passed, they noticed that he never moved. He just sat quietly in the mud and stared in the same direction. Presently they began to get used to him, until finally some young, bold, bad frogs ventured to swim close to him, and then one of them touched his nose.

And still Gogo said and did nothing.

"Bah! He's not a king!" they shouted. "He's not even a frog. He's just an old stone and couldn't hurt anyone." And they swam round him until they were dizzy, and jumped all over his back, and went away and spoke rudely about him to their elders.

At first none of the elders believed them. They had told their children Gogo was a king, and a king he had to be, but soon it was impossible to deny that the children were right, and then . . . Well, the noise began again, and things were as they had always been, only worse. Terrible!

The wise, wise old frog sighed and set out to see Mmumi again, who was not at all pleased at being woken again.

"All right!" he shouted in a rage. "All right! You aren't satisfied with the king I've given you. Is that the way it is? Very well, you shall have another, and I hope you like him."

And the very next night he gave them Mamba the Crocodile.

Gogo had come to his people with a splash that shook the lake, but Mamba slid into the water with only a whisper and left but one small ring spreading gently to show that he had come. Then he swam, silent as a shadow, lithe and long and secret, his jaws grinning like a trap. Gogo had never visited the people he had been given to rule, but Mamba visited them often and suddenly. And whenever he met a subject, the great jaws gaped and closed, and often it was the last of that frog.

The frogs developed great respect for their new king and lived quietly, looking over the backs of their heads as frogs can. Now and again at night they break out, but they keep their ears open, and if you go near the lake, they shut up.

They think that it's Mamba coming to put a little order into them, and they keep quiet.

TREASURE OVERBOARD

by Robert Silverberg

A fantastic treasure of gold and silver lies in the sea waiting
for someone to find it. Maybe it will be you...

At the bottom of Vigo (vee′go) Bay, off the northwest coast of Spain, lies one of the richest of all sunken treasures. For 250 years people have been trying to find it. How it came to be there is a strange story indeed.

It was late in the summer of 1702. England and the Netherlands were at war with Spain and France. For three years, no treasure had been shipped from Spain's rich possessions in the New World.

The Spanish had forced millions of Indians to mine gold and silver for them in South and Central America. They had let the treasure pile up there, rather than have it captured by English pirates. Now, though, it was decided to ship the treasure to Spain.

A fleet of seventeen Spanish treasure ships set sail from America under the command of Admiral Manuel de Velasco (mahn-yoo-el′ day vuh-lahs′ko). Two dozen French warships went with the treasure fleet to protect it against pirates.

The treasure was fantastic. There were 3,400 tons of gold and silver, worth hundreds of millions of dollars!

The treasure fleet was to sail to Cádiz (kuh diz′), Spain. But Cádiz was under attack by English ships. They had been driven off, but they did not go far from the Spanish coast. The French commander, Admiral Chateau-Renault (chah-toh′ ruh-noh′) suggested that the wisest thing to do was to take the treasure to some French port until the English had set sail for home.

Admiral Velasco would have no part of such a plan. "The treasure is supposed to be brought to Spain," he declared stubbornly. "And to Spain it will go!"

Cádiz was blockaded, though. The treasure ships could not get through. And now a new British fleet of twenty-seven ships-of-war got word of the treasure and sailed to head it off. Velasco, caught between two enemy fleets, made a run for Vigo, the nearest Spanish port.

The treasure fleet reached Vigo safely and dropped anchor in the bay. Safe, the admiral thought! But red tape now ensnarled

everything. The admiral wanted to unload his treasure before the English could seize it, but the port officials would not allow it.

Pointing to his papers, they solemnly declared, "The treasure is bound for Cádiz. It can only be unloaded there."

Admiral Velasco raged and stormed, but nothing could be done. He was told that rules had to be followed. The consent of the King was needed to change the port of unloading, and even then many papers would have to be filled out.

For an entire month, the admiral fretted in Vigo while the foolish port officials kept the treasure from being unloaded. And finally the English came along. Twenty-five English and Dutch ships appeared in Vigo Bay. The harbor had been blocked by a floating chain of logs and cables, but the invading fleet easily smashed through it.

French Admiral Chateau-Renault struck back with every ship he had. But the invaders tore right through the defending French warships and sent seventeen of them to the bottom in two hours. The Spanish treasure fleet was trapped!

Sinking ships were everywhere in the bay. Admiral Velasco saw his defenders ablaze and going under. He gave an order that must have hurt him bitterly.

"Get rid of the treasure! Dump it overboard! Don't let the enemy get their hands on it!"

Quickly the sailors began dumping fortunes in gold and silver into the bay. But they were not quick enough. The English and Dutch were closing in.

A new order went out: *"Sink the treasure ships!"* Decks were set afire. Spanish sailors manned the lifeboats and rowed desperately for shore as the great treasure fleet sank. By the time the invaders reached the fleet, most of the galleons were on their way down. But several were captured still afloat, and their treasure, worth more than $35,000,000, was taken off to England. The rest went to the bottom. It was an unhappy day for Spain.

Not all the captured treasure reached England, though. One galleon bearing half the English loot struck a rock at the mouth of Vigo Bay and sank with three hundred tons of treasure aboard. Most of what did get to England was silver. It was melted down and turned into English coins stamped with the word *VIGO* in honor of the great victory.

Uncounted millions lay beneath the sea after the battle. The war ended before long, and the Spanish government set about to recover its sunken loot. They thought it would be easy. The wrecked ships lay in only sixty or seventy feet of water.

But the bottom of Vigo Bay oozes with mud. More is dropped there all the time. Quickly the sunken ships were buried under many feet of silt and slime.

Still, the treasure seekers went to work. Nearly every year, someone tried to find the gold of Vigo Bay. The biggest excitement in those early years came in 1728, when a French salvage firm managed to get chains around one ship and drag it to shore. But to their disgust, they found they had not found a treasure ship at all. It was only one of the sunken French warships!

Twenty years later, a man named Juan Antonio Rivero (hwahn ahn-to′nee-yoh ree-vair′o) recovered some 200,000 silver pieces of eight. And in 1772, an Englishman named William Evans went down with a specially designed diving bell and came up with a good deal of silver. But little else was taken from the great treasure during its first hundred years in the depths.

In 1825, a mysterious English expedition visited Vigo Bay and may have been very successful. We will never know. One of the Spanish men hired by this group complained that Spanish divers were sent down during the daytime to clear away mud and wreckage, and then in the night English divers secretly went down to collect gold and silver. After a year's work, the Englishmen left suddenly. They claimed to have found nothing, but legend says that they took millions from the bay.

During the next forty years, many treasure hunters tried their luck and found almost nothing. In 1869, a French expedition arrived with some new inventions, such as a diving bell that had electric lights. They brought up some silver plates and several cannons, but they had to give up work when the Franco-Prussian war broke out.

At the same time an American named Colonel John E. Gowen formed a company and sent down divers. Several wrecks were dynamited, but no treasure was found in the thick mud. Gowen's company gave up, but other Americans tried again in 1885. Like the English hunters of sixty years before, they claimed to have recovered nothing, but some people say that they really found a great deal.

With the turn of the century came thirty-five-year-old José Pino (ho-zay′ pee′no), who showed up armed with all kinds of new pumps, magnets, and diving equipment. Pino charted the location of most of the wrecks and had a good deal of luck finding treasure. His men found gold statuettes, Mexican gold coins, bars of silver weighing up to eighty pounds, cannons, anchors, and other valuable items. Pino worked on and off in Vigo Bay for twenty-five years. He enjoyed more success than any of the other seekers after gold, for he found at least four million dollars.

After Pino came a Dutchman named van Wienen (vahn vee′ nuhn). He invented a tube designed to bore through the mud to the treasure galleons. By now thirty to fifty feet of mud covered the ships.

Van Wienen's work was interrupted by World War Two. In 1955, the Spanish government granted a three-year license to an American-owned company for work in Vigo Bay. They raised cannon balls, pottery, porcelain pieces, and other interesting treasures.

What about the gold? It is still there.

More than two and a half centuries have passed since Admiral Velasco ordered the treasure fleet to be sunk. Today, little remains of the sunken galleons but pieces of rotted wood. But the bulk of the treasure is still down there in the mud.

The *Monmouth's Prize*, which was the captured galleon sunk as it headed for England, had ten million dollars worth of silver aboard. The ship has never even been found. And many other treasures have escaped the searchers. For every gleaming gold doubloon brought up, dozens more lie hidden below.

Beneath a blanket of ooze and slime, Spanish doubloons wait in Vigo Bay, bars of gold and silver worth millions, glittering jewels that could ransom a king. The prize is there—a hundred million dollars or more—patiently waiting for someone to find it.

AUGTHOR

Robert Silverberg was born in New York City, where he now lives in a big old house he shares with his wife, their numerous cats, and thousands of books.

He is the author of hundreds of short stories and articles, and many books. His books include both science fiction and non-fiction. Among them are *The Man Who Found Nineveh,* a book about archaeology and exploration, and *The Time of the Great Freeze* and *Revolt on Alpha C,* both science fiction novels. The selection you have just read came from his non-fiction book *Treasures Beneath the Sea.*

Mr. Silverberg likes to travel when he isn't writing. He has visited most of the United States, much of Europe, the Caribbean area, and Israel. Among his hobbies are skin-diving, collecting rare books, and listening to classical music.

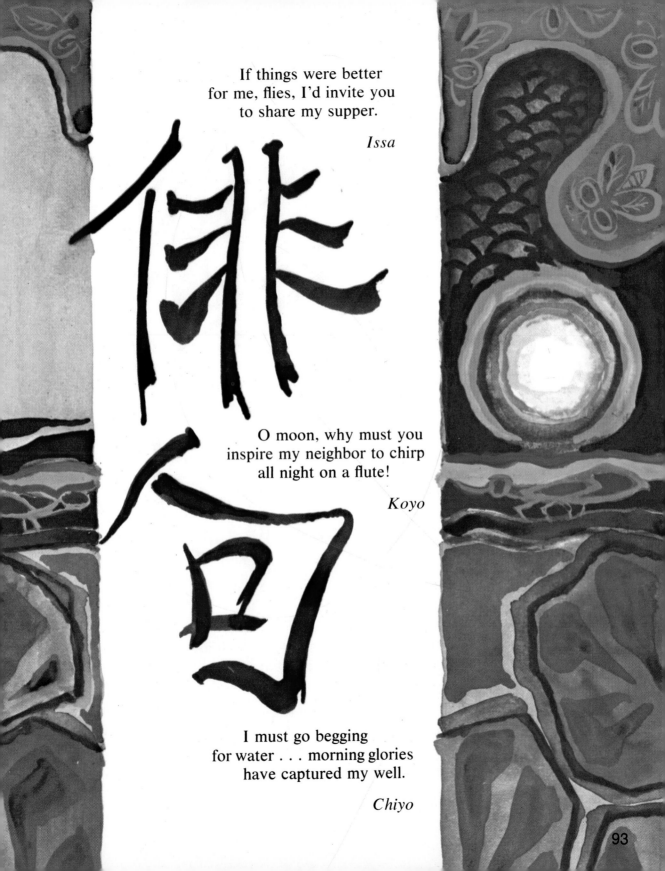

If things were better
for me, flies, I'd invite you
to share my supper.

Issa

O moon, why must you
inspire my neighbor to chirp
all night on a flute!

Koyo

I must go begging
for water . . . morning glories
have captured my well.

Chiyo

from
...and now Miguel

by Joseph Krumgold

The trouble with Miguel Chavez (mee-gel′ chah′ves) was that he was too young to do an adult's job and too old to enjoy children's play. He longed for a chance to prove to his father that he was ready to do a man's part of the work on their New Mexico sheep ranch. When an unexpected storm scattered part of the flock, Miguel thought his chance had come at last. But his father would not let him take part in the search for the missing sheep. Disappointed, Miguel headed for school.

Juby is my oldest friend. He lives in Los Cordovas (lohs kor′ doh-vahs) where the schoolhouse is. Ever since I can remember doing anything, fishing or playing ball or just talking, most of these things I did with Juby. And as long as I can remember Juby, he's been wearing this same big black hat with a wide brim on it curved up on the sides like the wings on a buzzard when it circles around, taking things easy in the sky. By now the hat is pretty old and has some holes in it, but it still looks all right on Juby, because it would be hard to tell what Juby looked like without it.

He was playing basketball when I came to the yard of the schoolhouse, my sister Faustine and my younger brother Pedro after me. That is, Juby and some of the others were playing just shooting for baskets, and as soon as he saw me, he waved his hand and quit, and came over.

"How're you doing?" he asked me.

I said, "Pretty good," because what's the use telling everybody your troubles?

"D'you folks lose any sheep?" he asked me.

"What?" I made one grab at his arm and held tight.

"Sheep," he said. "What's the matter?"

"Now look, Juby," I said. "What's the use talking, you and me? How do you know we got missing sheep? What about them?"

"I saw them."

"What?"

"At least I think they're yours. From the shape of the numbers they look like yours."

We don't put our brand on the sheep until after we shear them. But our numbers have a different shape to them from any of the others in the neighborhood.

"Where?"

"Then you did lose some sheep?"

"Juby!" I was a little excited. "What's the use, Juby? Just to talk? Where did you see them?"

"Well, you know Carlotta?"

"Who?"

"Our milk cow."

"Cows? What about the sheep?"

"I'm telling you. She got loose last night, Carlotta, and when I went to herd her back, I saw these sheep."

"Where? Where? Where?"

"What's the matter with you, Mike? Something wrong?"

"Juby," I said. "You and me, you're my oldest friend, aren't you?"

"Sure."

"Then tell me, where are the sheep?"

"Give me a chance. I saw them across the river. Maybe fifteen, ewes and lambs. They were heading straight for Arroyo Hondo (uh-roy'oh ohn'doh)." It was just in the opposite direction from where my older brother Blasito and the sheep wagon were, from where he had looked that morning. "Were they yours?"

"You don't know what this could mean, Juby. That is, for me."

But just then the bell started to ring, and Mrs. Mertian, who is the teacher of our school over there in Los Cordovas, she came to the door and told everybody to come in.

"Let's go." Juby went with the others into the class.

And that's the way things stood.

On one side, Mrs. Mertian with the bell ringing. And on the other side, the big mountains, looking very dark and a little mad, if you can think of mountains being mad. But that was the way they looked, and at that moment, there came thunder from behind them.

And in the middle, I stood. If it ever happened that I came home with the missing sheep? Could anything ever be better?

Mrs. Mertian said, "Miguel."

From the Sangre de Cristo (sahn′gree duh kris′toh) Mountains, there came thunder, very low.

I did not stand too long. Because there was no question about it! Nothing, that is to say, nothing at all could ever be better.

I headed straight for the boys on the other side of the yard.

"Miguel!" It was Mrs. Mertian yelling. I didn't even look back. I jumped into this whole bunch of bushes and started down the hill.

Big champion jumps, every one breaking a world's record: that's the way I came down that hill. With each jump, everything went flying. My books banging at the end of the rope in my hand, swinging all round. My arms, feeling like I had a dozen of them, each one going off by itself. My feet, like being on a bike, working away to keep my balance. But I couldn't balance. Except by jumping. I couldn't stop. Each jump bigger than the last. I cleared a bush, then a big cracked rock. Then, I wasn't going to make it but I did, a high cactus. Each jump I thought was the last. Each jump was going to end with a cracked head, a split rib, or maybe two broken legs. But it didn't. I don't know why. There was nothing I could do. I came down that hill like a boulder bumping in bigger and bigger bumps, bumping its way down a cliff. Straight for the river. Until I wasn't scared of falling anymore. I had to fall! Or land in the river. But how? I grabbed a bush. That didn't stop me. And then my books caught, between a couple of rocks. I slipped, grabbed at another bush. Slid a couple of feet, and then took off again. And then I landed. On my face. I landed in a whole piled-up bunch of mesquite. No one, I'm sure, ever since that hill was first there, ever came down it so fast.

I wasn't hurt. Except for a scratch stinging near my eye, I was all right. It didn't even bleed. All I needed was to catch my breath. I lay there in the bushes until I did. Breathing and listening for Mrs. Mertian, in case she came to the top of the hill and was yelling down at me. But I didn't hear any yelling. When I looked, she wasn't there. The school bell stopped, too. All there was to hear was the thunder, now and then, far off, and the wind blowing.

I got up, thinking I'd done it. After what Juby told me, there was only one thing to do, and now I'd done it. Here I was, just me, Miguel, getting the sheep that were lost, all alone. And there would be no one bringing them home but me. All I had to do was to get up there, on the mesa across the river, round up the bunch, and march them back to where everyone could see. It would be something worth watching, me herding the ewes and lambs that were lost back into the corral at home. My father would tell me how sorry he was about breakfast, the way he wouldn't let me go help. And I would tell my father, it was nothing, he didn't have to feel sorry.

I felt good. Looking at the mountains, and the mountains looking down at me as if to see what I was going to do next.

I hopped across the river. The easy place to cross was downstream a way, where there were more rocks to jump on. I didn't bother to go to the easy place. I could have made it even if the rocks were twice as far from each other, feeling good like I was, and all in practice from the way I'd come jumping down the hill. I only slipped into the water twice, without much water getting into my shoes at all.

To get up the cliff on the other side was not easy. It was steep in this place and wet and slippery with the rain, the stones high and smooth with nothing to grab on to, except sometimes a juniper bush. And, besides, having the books in one hand. It would be better without the books. But I couldn't leave them around or hide them, seeing they might get wet. I made it all right, pulling and crawling my way up. Steep places and books, that wasn't too hard. Not to find a bunch of lost sheep, it wasn't.

When I got up to the top and looked, I didn't see them. I guess I did expect a little bit they'd be up there waiting for me. But they weren't. I didn't mind too much. The kind of thing I was doing had to be hard. Such a big thing couldn't be too easy. It'd be like cheating. I set out, walking to the north.

Up on the mesa, it looked empty. Like one of those pictures that Pedro draws. One straight line across the middle of the page and big zigzags off to one side for the mountains. Then dark on top for the clouds, which he makes by smudging up all the pencil lines. And dark on the bottom for the mesa, which he makes with a special black crayon. That's all there is in the picture. And that's why it's a good picture. Because that's all there is. Except for some little bushes, juniper and chaparral and sagebrush. With nothing sticking up, only a high soapweed or a crooked-looking cactus. Nothing else.

Especially, no sheep.

I walked from one rise to the next. Every three or four steps turning all around as I walked. And when I got near to the top of each rise, I had to run. Because I thought in the next ten, fifteen steps up top there, sure, I'd see them. The first few times I saw nothing, which I didn't mind too much. And the next few times, I saw nothing, too. Pretty soon I was getting ready to see them, because after an hour or so of walking and turning around and running, I figured it was hard enough. Even for something big.

Besides, I had a pebble in my left shoe. I felt it down there coming up the cliff. I didn't mind then, because it only made everything even harder. And that was all right with me. But now it was getting to hurt good. And I couldn't sit down and take it out. That would be like giving up.

Besides, I didn't have any time to waste. The mesa spread out, as far as you could see, with many breaks—everywhere little canyons and washes. And it was sure that on top of the next canyon, maybe, I was going to see them, those sheep. If I didn't waste time getting up there. Which I didn't. But all I saw was the same kind of nothing that I saw from the last high place, just this wide straight line stretching right across the middle.

Walking down was harder than walking up. For one thing, walking down on my left heel made the pebble bigger. It was getting to feel like a rock. And for another, walking down, you've already seen what there is to see all around, and there's nothing to look forward to until you start to walk up again. It got so I was running more than I was walking. Running downhill because I wanted to get that part over with, and running up because I couldn't wait to get to the top. And all the time, turning around. I got pretty good at being able to turn around and keep running at the same time.

Except what good was it, getting pretty good at anything? When the only thing counted was to get one look, one quick look at those sheep.

All the turning around did was to get me so mixed up I didn't know whether I was going north, south, east, or west. Not that it made any difference, I guess. The sheep weren't particular which direction you went to find them. They weren't in any direction. There were just no sheep. There was all the dark sky, and all this straight flat plain you'd ever want to see. But no sheep.

And after a couple of hours of seeing no sheep, I would've been glad to see any sheep, even if they weren't ours. I kept trying to see sheep so hard, it was as if my eyes got dry and thirsty just to see sheep. To see nothing for two, three hours, especially sheep, it gets hard on your eyes.

It was getting hard on my left foot, too, with that big rock pressing in.

And it wasn't so easy on my hands, either, on account of the books. The books weren't very heavy, but when you keep that rope wrapped around your hand, it can pinch. And even if you take it off one hand and put it on the other, it isn't long before it's pinching that hand, too.

Another thing was, it got to be hard breathing. Because there was no time to stop and get a good breath. There was always somewhere to go take a look, and you couldn't stop because maybe that very second the sheep were moving away out of sight, and that very second if you were up on a top you'd see them.

After so many hours of it being so hard, I figured it was hard enough by then. It was getting long past the time I ought to find our sheep. Only it didn't make any difference how I figured. They weren't there to be found. Not anywhere.

And after a while, walking, walking, every place started to look as if you'd been there before. You'd see a piece of tumbleweed. And you were sure it was one you saw an hour before. It didn't help to think that maybe you were just walking up and around the same hill all the time.

Then looking, looking, I thought I heard a bell. I listened hard in the wind. One of the ewes that was lost might have a bell. In the flock, there are ten or a dozen sheep with bells. Each one is like the leader of a bunch. I stood still, listening. Then I heard it again, and it was for sure a bell. But it was the school bell, far away, back in Los Cordovas. It must've already become noon, and that was the bell for noontime. Soon the ringing far away stopped. And there was nothing to listen to again, except the quiet wind.

It was never the same, after I heard that bell. It made me feel hungry. Because the bell meant going home to eat. And feeling hungry, I got to feel not so good in the other parts of me. Like lonely. At the beginning, being alone was the best part of it, going off by myself to bring home the sheep. But now it was getting to look as if I wouldn't be bringing home any sheep. And that made a lot of difference about being alone, while everybody else was back there going home to eat. The only way I could go home was to find them. It wasn't only so I could bring the sheep back. I had to find them so I could go back, too.

From then on, I got very busy. I didn't stop to walk anymore. I ran. Everywhere I went, I kept up running, and I did most of my breathing going downhill when I didn't have to try so hard to keep running. There was hardly any breath left over to keep looking with. And that was the hardest part of all, the looking. Because there was never anything to see.

And after a long while, I heard the bell again. School was out for the day.

It was hard to figure out what to do next.

I could leave home. That's about all that was left. I couldn't go back without the sheep. Not after what my father said at breakfast, and especially not after the way he looked. And it was clear enough that, in all this whole empty place, I was never going to find them, those sheep. I could just as well stop, that's all. I could take some time and do a lot of breathing. I could bury my books under a bush. I could sit down and take off my shoe and get rid of that rock with all the sharp edges on it. Then I could go somewhere until I saw a lot of sheep and sit down and look at them, till I got enough again of looking at sheep. And then I could decide where I was leaving home to go to.

Maybe even to the Sangre de Cristo Mountains. On my own, by myself.

But when I looked at the mountains, I knew that was no good. It was impossible. There was only one way to go up into the Mountains of the Sangre de Cristo. And that was to make everyone see you were ready, and then you would go.

Indeed, in order that I should go this way, that's why I was looking for the sheep right now. And if I gave up looking for the sheep, then the idea of going up into the mountains, I had to give that up, too. I guess, if you are going to leave home, you just leave home, that's all, everything.

Except, it wasn't up to me anymore. It wasn't a question that I should give up looking for the sheep.

It was just no use.

I could keep running from the top of one rise up to the next, looking, looking with my eyes getting drier and drier, without any breath, and the bones in my hands like they were cracking, and the heel of my left foot like it was getting torn away, listening to nothing but the wind. I could keep on doing that forever. It wasn't a question of me giving up, it was a question that just everything had given up, me and everything.

So I sat down. I took a deep breath. And I started to untie the laces from my left shoe. And then — what do you think?

I smelled them.

It is not hard to know that what you're smelling is sheep. If only there are some sheep around to smell. They smell a little sweet and a little old, like coffee that's left over in a cup on the table with maybe used-up cigarettes in it. That's sort of what they smell like.

So when there was this smell, I looked around. I found out from which direction was the wind. And in that direction I went to the top of the next rise, a dozen steps. And no farther away than you could throw a rock, there they were coming up the hill toward me, about fifteen ewes and their lambs, ambling along, having a good time eating, just taking a walk as if there were no trouble anywhere in all the world.

Wahoo! I took off. Around my head in a big circle, I swung my books like a rope. I was going to throw a loop on all fifteen at once. Wahoo! I took off down that hill as if I were a whole tribe of Indians and the sheep were somebody's chuck wagon that was going to get raided. Wahoo!

The sheep looked up, a little like a bunch of ladies in church interested to see who was coming through the door.

I showed them who was coming through the door. Before they knew what was happening, they were moving. *Whoosh* — I let my books swing out, and I hit one right in the rump. *Whish* — I kicked another one with my foot that had the rock, so that it hurt me more, I think, than the sheep. I picked up a stone and — *wango* — I let a third one have it in the rear. I got them running right in the opposite direction from the one they were going.

I kept them going at a gallop. Running first to the one side, then to the other, swinging the books around my head all the time. Yelling and hollering so they wouldn't even dare slow down. They looked scared, but I didn't care. I had waited too long for this. And now I wanted them to know that I was here. I ran them down the hill fast enough to be a stampede. And whichever one ran last, he was the unlucky one. There were a lot of rocks around, and I throw rocks good.

At the bottom of the hill, I quieted down. Why was I acting so mad? I had no reason to be mad at the sheep. It wasn't as if they started out to get me in trouble. Indeed, because of them, here I was doing a great thing. I was finding them and bringing them home. If they hadn't taken it into their heads to go out and get lost, I never would have this big chance.

I quieted down. I stopped and I breathed. The air was good. After the rain, it was clean and it smelled sweet, like a vanilla soda in Schaeffer's Drugstore in Taos (towse) before you start to drink it with the straw. I took in the air with deep breaths. I sat down and took off my shoe. I found the rock down near the heel. But my goodness, it wasn't any kind of rock at all. Just a little bit of a chip off a stone. In my foot it felt like a boulder. But in my hand it didn't look like anything at all.

I was quieted down. We started off. It was going to be a long drive home. I didn't mind. There were so many good things to think about. What my father would say to me, and my grandfather.

It is no great trouble to drive a small bunch of sheep. You just walk behind them, and if one begins to separate, you start in the same direction that it starts and that makes it turn back and bunch up again. It was very little work. So there was much time to think what my uncles would say, and

my big brothers. And how Pedro would watch me.

There was much time to look around. At the mountains, not so dark now and not so mad. There was much to see, walking along thinking, breathing, and looking around. How the clouds now were taking on new shapes, the dark ones separating and new big white ones coming up. And on the mesa everything looked fine. I saw flowers. Before, when I was looking, there were no flowers. Now, there they were. The little pink ones of the peyote plants. And there were flowers on the hedgehog cactus, too, kind of pinkish purple some, and others a real red.

After a little while, I had something else to do. One of the lambs lay down. Whether it was tired or why, I don't know. I picked it up, the lamb under my arm, and in the other hand the rope with my books. It was not so bad. Even the rope didn't pinch anymore. And when the lamb got heavy under one arm, I put it under the other.

I felt better, now, than in a long time.

Even when I had to pick up this second lamb, which was straggling

behind, I still felt good. It was harder this way because now I couldn't use one arm after the other when the lambs got heavy, and there were the books I had to carry in addition. By now, though, we were coming down the dry wash that led to the river. There was not much farther to go.

They were a good bunch of sheep, all of them. When I brought them to the place in the river that was not so deep, they waded right across without any trouble. As for me myself, I almost fell in, but all the way this time. I was balancing myself all right on the rocks going across when one of the lambs started to wriggle as if it wanted to shake itself apart. But I held on, and I kept my balance and didn't fall in. I wouldn't have minded, anyway, if I had. If I came to the house with all my clothes wet, that would make what I did look as if it was even harder than it was.

Blasito was the first one to see me.

He was walking across the top of the hill near the corral when I came around the bend from the river.

"Hey, Mickey," he yelled, "where you been? What's those sheep you got?"

"Yours," I shouted back.

"Mine? What do you mean mine? The lost ones?"

"That's what," I yelled. "The lost ones!"

"No! No fooling?" He turned away from me. "Ai, Grandpa. Padre de Chavez. Mira! Miguel's here, with the bunch of sheep that was lost!" He looked back to where I was coming up the hill. "Bravo, Miguelito (mee-guh-lee′ toh)! Where'd you find them? How did it happen?"

"I'll tell you." I needed my breath to get up the hill with those two lambs under my arms. "Wait'll I get there."

The two of them were waiting for me, Blasito and my grandfather. Grandpa took one of the lambs from my arms. I let the other one down. Blasito shooed the bunch into the corral. And all three of us talked at once.

"Where did you find them?" asked Blasito.

"How did this happen?" said Grandfather.

"I'll tell it to you all," I said, "from the beginning. On the way to school this morning, I started to think."

Blasito interrupted. "Can't you tell us where you found them?"

"But that's what I'm trying to do. It started on the way to school."

"Miguel!" Grandfather wouldn't let me talk. "That part, you can tell us later. Where were they, the sheep?"

"Well, I'll tell you that first, then. I found them on the way to Arroyo Hondo, about twenty or thirty miles from here. But the way it started——"

"How many miles?" My grandfather looked at me with a smile.

"Oh, many miles. Many, many. What happened was——"

"How come you went north?" asked Blas. "All morning we've been riding toward the Arroyo del Alamo. In just the other way."

"First comes the way I went down the hill," I tried to explain. "With world-record jumps."

"Why is it that you don't want to answer your big brother Blas?" asked Grandpa. "How did you know where to look?"

"But why can't I tell it the way it happened? There was much trouble and it's very interesting."

"Later," said Grandpa. "Now, how did you know?"

"Well, I figured it out, and then I kept my ears open to hear things."

"What things?" said Blasito.

"Things people say."

"Like who?"

"Like Juby."

"He told you?"

"Look," I said to Blasito. "If I can't tell you in my own way, then what's the use? The kind of questions you ask, it makes it all sound like nothing. If I have to tell it this way, just to answer a few little questions, then what's the use my going out and finding the sheep anyway?"

"Use?" Blasito started to laugh. He banged me on the back. "It's a great thing, finding those sheep. I mean it, Miguel. You did fine!"

"What did you say?"

"I said great, fine!"

Grandfather took me by the hand and shook it like two men shaking hands.

"It's the truth," he said. "This that you have done, it was good."

"What?" I asked my grandfather.

"It was good."

"Better than the rest of us could do," said Blasito.

"What?" I asked Blasito.

"Better than the rest of us!" Blasito shouted so I would hear.

Grandpa still held my hand, and he shook it again. "You brought them in all right, Miguel. Like a real pastor."

"What?" I asked my grandfather. I wanted to hear everything twice.

"A real pastor," Grandpa said again, and we all looked at each other and smiled.

"Anything else?" I asked.

Before anyone could answer, there was a great shout from the house. "Miguel!" It was my father. It was a shout that sounded like thunder. "Miguel, get over here!"

He stood, he and my mother both, they stood in front of the house. And with them was Mrs. Mertian, my schoolteacher. They stood with Mrs. Mertian, who had come from the school in Los Cordovas, and they talked together.

My father looked around at us once again. "Miguel!"

Grandpa nodded to me that I should go to my father. "Take off," said Blasito. "You'd better get going."

I went. What else? It was too bad, real bad, my teacher should talk to my father before I even got a chance. I knew now that the things I was thinking about on the way home, of what my father would say to me, I knew that these were probably not the things he was going to say to me now. I walked to the house, where they stood, and Mrs. Mertian smiled at my mother, and they shook hands. Then she smiled at my father and shook hands with him. Then everybody smiled at each other and she left. But when they turned to watch me coming up the path, my father and mother, nobody smiled.

"Where'd you go?" said my father.

"Up there to the Arroyo Hondo. Many miles."

"What's in Arroyo Hondo?"

I knew my father didn't want to know what's in Arroyo Hondo. He knew as well as I. Just a grocery store and some houses. If I told him that, then everything would get all mixed up.

"It was not for what's in Arroyo Hondo. It's that I went after the sheep that were lost."

"This morning at breakfast, didn't we talk about the lost sheep?"

"Yes." I knew what he meant. "And you told me to go to school. And I did, I went to school."

"That is true. But it is only one small piece of what is true. The rest is, you didn't go in."

"Because of Juby. He is my oldest friend."

"And why is it, Miguel, that you will obey your oldest friend? But your parents, who are friends to you even older than your oldest friend, what they say means nothing."

"But Juby told me where were the missing sheep. So I went. I got them. I brought them home."

This is not the way I wanted to tell it at all. It was worse than with Blasito and Grandpa. It didn't sound hard this way, or like a big thing. It was like going down to the spring for a pail of water, no more. But what else was there to do? If things kept up like they were, it could get bad.

"You brought what home?"

"The missing sheep. They are in the corral."

My father and mother looked. Blasito and my grandfather, who were watching us, they pointed out the bunch in the corral.

"Well!" My father, at least, he didn't sound so mad anymore when he looked back to me.

"That's why I didn't go to school."

"Well." My father put his hands in his back pockets and looked down at me. "That's different. But not so different to make too much difference, Miguel. The sheep are important. Sure! But you, too, that you go to school is important. Even more important. Always there has to be something done with the sheep. And if every time something had to be done, you stayed away from school, my goodness, you'd grow up to be a burro. And you tell me, do we need a burro around this place?"

"No. Only mules and horses."

"And even more, what we need is young men who are educated, who have learned to know what is the difference between what is right and what is wrong. Do you understand?"

"I understand. And I promise. I will never miss my school again."

"Good. Now get into the house. Mrs. Mertian brought the lessons from today. So go in and do them and write your homework for tomorrow."

My mother took me by the back of the head to go into the house with me. And then my father did a wonderful thing. He gave me one good spank. And when I looked around up at him, he was smiling.

"It would not be true," he told me, "if I didn't say also I am glad to have the sheep back. How you did it was wrong. But for what you did, I want to thank you."

And then he went off to go to Blas and Grandpa where they were working on the tractor. My mother took me with her into the house.

"Come, Miquito (mee-kee'toh). That's enough for today. Good and bad, you've done enough."

How will Miguel finally prove to his father that he can do a man's job? You can find out by reading the rest of Joseph Krumgold's book . . . *and now Miguel.*

ABOUT THE AUTHOR

Joseph Krumgold was born in Jersey City, New Jersey, in 1908, and grew up near New York City. When he was young, his father owned and operated several movie theaters, so it was only natural that Joseph became interested in making movies. This interest eventually led him to Hollywood, California, where he began his career as a writer by writing stories for the movies. Mr. Krumgold says that his courses in chemistry and physics in high school and at New York University helped him learn about the technical production of movies, and his studies of English and history gave him ideas for stories.

Mr. Krumgold became interested in making documentaries, films that tell about real people and places. He left Hollywood and traveled and lived in many places, including France, Israel, and Italy, to make such films. His films won a number of prizes in the United States and abroad.

One of the films which Mr. Krumgold wrote and directed was made in New Mexico. It is about real people, the Chavez family, and was filmed while the story actually happened. Mr. Krumgold felt that he had more to say about Miguel Chavez than he could say in the movie, so he wrote the book . . . *and now Miguel.*

In 1954 . . . *and now Miguel* won the Newbery Medal, which is awarded each year to "the book which has made the most distinguished contribution to literature for children." The award encouraged Mr. Krumgold to write two other books on how a child grows up in different parts of the country. They are *Onion John,* awarded the Newbery Medal in 1959, and *Henry 3,* published in 1966.

Mr. Krumgold and his wife live with their one boy, Adam, on a farm near Hope, New Jersey, but a great deal of his time is spent abroad where he works on films and books.

MORE BOOKS TO ENJOY

A BEAR CALLED PADDINGTON, *by Michael Bond*

Paddington is a lovable bear who comes to live with the Brown family and manages to blunder into all kinds of mischief.

THE ENORMOUS EGG, *by Oliver Butterworth*

A boy's hen has been sitting on an enormous egg. When the egg hatches into a dinosaur, it creates excitement in the New Hampshire village and throughout the country.

LITTLE VIC, *by Doris Gates*

Pony Rivers, a stableboy, has great faith that Little Vic will become a great race horse. He and the horse stay together through difficult times to prove it.

OWLS IN THE FAMILY, *by Farley Mowat*

A family adopts two owls and has hilarious adventures with the new pets.

A WONDERFUL TERRIBLE TIME, *by Mary Stolz*

Two city girls who are close friends are given a surprise summer vacation. Their new experiences seem both wonderful and terrible to them.

TRULY ELIZABETH, *by Edna S. Weiss*

A girl from a farm tries to get used to living in the city. Because of her helpful, adventurous ways, she often gets into trouble, but she also makes friends.

CORNUCOPIA

CORNUCOPIA

THE TRAINED KANGAROO

How would you like to train a kangaroo? This true story by Bob Barton tells how he trained Bouncer, a very lively kangaroo, to be the star of an unusual circus act.

When Colonel Miller's show disbanded during the winter of 1897, I had expected to go north again for theater work. But one evening the boss stopped me as I came from the mess tent. "Come along over to my wagon, Bob," he said. "I have something to offer you."

I followed him around the corner of the big tent and over to where his wagon was lined up with the others. We climbed the stairs at the rear and entered the tiny compartment which was both his sleeping room and office.

"People are looking for something new these days," the Colonel began. "We can't go on the road next season with exactly the same show that we had this fall. I am thinking of keeping three or four of you somewhere in South Carolina to work with the animals. Would you care for the job?"

"Would I!" I shouted. "I'll train any kind of animal you can get hold of."

Colonel Miller smiled. "Perhaps you won't be so sure when I tell you that I am having a kangaroo shipped over here from England."

I quickly lost my enthusiasm. "But not a kangaroo!" I exclaimed. "That's impossible."

I told him some of Colonel Hartshorn's stories about his experiences in Australia. He said the kangaroos were the wildest animals he had ever seen. It was difficult for him even to get within gunshot of them. He said he tried many times to capture one, but found them faster than our North American deer.

"Not only that," I continued, "but he said they are mean animals. He saw one hop away from a fight with a huge snake. The snake was crushed to a pulp by the kangaroo's powerful back legs. No," I concluded with a definite shake of my head, "you can't expect us to train a kangaroo."

Colonel Miller waited until I was finished. I was a little angry when I saw that he was smiling.

"Maybe you don't want the job," he said. "Just forget it. I'll get somebody else."

"Wait," I cried, "I didn't mean that I wasn't willing to try. What do you expect me to train the kangaroo to do?"

"I don't know," said the Colonel frankly. "I haven't the least idea just what tricks are possible. A traveling show in England has used a pair for two years now. Perhaps they have done nothing more than exhibit them in a cage. Maybe that is all we shall be able to do with ours, but I have a feeling they can be trained for an act. You go down to Charleston with the others and I'll have the kangaroo shipped there as soon as he arrives in New York. You can work with him and find out what he will be able to do."

I was as impatient as any kid performer while waiting for the kangaroo to arrive. I talked with many of my friends about what stunts I might teach him. No one had any idea. They all laughed aloud at the very thought of training a kangaroo to take a place in the tent.

Colonel Miller's letter saying that the new performer had been shipped from New York came on the day before he was due to arrive. I could hardly wait until time to go down to the train.

The baggage men lifted the cage out of the car. I ran forward, anxious to get a first glimpse of my new trouper. Even then I could see that he was frightened. The train ride, the bouncing about during the transfer from the baggage car to the truck, and all the strange eyes peering at him had made the kangaroo wild with fear.

the dish. When I kept talking in a soft and soothing voice, he began to edge nearer and nearer. He ate his supper while I stood outside the cage only two feet away.

For the next three days I did most of my training when it was time for the kangaroo to eat. It took only a single day to teach him to come quickly for his meal when I put it into the cage. On the second afternoon I was able to reach out my hand and touch him. Time after time he scampered away as soon as he felt my hand on him. At last, however, he stayed to eat his supper while I patted him and talked softly to him.

Those of us who were in the camp had many arguments about the name for the kangaroo. Somebody suggested "Aussie" because he came from Australia. I thought such a name was too hard for children to say and understand.

In the end he was named by a small boy from Charleston who happened to be on the lot during the kangaroo's first adventure out of his cage. We had erected a corral in which to do the training. We carried the cage into this while the kangaroo was still inside. Then we opened the door.

I hustled the cage into one of our show wagons and got away from the crowd as soon as possible. It was clear to me that lots of training would be necessary before the kangaroo would be ready for the show. There was hard work ahead, and I was anxious to start it as soon as possible.

The letter from the Colonel had said that bread and milk were good food for a kangaroo, so that evening I prepared his supper with my own hands. I carried it to the cage and set it inside. At first he shrank into the corner and would not come near

The word kept coming back. "Bouncer! Bouncer!" I repeated to myself.

"There is a name for him!" I declared. "We'll call him Bouncer."

From then on the kangaroo was Bouncer to all the show people as well as to the boys and girls who came to see him.

This gave me an idea of what the kangaroo would be able to do for an act. He could leap so easily and so high that I felt we might make a tiny platform reaching fifteen or eighteen feet into the air, and teach him to hop up on it. I could even seem to hear the shouts of the crowd when the act was finished and the band struck up a tune.

It was only after many failures that I began to understand Colonel Miller's point of view. Perhaps a kangaroo was intended to be left in the wilds and not to work in an act. I had never used a whip in training animals, but I was sorely tempted to lay one heavily upon the kangaroo's back. It was discouraging to prepare all the equipment for an act only to have Bouncer forget my instructions and chase after a dog or stop to wrestle with Teddy, our trained bear.

Then for several days everything seemed to go well. The platform

Only those who have watched a rabbit hop can appreciate how strange the gait of a kangaroo is. We all laughed whenever he took a jump. The small boy who was peering through the fence was carried away with enthusiasm. "Say! Isn't he a bouncer?" he exclaimed.

upon which Bouncer was to jump had been raised from five feet to eight feet, and I felt certain that we could put it up to ten feet before the end of the month. It seemed that the hardest part of the training was over.

But another disappointment was in store for us. One morning Bouncer was mounted upon a small barrel waiting my signal for the great hop to the top of the platform. All my previous commands had been followed and I had every reason to believe we would finish the act successfully. Suddenly Bouncer raised his nose into the air as if smelling the wind. I gave a command to attract his attention, but it went unheard. Without warning the kangaroo hopped off the barrel, took one jump toward the fence, and went over the top with a great leap.

"Help! Help!" I screamed as I ran through the gate. "Bouncer has—"

I stopped, spellbound. Just before me was Bouncer, wrestling with the trained bear. Evidently he had sensed that Teddy was near and wanted to play. He made no move to run away when I came near, nor did he seem to object when I dragged him back to the corral.

"That kangaroo seems to care for nothing except wrestling," said Billy when I told him about it. "You had better forget the kangaroo act and work on something which will be of use on the road. Bouncer is an interesting animal all right, but he'll never make a performer."

I agreed with Billy at the time and decided to give up the daily training periods. But that night as we sat around the fire, I had an idea. At first it seemed so silly that I didn't mention it to the others.

Later in the evening I found courage enough to speak up about it. "What would you say," I asked, "to our working out a boxing act for the kangaroo? He is playful and seems to punch anyone in sight. Perhaps we could teach him to do some real boxing. It surely would be good for a few laughs."

My friends all thought the plan was foolish, while admitting that it would be a hit if the kangaroo would box or wrestle with his trainer.

"But it wouldn't be worth the trouble," concluded Billy. "You never could depend upon Bouncer to do his part."

Billy's opinion sounded reasonable, yet I thought about the idea a great deal in the next few days. Then another suggestion seemed worth trying. I didn't tell anyone about it, but I asked Harry Burton to make a pair of purple tights to fit Bouncer. Then I went downtown to find some boxing gloves large enough to go on the kangaroo's front paws.

Bouncer objected strongly to wearing the tights and gloves. He whaled me with both his front paws and tore his first pair of silk tights to shreds. I was patient, however, and it was not long until Bouncer was dressed and ready for a workout. All of us laughed at him. He looked with sad eyes at one glove and then the other. He worked desperately trying to yank them off.

After putting on a pair of gloves myself, I walked over toward the kangaroo. I touched him lightly with my glove and then lifted his paw the second time against my chest. A third time I punched him easily and this time it was not necessary for me to lift his paw. He had already struck me.

It was surprising how quickly Bouncer learned to box. He had seemed so dumb when we tried to teach him the trapeze act that no one felt he would learn to handle the gloves. The truth of the matter was that Bouncer was not taught to box. He took to it naturally. He boxed as he played. The act was a good one because it was a natural.

The kangaroo was often very funny without intending to be. One day we were milling about in the corral. He was striking me often, though usually not very hard. His greatest fault lay in his attempts to come close enough to hug me. I had a feeling that such a habit might spoil the act, so whenever he threw his front legs around my neck, I hit him rather hard with my boxing gloves. This day he was very friendly and got a grip around my neck which it was almost impossible to break. Partly in self-defense and partly because I wanted to teach him to keep away, I struck Bouncer very hard. The kangaroo slid away from me and sat down heavily on the ground. He looked up as if uncertain what to do next. He blinked his eyes and looked first at me and then at his gloves.

I was afraid that my unintended blow had ruined our act, for when I went over to help him up, Bouncer scampered away on all fours. He had evidently had enough. It took all the persuasion of nearly a full box of sugar before he would exchange blows. The sugar had a magic way with him, though, and Bouncer would do almost anything to get it. He forgot his hurts and was soon busy again with his boxing.

The first time the kangaroo act was used in the tent it caused a great sensation. I wore bright-yellow tights and arranged to have the act announced as if it were a championship fight. The crowd howled with laughter when we entered the ring. Bouncer carried on like an old trouper. He did every part of the act as we had planned it. When the time came for him to strike the blow which was to send me to the sawdust, he delivered it with considerable strength. He jumped up and down with glee as I lay on the ground.

Bouncer was not as dependable as some of the other animals in the show. There was always the possibility that he would do something unexpected. He had no formal stunts. The boxing act, however, allowed for his strange ways.

Our kangaroo didn't play his part only in the tent. He was a boxer all the time. He was apt to strike anyone who interfered with what he wanted to do. On one occasion, however, he tried to use his skill to help a friend.

Bouncer had become very fond of Billy. I was walking around the grounds one evening holding the kangaroo by a chain when suddenly we came upon a strange sight. It was Billy's birthday and some of the boys were tossing him in the air in a blanket.

Billy was shouting: "Hey, that's enough! Let me down!" Bouncer thought he was calling for help. He broke away from me and hopped over to the crowd. Then he began punching right and left. His blows were not hard and the boys took it in good fun. I couldn't help admiring the loyalty of the kangaroo to the one he recognized as his friend.

It was always great fun to give Bouncer a bath. Show people often went down to some brook or stopped beside a lake to wash. Most animals dislike the water and Bouncer was no exception. For some time it was impossible to get him close to it. The best we could do was to lead him down to the edge of the stream and there sponge him off. Gradually, however, Bouncer began of his own choice to wade into the water a short distance. It was not long before he enjoyed every chance to splash in a stream. We always heard his strange and pitiful cry if we went bathing without him.

The kangaroo was a peculiar beast. Many of the show people were certain, at first, that they could never become very fond of him. But Bouncer was loyal to all his friends, and came to be one of the best loved animals in the show.

AUGHOR

AUTHOR

As a young boy, Bob Barton developed a strong interest in circuses and circus life. When he was only twelve years old, he left home to join a traveling gypsy caravan show. With him, he took his pet dog whom he had taught to do many tricks. Later, he joined a type of circus called a covered wagon show. He was a clown and animal trainer with the show for many years. The story you have just read was taken from a book Mr. Barton wrote about his experiences.

There was an Old Man of Koblenz,
The length of whose legs were immense;
He went with one prance
From Turkey to France,
That surprising Old Man of Koblenz.

Edward Lear

Jeremiah, a thrifty young fox,
Wore some of the gaudiest sox.
When asked why this was,
His wife said, "Because
He buys them on sale by the box."

Edward Mullins

LIMERICKS

There once was a finicky ocelot
Who all the year round was cross a lot
Except at Thanksgiving
When he enjoyed living
For he liked to eat cranberry sauce a lot.

Eve Merriam

USING AN INDEX

How do you find the information that a book has on a given topic or a question you want answered? Do you open the book just anywhere and keep turning pages to the left or right until you come to the information you want? There is no need for you to use that slow way of finding what you are looking for. Instead, you can use the index that is at the back of most books you use in studying.

Look at the part of the index of a book on the next page. The words printed in heavy black print and farthest to the left in each column are called **main topics.** They name people and things that the book tells about, and they are arranged in the order of the letters in the alphabet.

When you use the index of a book to help you find the information the book gives on some topic or question, you must decide what word to look for among the main topics. We call that word a **key word.** Always try to choose a key word that names what your topic or question talks about.

Sometimes the key word to use for a question is in that question. What word would you use as a key word for each of these questions?

1. What are the different uses of helicopters?
2. What did the first automobiles look like?

Sometimes there may be in a question more than one word which you should use as a key word. For example, take the question *How does climate affect travel?* If you used only the

Africa, automobiles in, 219; bridges, 255; burdens carried by men, 314; burros, 331; railroads, 182, 185; roads, 210; wagons, 293

Airplanes, first, 8, 9 *p;* how controlled in the air, 15; how supported in the air, 16; how they came to be, 10–14; uses of, 63–72

Airports, in mid-ocean, 97–98; in the United States, 70–72; on air-mail routes, 65

Automobiles, different uses for, 217–219; how they came to be, 221–224; how they helped to improve roads, 207; increase in production, 227, 228 *t;* what the first ones were like, 224–226

Balloons, first crossing of the Atlantic, 87; first crossing of the English Channel, 89; first successful dirigible, 83; hot air, 74–78

Bicycles, how their use helped to improve roads, 206; how they came to be, 250; used in many parts of the world, 214

Boats, ancient, 411–412; native in different parts of the world, 418–420

Bridges, built by natives, 255–258; famous, 249–252; importance of, 111, 243

Burros, in the United States, 189–191; work they do, 208, 314–315, 386

Canals, George Washington's interest in, 2; in China, 350, 419; in Europe, 384, 385; in the United States, 380

Cargoes, how loaded and unloaded on ships, 382, 401; kinds of, 356–358, 362, 382, 401, 406, 409

Cars, early railroad, 105, 136; electric, 236–237; modern railroad, 109–117. *See also* **Pullman cars**

Chicago, great railroad center, 117, 118 *m;* reached by foreign planes, 47; reached by ocean liners, 383

Coke, *see* **Fuel**

Dirigible balloons, advantages of, 96; defined, 182; early experiments with, 83; how brought to earth, 92–94; how managed in the air, 91; modern, 85; uses for, 96

Dog teams, of the Eskimos, 303; used by Arctic explorers, 59

Donkeys, in China, 333; in Egypt, 333; in Mexico, 293; in Sicily, 295; on lower slopes of the Andes, 352. *See also* **Burros**

Drags, used by the Indians, 299

Drawbridges, 244

Dredges, in a busy harbor, 363

Dry lands, Sahara Desert, 186; 345–349; transportation in, 344

Dugouts, in ancient times, 411; in Central America and Africa, 412, made by American Indians, 411 word *climate* as a key word, you might miss some of the information the book gives. That is why you may also need to use the word *travel* as a key word.

What two words would you use as key words for each of the following questions?

3. Is coal mined in Illinois?
4. How is radio used in fighting crime?
5. Why is cement used in building bridges?

Sometimes a word you need to use as a key word is not in the question. For example, take the question *In what states are the most peaches and apples grown?* If the index did not list the words *peaches* and *apples* among its main topics, would you decide that the book gave no information you needed? You should not do that. You might get the help you need by using the word *fruits* as a key word.

Suppose that an index you are using does not have among its main topics either of the italicized words in each of the following sentences. What other word that is not in the question would you try to use as a key word?

6. For what purposes are *tin* and *copper* used?

7. Are both *wheat* and *corn* grown in the same places?

Look again at the part of an index used in this lesson and find the main topic **Airplanes.** After it you can see five groups of words. They are *first, how controlled in the air, how supported in the air, how they came to be, uses of.* Each of these groups of words is called a **subtopic.** The subtopics show what the book tells about the main topic **Airplanes.** In some indexes, the subtopics are arranged in the order of the letters of the alphabet. In others, they are arranged in the order in which they are talked about in the book.

After each subtopic are one or more numbers. Each of them is the number of a page on which information is given about that subtopic. A dash between two numbers, such as 63—72, means that information on the subtopic begins somewhere on page 63 and ends somewhere on page 72. In some indexes the letter *m, p, d,* or *t* is used after a page number to tell you that on the page is a map, a picture, a diagram, or a table. For example, after the main topic **Airplanes,** you will find: first, 8, 9*p.* This means that on page 9 there is a picture of the first airplane.

What subtopic in the part of an index you looked at would you use to find information on each of these questions?

1. How are cargoes loaded on ships?

2. In what ways were the first bicycles different from those we use today?

It is easy to choose the right subtopic to use for the first question, because one or more important words in the question are also in the subtopic. It is not so easy to choose the right subtopic for the second question, because none of the important words in the question are in the subtopic. You need to look at all the subtopics that come after the main topic **Bicycles** and

try to decide which is the best one to try. Probably the sub-topic *how they came to be* is the one to use.

Find the main topic **Coke** in the part of an index. No sub-topics come after that topic, but you will find there the words "*See* Fuel." Those words mean that by using the main topic **Fuel** you may be able to find the information you want about coke.

Find the main topic **Donkeys** in the part of an index. After the subtopics you can see the words "*See also* **Burros.**" Those words mean that by looking under the main topic **Burros** you can find where to look for other information about donkeys.

Discussion

Help your class answer these questions:

1. How can using an index help you find information on a topic or question?
2. How are the main topics in an index arranged? In what ways may the subtopics be arranged?

3. What is the key word for each of questions 1 and 2 near the beginning of this lesson?

4. Why will you sometimes need to use more than one word as a key word for a question? What words should be used as key words for questions 3, 4, and 5?

5. When would you need to use a key word that is not in the question? What word should probably be used as a key word for each of questions 6 and 7?

6. Why may it sometimes be harder to choose the right sub-topic than it is at other times?

7. What does the dash between two page numbers tell you? What does the word *See* tell you? What do the words *See also* tell you? What do the letters *m, p, d,* and *t* in an index tell you?

On your own

On what pages listed in the part of an index on page 126 would you expect to find information on each of the following questions? Write and number your answers on a sheet of paper.

1. What are some of the main canals in the United States?
2. What heavy loads do men in Africa carry?
3. Were more automobiles made in the United States in 1964 than in 1960?
4. In what countries in Europe are bicycles commonly used?
5. Where were the first airplane flights made?
6. What improvements have been made in railway cars?
7. What are the main airports in Chicago?
8. What were the first balloon flights over large bodies of water?

Checking your work

If you are asked to do so, read aloud the answers you wrote for some of the questions. If you made a mistake in any answer, find out why it is a mistake.

Our Friends-The Bees, Wasps, and Hornets

By Russ Kinne

Are you afraid of bees? Most people are. Did you ever notice, when a large insect flies near people, how many will try to duck or shoo it away? If you ask them what kind of insect it is, they will probably say, "A bee." Now, with your sharp eyes, you may have noticed that these "bees" are not all the same size. Furthermore, they come in a good many different color combinations. Are *all* of them really bees?

No, they are not. There are many of these insects, but they all belong to the same family. Scientists have named the family *hymenoptera* (hie′muh-nahp′tuh-ruh).

Since most of the hymenoptera can sting, parents are wise when they tell their children to stay away from them. For the very few persons who are extra sensitive, or even allergic to stings, a single sting can be a very serious matter indeed. In most cases stings are unpleasant, and usually unnecessary. But that doesn't mean you can't look and learn. If you move slowly and gently, chances are you won't have any trouble. But if you hit at these insects, or hurt them, they will sting you. So, *don't do it!*

Around flower gardens, the honeybee is the most common.

A honeybee sucking nectar from a coneflower.

A honeybee stinging. Tiny barbs on the shaft hold the stinger in the victim's skin and cause the stinger to be pulled out of the bee's body. This injures the bee to the extent that he will soon die.

A honeybee leaving a flower carrying a load of pollen on its legs.

Honeybees on a honeycomb looking for cells in which to deposit their load of pollen.

A beekeeper removing honey from a bee hive.

It is about three-quarters of an inch long—the size of a penny—and its color ranges from black to light brown in color. You may notice blobs of bright yellow pollen on its hind legs, and as you watch, it may suck a drop of sweet nectar from each flower. It uses pollen as food and makes honey from the nectar. We don't know why, but a hive of bees makes far more honey than it can possibly use. The hive normally makes its home in an old hollow tree. Long ago both bears and men learned about honey. They began to raid these "bee trees" and take the honey stored inside. Bears still do. But man has discovered that bees will live quite happily in special wooden boxes in backyards and orchards and let the beekeeper take away the surplus honey every few weeks. This is where the honey that you find in the market comes from.

But this is not the most important thing bees do. The pollen that sticks to the bee's body is carried from one flower to another. This is called cross-pollination. Cross-pollination helps to make healthier plants and bigger and better fruits. Without cross-pollination, some plants cannot produce seeds at all. In commercial apple-growing country, men even pay the beekeepers to let their bees loose in the orchards. So you can see how important the little honeybee can be!

Almost everyone in the world knows the big black and yellow bumblebee. It's the largest of our native bees and wasps. It feeds on nectar and pollen, and is a valuable pollinator. It may be that some plants, like the red clover, could not survive without this insect's services.

Do you know where the bumblebee's home

is? The nest is underground. Bumblebees make honey too, but not nearly so much as the honeybees do.

Another large bee is often confused with the bumblebee. This is the black carpenter bee, which drills cavities in soft wood. There are even some nesting in the roof of my house! Once in a while, these bees will drill deeply enough to weaken a piece of wood, but this is rare. I enjoy watching "my" bees, and they are welcome to stay. Carpenter bees have an all-black abdomen, while the bumblebee's abdomen is black and yellow. With a little practice, you can tell them apart quite easily.

You may see a black and yellow insect, about the size of a honeybee, that you will recognize at once—the yellow jacket hornet. If you have met it before, you may know that it has a short temper and will sting immediately if anything disturbs it! If you move slowly and gently, however, it may let you come close enough to watch it. I even let them feed from a drop of honey on the end of my finger—but I wouldn't advise you to try this!

All these insects will let *us* alone if we let *them* alone. But beyond this, they all have their own "personalities," and it helps to be able to recognize them by sight.

Sometimes you may notice a yellow jacket almost three times as big as the common ones. Lots of people think they are yellow jacket "queens," but they are more likely to be European hornets, which have become established in the United States. If you can get a good look, you will see they are really brown and yellow.

A bumblebee on a red clover blossom.

Head-on shot of a bumblebee. Note the large compound eyes and mouth parts.

A carpenter bee.

Yellowjackets in their nest.

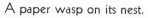

A paper wasp on its nest.

Yellow jackets usually build a nest underground. The European hornet sometimes makes its nest from a branch of a tree or under the eaves of a building where it is protected from rain and wind. These nests are very complicated structures that the insects build out of paper. They chew up bits of wood, mix it with saliva, and mold it into shape. When it dries, it is very strong and light in weight.

One of the most common of all wasps, found all around the world, is called the paper wasp. These wasps are almost tame. They usually build a comblike nest under the eaves of a building. It is not hard to find one. These wasps are over an inch long and are usually brown or brown and black. They are very helpful and should not be destroyed. They go quietly about their own affairs, almost never bother people, and eat thousands and thousands of harmful insects. We should be glad to have them around!

There are many other kinds of bees and wasps and hornets, but no one should be scared when they appear. In fact, many of them don't even have stingers! There are also flies and other insects that look a great deal like bees and wasps, and, of course, these can't harm us at all.

Bees, wasps, and hornets are fascinating to study and watch. If we follow the advice of "look but don't touch," we shouldn't get into any trouble.

Henry Reed is spending the summer with an aunt and uncle in Grover's Corner, New Jersey. There isn't much to do in Grover's Corner, which consists of only nine houses. Even if there were, there is only one person to do anything with—Midge Glass—and Midge is a girl! Still Henry manages to find plenty to fill the daily journal he is keeping.

The following entry from Henry's journal is one of the many that appears in the book, *Henry Reed, Inc.*

A Day in the Life of Henry Reed

by Keith Robertson

Not too much has happened since my last entry. Last night I went with the Glasses to the outdoor movies, which I enjoyed a lot. The reason we went to the outdoor movies was that we didn't have any lights in Grover's Corner last night. The reason we didn't have any lights is connected in a way with something Midge and I did.

The Ainsworths, who live down near where the new house is being built, had a wasps' nest in a mulberry tree out near their chicken house. Midge heard about it and went over to look at it several days ago. It was one of those great big gray paper nests that wasps build, and I'd only seen one of them before. Most of the wasps around here just build sort of open cones underneath the eaves of buildings and don't make a paper covering around them. This was one of the biggest wasps' nests I've seen, even bigger than the ones in the Museum of Natural History when I visited there two years ago.

"I'd like to have that," I said.

"Why?" Midge asked. "Is it full of honey?"

I explained that wasps don't store honey like bees do. They kill spiders and flies and store them away instead. Midge doesn't know even the simplest facts about insects and animals.

"Then what do you want it for?" Midge asked.

"I'd like to look at it," I said. "The wasps knew how to make paper before people did. Besides we might be able to sell it."

"Who would want a wasps' nest?" Midge asked.

"A museum," I replied.

She didn't think much of the idea, but I asked Mrs. Ainsworth if she minded if I took the wasps' nest. She said certainly not. In fact, she would gladly pay me a dollar if I would take it away. Midge was a little more in favor of the idea then and agreed to help me.

"We could hang it up near the barn," I said, "and the wasps would eat all the spiders on the second floor."

"Nothing doing," Midge said flatly. "There's not room enough in this firm for the wasps and me, too. Have you ever been stung by a wasp?"

I'd never been stung by a wasp, although I have been stung by bees. Midge said it wasn't the same thing at all. Finally I agreed that we wouldn't try to preserve the wasps, just the nest. We found a five-gallon can that seemed like the perfect container, and we went over to get the nest.

I borrowed Mrs. Ainsworth's ladder and got it up against the tree without any trouble. I was about two-thirds of the way up the ladder with a saw in my hand, planning to saw off the limb where the nest hung, when I got stung. Midge was right. A wasp's sting is nothing like a bee's sting. It really hurts. I decided right then and there that I wasn't going to get the nest until I had the proper equipment.

I asked Uncle Al that night if he knew where I could buy a can of smoke that beekeepers use. Naturally, he wanted to know what I was going to use it for. I told him that I wanted to get rid of some wasps.

"Your mother liked bees and you like wasps," he said, shaking his head. "I suppose you'll be stung less if you have the smoke than if you don't have it. Frankly, my advice is to stay as far away from wasps as possible. I have put off painting the eaves of that garage out there for two years because of those wasps."

He got me the smoke yesterday morning, and I got out my mother's old bee equipment. The net was full of holes, but Aunt Mabel made me a new net out of an old curtain. The net is attached to the hat at the top and comes down over my shoulders. There are two drawstrings to pull it tight around your chest and under the arms. After I got the net on, I put on a jacket and some long gloves. Then I was practically sting-proof.

I tried out my suit first on the wasps' nests under the eaves of Uncle Al's garage. These weren't the kind of wasps that build the big paper nests, of course, and they weren't very interesting, but my net worked perfectly and I didn't bother using any smoke. I simply climbed up on the stepladder and knocked all the cones down. The wasps buzzed around my head, as mad as could be, but they couldn't get through to sting me.

Next we went over to Mrs. Ainsworth's, and I put up the ladder again. I climbed up to the top, not paying any attention to the wasps. When I got up to the nest, I gave it several shots from my smoke can. I wasn't worried about them stinging me, but I knew that when I started sawing off the limb they would really get mad. Midge was holding the ladder, and she didn't have any net.

Everything went perfectly, which shows that if you plan in advance you can do almost anything without any trouble. I sawed off the outer end of the limb first, then sawed it again between the tree and the nest. That left the nest hanging to the little piece of limb, about a foot long, which I was holding.

I had poked a tiny hole in the lid of the can and had threaded a little piece of wire through this. I climbed down with the nest, hung it to the little wire loop in the lid, and put the lid carefully on the can. Midge had retreated to the corner of the house where she stood watching.

There were quite a few wasps who were out hunting, and I stood there for a few minutes watching them as they came back. They looked pretty silly zooming in, expecting to find a great big nest and instead finding nothing but empty space. I suppose a person would feel the same way if he arrived home to find that a hurricane had blown away his house. I felt a little bit mean, because I certainly played those wasps a dirty trick.

I felt even sorrier for the wasps that were in the nest inside the can. They were prisoners and would starve to death. At least the others could start over again. Midge didn't seem to feel a bit sorry for any of them, though. She said that she hoped all of them got their stingers doubled over trying to sting the tin can.

I picked up the can and we started back toward the barn. As

we passed the new house, we noticed that a bulldozer was digging a hole off to one side of the house.

"Maybe they're going to have a swimming pool," Midge said hopefully. "But I don't know why they didn't start on that first instead of the house. Half the summer's gone."

"I doubt if it's a swimming pool," I said. "It doesn't look big enough."

"Then what is it?"

The bulldozer was digging dirt out of the hole and pushing it into a low spot up near the front of the lot. "Wait until he comes back up here and we'll ask him," I said.

I set the can down beside the road and climbed up the bank to watch the bulldozer. Midge joined me a minute later. The bulldozer came chugging toward us, and Midge waved her hand.

"Is that a swimming pool?" she shouted.

"No such luck," the driver shouted back. "Digging out for the footing for a garage."

He had stopped the bulldozer to answer Midge but now he started again, distributing the dirt around evenly along the front part of the lot. A plumber's truck came tearing down the road and turned in the driveway. The man was driving much faster than he should have been, and I suppose he didn't realize that he had reached the driveway until the last minute. He slammed on his brakes, his tires screeched, and he skidded around the turn into the driveway. I had set the can well out of the way, I thought. It would have been for any ordinary driver, but not for this cowboy. His rear bumper just touched the can, but that was enough to knock it over. It rolled down into the ditch and the lid came off.

"Look out! Wasps!" Midge shouted at the top of her voice, and she took off like a streak for the front of the lot.

I had put my bee hat and net and gloves and can of smoke on top of the can when I'd set it down beside the road. They fell down in the ditch with the can and I couldn't get to them.

I waited a few seconds, but when I saw those wasps coming out of that can like a black cloud, I decided to follow Midge.

"Look out! Those are wasps!" I yelled to the bulldozer driver in case he hadn't heard Midge.

He said later that he hadn't heard either one of us. The first thing he knew about the wasps was that he had been stung on the neck. They zoomed in on him like a bombing squadron and were all around him at once. He started swinging his arms around like mad, and then he noticed that he was headed for the ditch. He gave the wheel a yank and started swinging at the wasps again. By this time they were really after him. Later he counted fifteen wasp stings, so I suppose most of the time he didn't know what was happening. Finally he decided that the only thing to do was to stop the bulldozer and to get out of there. By that time it was too late. Just as he stopped it, it banged against the light pole beside the driveway. The bulldozer wasn't going fast but the ground was soft beside the light pole, and it was just a temporary pole. It didn't break off, but it leaned over at about a forty-five-degree angle. It reached far enough to hit against the main lines at the road and snap one of them.

By this time the wasps had reached the house, and they were still after blood. They chased the mason and the two carpenters out of there and stung all three of them. The man who had caused all the trouble, the plumber, didn't get stung at all.

After a few minutes passed, I found a long stick and I slipped back out by the road. I managed to get my hat and net and put these on. Then I walked down into the ditch, got my gloves, and put the lid back on the can. Most of the wasps had left the nest. It had broken into three or four pieces. I was pretty sore at that plumber for ruining my wasps' nest, but there wasn't much point in complaining. I couldn't ask him to pay for the nest because I didn't know what it was worth. I decided to say nothing. Besides, I thought it might be just as well if that bulldozer operator didn't know where the wasps came from.

I dumped what remained of the nest out in the alfalfa field in back of the lot and put away my bee equipment. I hadn't seen a sign of Midge since the can was knocked in the ditch. As I came out of the barn, she came across the street.

"Where have you been?" I asked.

"I went back to collect that dollar from Mrs. Ainsworth," she said. "I thought maybe I'd better get it before she tried to cook dinner tonight."

"What's that got to do with it?"

"She's got an electric stove," Midge said. "In case you haven't heard, there isn't any power in Grover's Corner."

She was right. Somebody phoned the power company and they promised to be out as soon as they could, but they hadn't appeared yet at dusk. Everybody in Grover's Corner last night ate dinner by candlelight. Of course, some people couldn't even cook dinner at home because they had electric stoves, so they went out to restaurants. Aunt Mabel has a bottle-gas stove so it didn't make much difference at our house. The Glasses have an electric stove, but Mr. Glass grilled a steak outside on the charcoal grill.

Mr. Glass had planned to do some work on a scientific paper that he is writing, but since there weren't any lights he decided to take the family to the outdoor movies and they invited me to go along. The power company worked fast, and by the time we got back from the movies there were lights again.

AUTHOR

Keith Robertson was born in Iowa, and grew up in the Middle West. Following high school, he joined the Navy and spent two years at sea. Later, he graduated from the United States Naval Academy, and during World War II he served aboard destroyers on both the Atlantic and Pacific Oceans.

After the war, Mr. Robertson left the Navy and worked several years for a publisher. During that time he began writing books for young people and has been doing so ever since. Besides *Henry Reed, Inc.,* he has written two other books about Henry Reed: *Henry Reed's Baby Sitting Service* and *Henry Reed's Journey.*

Mr. Robertson is married and has three children. He says that his children and their young friends supplied him with most of his ideas for the Henry Reed books. But now his children are grown up, and he has to find new sources of ideas for his books.

The Robertsons now live on a small farm in central New Jersey where they have surrounded themselves with farm animals and good books— two things they enjoy very much.

Flight to Freedom

by Frances Humphreville

Harriet Tubman had as much courage, intelligence, and daring packed into her small body as any of the heroes you have read about. Born a slave on a Maryland plantation, she had a deep longing for freedom, not just for herself but for all her people. She was in her twenties when she made her own escape. During the next twenty years, she guided so many slaves to freedom that a $40,000 reward was offered for her capture. Many times her determination and her knowledge of woodlands saved her and her charges from being captured by slave hunters and their dogs. During the Civil War, she served the Union Army not only as a cook and a nurse, but also as a spy and a scout. She died in 1913, a tiny lady whose life spanned nearly a century of adventure.

This story, taken from Frances Humphreville's book HARRIET TUBMAN: FLAME OF FREEDOM, tells of Harriet's daring escape to freedom.

One day Harriet was working near the road. She had been sent to trim some of the hedges that screened the highway from the fields.

A carriage stopped near her and a woman got out. She was dressed in the clothes of a Quaker. Pretending to fix the harness on her horse, she stood very close to Harriet.

"How did you hurt your head?" she asked. Her voice was low and kind.

Harriet knew that Quakers did not believe in slavery. She told the woman about the accident, a bad blow on her forehead, which had happened while she was trying to protect a fellow slave who was escaping.

"Have you ever heard of the Underground Railroad?" asked the woman.

"I've heard the men talk to my father about it," Harriet answered. "I know it isn't a real railroad. It's made up of people who help the slaves to freedom, isn't it?"

"Indeed it is. Over three thousand people help run our railroad. We've taken almost one hundred thousand slaves to free states."

"Why, that's wonderful!" Harriet exclaimed.

The Quaker lady glanced around her and then got into her carriage. Looking straight ahead, she said quickly, "If I were to travel north, I would follow the Choptank River. I would go up to its beginning. That is just at the border between Delaware and Maryland. Then I'd go north by northeast. It's fifteen miles from the border to John Hill's farm in Camden, Delaware."

In a few minutes she was gone. Harriet repeated the directions to herself so she would not forget them. It was good to know that somewhere there were people who believed that the slaves should be helped to freedom.

Harriet had always loved the Bible story that told of how Moses led his people, the people of Israel, out of slavery in Egypt. One of her favorite songs was "Go Down, Moses," but the slaves were not allowed to sing it now.

Go down, Moses,
Way down in Egypt's land.
Tell old Pharaoh,
Let my people go.

Then one night when Harriet was bringing in her last basket of cotton as the full moon was coming up, her spirits rose with the beauty of the evening. With her sturdy back erect and her head high, she was humming softly "Go Down, Moses" when a big black whip came down in a searing lash across her shoulders.

"How many times do you have to be told not to sing that song?" the overseer demanded. "I'm in charge here now, and you are no longer wanted. I'm going to take care of you this week once and for all when the cotton's in." The whip cracked around her bare ankles. "Think about that while you wait for the trader!"

When a slave was traded, he had to go wherever he was sent. Harriet knew the time had come. She must make a break for freedom or forever be a slave.

Later that night, Harriet crept from her bed and made ready for the journey. She had planned the route she would follow and the food she would need. Now, in a small bag, she packed some corn bread and some scraps of pork. She took the few coins that were left from her earnings. Though she felt a pang of regret, she put the family's best hunting knife into her pocket.

She walked to the nearby cabins for two of her brothers, keeping carefully to the shadows. Benjamin and William Henry did not really want to go with Harriet. They talked in hushed whispers to her now. They reminded her of the bloodhounds that could track them down so easily. They talked about the unknown route and the cold weather of the North.

"You know the rewards are getting larger," William Henry said. "The punishment gets worse for each runaway. Let's wait and see what happens here."

Harriet was furious. "Stay here, then," she said, and her voice shook with anger. "It's now or never for all of us. The trader will be here again in the next few days."

"We'll go with you," Benjamin said after a moment.

So they moved out singly and met beyond the cornfields near the woods. They hadn't walked far before a fog shut down. Harriet was used to it, for mist and fog often hung over the land along Chesapeake Bay, but it made her brothers uneasy. They couldn't see ahead of them for more than a few feet. There were no stars to help tell directions.

After a while a light rain began to fall. The men fell into holes at the swamp edge. They walked into small bushes and briers that tore at their clothes. They were terrified of the many night noises. They pleaded with Harriet to turn back. They stumbled, fell, and argued with her about the fast pace she had set and the direction she had taken.

Harriet moved as though guided by an unknown force. She seemed not to hear their pleading or their whining.

When they finally stopped for a short rest, her brothers declared they had decided to turn back.

Benjamin said, "We're going home. You'd better come, too. The dogs'll find you in an hour or so in the morning. We can't have walked very far. Come on back, Harriet. The risk is too great."

Harriet shook her head. "I want liberty," she said. "No man will ever take me alive. I don't intend to give up easily, now or later. I will fight for freedom as long as my strength lasts. What better way to go than that?"

Her brothers hugged her and turned away. William Henry's face was wet with tears. Harriet waited, hoping that her brothers might change their minds and return, but the fog swallowed them up, and she was alone.

As she started out again, the fog lifted. Soon the bright North Star was shining down to help her on her way. Harriet had a feeling of wild joy, as if this were a sign of approval for her lonely journey.

At the first sign of daylight, Harriet headed for one of the great swamps that ran behind many of the large plantations. She was almost frantic with fear as she saw two water snakes slither down into one of the swamp pools. At the next deep pool, she closed her eyes and waded in. Dogs could not track her if she walked through water.

Picking her way carefully, she kept to the sluggish pools. She walked around the hummocks, and traveled as fast as she could until the sun had risen higher. Now was the time of real danger. She found a small island in the tall swamp grass and lay down to rest. Twice during the day, she heard the distant shouts of men, but she forced herself to lie quiet and even managed to take short naps.

When it was almost dark, Harriet came out of the swamp and looked about her. Now was the time to follow the Quaker lady's advice. Harriet headed in the direction of the Choptank River.

Harriet walked at night and hid by day. She crawled into the thick underbrush and slept when she could. Once she awoke hearing voices. Three men on horseback had stopped not far from her. They were hunting for runaway slaves. She held her breath until they moved on.

Now she must try to keep her wits about her. She stopped often to check her direction by the stars. She limited herself to using only a part of her few supplies each day. She looked for and found wild grapes to eat and clean water to drink. She moved very carefully among the trees and hid whenever she heard voices or horses' hoofs. She made wide circles around farm buildings, for dogs might bark and bring out the owners to investigate.

When she reached the Choptank, she took off her shoes and waded in up to her waist. The sight of the river comforted her. The water was soothing to her tired feet. She sang softly. For the first time since she had left home, she felt a calm courage.

Harriet waded upstream until only a thin stream of water came down over the rocks. This, then, was the spot where the Choptank River began.

Now she would have to face the fifteen-mile walk to Camden. This part of the journey might prove the most dangerous of all, even at night. She would have to leave the river and the safety of the woods for the open fields and the highway.

It was almost daylight when she saw in the distance the buildings of a town. She stopped at a group of shacks that looked like the shacks slaves lived in. She dared go no farther lest she take a wrong path.

The Negro woman who answered Harriet's light tap on the door was already dressed in her cook's apron and cap. Before Harriet could ask a question, the woman said softly, "That's the Hill farm in the little hollow. Go to the haystack nearest the big barn. There's loose hay near the bottom. Crawl in and wait until about mid-morning. Then go to the door and give two short raps. That's the Underground's signal. Hurry!" The door closed.

Harriet followed the directions. The haystack was warm. She had a fine, safe view of the house and barns. She fell asleep. She was awakened by the sound of horses' hoofs. Two men were riding away from the farm. Much later, a woman dressed in the Quaker garb came out to feed the chickens. Harriet waited and watched until the woman went back into the house. When she felt sure that the woman was alone, she went quickly to the door and gave it two quick knocks. The lady who had been feeding the chickens drew her into the house at once.

"Welcome," she said. "I'm Mrs. Hill. You look as though you need some food and rest right away. And a good hot bath will make you feel better, too. We can talk later."

So Harriet bathed and ate. She slept almost all day in a hidden room behind a fireplace.

In the late afternoon Mrs. Hill came into the room and sat down in a chair by the bed. "Stay right where you are," she said as Harriet sat up in bed. "Travel has to be done after dark. There's no great hurry. You just rest as long as you can."

Then, from Mrs. Hill, Harriet learned the true meaning of the Underground Railroad. She liked Mrs. Hill and enjoyed talking with her.

"I know the Railroad is a way to help my people escape to the northern states," Harriet said, "but it's not very clear to me how it works."

"The Underground is not a railroad, and of course, it doesn't run under the ground," Mrs. Hill said.

"My father used to tell me about it when I was a little girl," Harriet told her. "For some time I thought he meant that trains really ran under the ground."

Mrs. Hill smiled. "It's called the Underground Railroad because of the fast and secret way it helps Negroes to travel north. We don't talk very much about the real facts. There's danger in too many people knowing the exact details."

"I understand," Harriet said. "I'm grateful for anything you can tell me to help me along the way. And I'm interested in having my own people help, too."

Mrs. Hill nodded her head to show that she agreed. "But many of the southern slaves do help," she said. "Even when they can't escape themselves, they help runaways. They give them food and clothing. They risk their own lives to take the runaways to safe hiding places."

"That's why I think all my people will be free someday," Harriet said proudly. "If the right spirit is there, we'll be able to help each other. I feel better already," she added.

"But you aren't safe yet," Mrs. Hill warned her. "You will be in constant danger until you're out of Delaware and into Pennsylvania or New York State." She waited a moment as though not sure of how much she should tell. "Philadelphia is our eastern headquarters. The city is a natural crossroads for our work. There are a great many workers there."

"What do they all do?"

"Well, some serve as guides or conductors," Mrs. Hill said. "Others make maps showing the stations. They draw skulls to mark the places to stay away from. They write travel routes in codes. Of course, whenever possible, we send fugitives on with a guide. When that's not possible, we give them a map. And we make them learn the directions by heart, in case they lose the map."

"I'd like to be a conductor someday," Harriet said.

"All the conductors are men," Mrs. Hill answered. "Very few of them get any praise, because they aren't known by name — except for Thomas Garrett in Wilmington. His fame for his work in helping escaping slaves has spread to all the northern states. He's been a fine example to all of us."

"He's a Quaker too, isn't he?" Harriet asked. "It was a Quaker lady who told me to come here and gave me such good directions."

"Yes, Quakers believe in freedom for everyone. But we aren't the only ones who help. Other stations along the way are kept by Methodists, German farmers, and many other people who are against slavery."

That night Harriet met Mr. Hill, who was as kind to her as his wife had been. He drove her in his wagon as far as he could along a back road. "I must be back by daylight to go about my business as usual," he said. "I've already been fined for helping slaves."

Harriet thanked him for herself and for her people.

"Follow this road to my brother's farm," Mr. Hill told her. "It's at the top of a hill. The house is white with a wide stone

wall around it. It has red barns exactly like mine. Meanwhile I will get word to Thomas Garrett to expect you in Wilmington."

Thomas Garrett! Harriet could hardly believe she would see the most famous conductor of them all.

James Hill was just as nice as his brother, Harriet decided. James warned Harriet to be very careful while traveling over the twenty-three miles to Wilmington and Thomas Garrett.

"There are posters everywhere offering five hundred dollars for your capture," he said. "Also, Thomas Garrett is very closely watched."

He drove Harriet part of the way and then turned her over to another conductor—a free Negro. This man had a plan to outwit the patrol stationed just outside the city of Wilmington.

He dressed Harriet in ragged overalls and a big old floppy hat. He gave her a rake and hoe to carry. Then, walking together as two Negro workmen, they passed by the guards and into Wilmington. In the early morning they crept through the streets to the shoe store of Thomas Garrett.

Thomas Garrett was a small, gentle old man. He and his wife, Sarah, were Quakers. They had moved to Wilmington, Delaware, about the time Harriet was born.

He was famous for his kindness to runaway slaves. He had been arrested a number of times for helping them to escape and fined so heavily that he had been left without a cent. At sixty he had opened a shoe store and gone on helping escaping slaves. Again he had been arrested and fined. He was criticized strongly by people who approved of slavery. Through it all, he kept his sense of humor.

Behind the shelves of shoes, Mr. Garrett had a secret room with no windows. "Rest here," he told Harriet. "Tomorrow you'll have new shoes and a ticket over the border." He smiled at her. "You are very close to being my two-hundredth passenger," he said. "Our work has spread. There's an Underground in all the northern states from Maine to Iowa."

After Harriet had rested, Mr. Garrett explained the route she must take. "Wilmington is only eight miles from the Pennsylvania border. Naturally the border is heavily guarded. Your best disguise is that of a working man. I'll take you as near to the crossing point as I can."

Very carefully he went over the directions and made Harriet repeat them until he was certain she knew them. "Head for Philadelphia as soon as you can," he advised her. "There'll be jobs there and other free Negroes to help you. You may want to visit the office of Mr. William Still. He's secretary to the committee that helps runaways. If he's very busy, you may not be able to see him, but one of his workers will help you with any problems you may have."

Harriet thanked him. She tried to put into words some of her gratitude and respect, but the words would not come.

Thomas Garrett seemed to understand. His farewell and his low bow were something Harriet would always remember.

It was only about a week after she left Maryland that Harriet crossed the border into Pennsylvania. She was tired out, the new shoes Mr. Garrett had given her hurt her feet, and she had no place to go, but she was free.

"I made it, Lord," she said aloud. "Now it's up to me to see that my family makes it, too—and all the others who want to be free."

AUTHOR

Dr. Frances Humphreville started writing short stories and poetry when she was only ten years old. By the age of seventeen, Mrs. Humphreville was teaching school and was having some of her short stories published. During her long career as a teacher, Mrs. Humphreville has taught every grade, from elementary school to high school to college. Despite her busy schedule, she has found time to do volunteer work with gifted, retarded, deaf, and blind children.

Mrs. Humphreville was born in Maine and now lives with her husband in a long, low ranch house in Shelton, Connecticut. There she is often visited by a variety of food-seeking animals which include a huge crow, a raccoon family, and many birds. The Humphrevilles have a pet cat who has learned to meow over the telephone. Besides her writing, Mrs. Humphreville enjoys swimming, taking pictures, and playing the piano, violin, and tenor saxophone.

USING AN ENCYCLOPEDIA

When you need to find information, you will often use special books called **reference books.** Reference books such as encylopedias, dictionaries, almanacs, and atlases contain information on many topics. The information in these books is organized so that you can find it quickly.

One of the most useful reference books for your purposes is likely to be an **encyclopedia.** It contains hundreds of articles which give information about famous people, about places, about things, about events, and about ideas. There you can find answers to such questions as: Why do volcanoes erupt? How were the first pyramids built? What causes tornadoes? Who invented baseball?

Because an encyclopedia contains so much information on so many different topics, it is usually made into a set of books. Each book in the set is called a volume.

The topics in an encyclopedia are arranged in alphabetical order. You will find on the spine (the narrow back edge) of each volume a guide letter or letters indicating the topics covered in that volume. In the picture at the top of the next page, notice the guide letter or letters and the number on each volume.

The guide letter or letters on each volume tell you the beginning letters of all the main topics listed in that volume. In the encyclopedia shown on the opposite page, so many topics start with *c* and *s* that there are two volumes for each of those

letters. The number on each volume helps you to place the volumes in order quickly, or to talk about a volume by its number.

In order to find information that an encyclopedia gives, you must first choose a key word to look for, just as you do when using an index. Suppose you need to answer this question: What is a star? You would use as your key word *star*. Since volumes 17 and 18 both contain topics beginning with the letter *s*, you will have to use the second letter in *star*. Because *st* comes between *so* and *sz* in alphabetical order, you would choose volume 18.

Often you will use more than one key word to find information on a topic. Suppose you need to answer the question: What is the difference between a planet and an asteroid? If you use only the word *planet* as a key word, you may not find all the information the encyclopedia gives. That is why you may also need to use the word *asteroid* as a key word. Thus, you should choose both volume **P** and volume **A** to find the answer to the question.

Topics having more than one word are usually alphabetized by the first word. You would find *North America* in the **N** volume and *Los Angeles* in the **L** volume. To find information about a person, you should use the person's last name as your key word. When you have selected the correct volume, you can find your key word quickly by using the guide words printed in heavy black type at the tops of most of the pages just as you use the guide words in a dictionary. What are the guide words on the encyclopedia pages shown in the first illustration on the opposite page?

Sometimes the title of an article, appearing in large type as the heading on a page, serves as the guide word. If there is a picture at the top of both facing pages, as in the illustration at the bottom of the opposite page, guide words are often omitted. If so, use as your guide words the first main topic on the left-hand page and the last main topic on the right-hand page. What words would you use as guide words for the pages shown in that bottom illustration?

When you have located the article you are looking for, you may find that it is a long one. Most long articles in an encyclopedia are divided into sections. Each section has a heading in heavy black type that tells what information that section contains. To find the information you are looking for, skim over these section headings until you find the one that seems to point to the information you want. In the bottom illustration on the opposite page, notice in the article on the BAT the headings *The Bodies of Bats* and *How Bats Navigate*. If you were trying to find information about how bats can find their way in the dark, in which section would you most likely find it?

As you read through an article in the encyclopedia, you may find the words *See* or *See also* followed by the name of another topic or topics. These cross-references name topics under which you can find more information on the subject of the article. Notice in the bottom illustration on the opposite page the cross-references at the end of the article on the BAT.

Sometimes you will find *only* a cross-reference after a topic you look up. For example, find the topic BATFISH in the bottom illustration on the opposite page. Notice that only the cross-reference *See SEA BAT* follows that topic. This means that all the information the encyclopedia gives about the BATFISH can be found in the article about the SEA BAT.

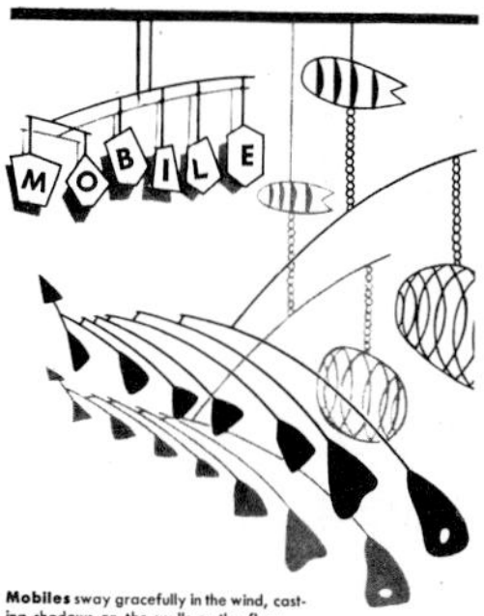

Mobiles sway gracefully in the wind, casting shadows on the walls or the floor.

MOBILE, *MOH beel,* is a contemporary type of sculpture. It is distinctive from other types of sculpture in that it achieves expression or meaning through movement. Traditional sculpture achieves its expression through the arrangement of solid forms. Mobiles are usually frail constructions of many rod-like projections loosely joined together. They are delicately balanced so they can swing freely in an infinite variety of moving arcs. The rods may end in *finials* (ending shapes) that recall the erosion effects of wind or water, or imaginative flight forms in space. Sculptors use many colors, textures, and materials for mobiles.

Most mobiles are suspended from above, so they can move freely overhead. Some are pivoted on a base. They are planned to present artistic interest not only in their actual shape, but also in the moving shadows they cast on walls and floor. Mobiles usually move as the result of natural currents of air, or the vibration of the earth. A few are designed for mechanical power.

A mobile's movement is of greater aesthetic value than its actual shape. The constantly swinging projections form arcs that cut shapes or volumes out of space. These volumes have no weight or substance, but they do remain fixed in our memory. The real design of a mobile is in this variety of space shapes, and in their abstract relationships with one another. Artists of many times and many places have created things that depend on movement for some part of their expression. But an American sculptor, Alexander Calder, was the first to create the true mobile, in which movement is the basic aesthetic purpose. Calder is regarded as the foremost creator of mobiles.

Wide acceptance of this new art form is obviously based on two significant facts. First, our art concepts have quite naturally grown to include the beauty of the machine in motion. Second, our minds have been freed to think and feel in terms of volumes of space that our eyes cannot see. BERNARD FRAZIER

See also CALDER, ALEXANDER; SCULPTURE (Form and Treatment; picture: Red Petals).

MOBILE, *moh BEEL,* Ala. (pop. 202,779; met. area 363,389; alt. 15 ft.), is the only seaport of Alabama, and one of the largest ports in the United States. Several streets of the city and its suburbs form the 35-mile Azalea Trail, featuring thousands of flowering azalea plants every spring.

Location, Size, and Description. Mobile is the second largest city in Alabama. It lies on the Mobile River at its entrance to Mobile Bay, 31 miles north of the Gulf of Mexico. For location, see ALABAMA (political map).

Huge moss-draped oak trees towering over historic Government Street form the entrance to the city from the west. Large trees and handsome homes line the residential streets. In the downtown district, small parks with giant shade trees provide relief from the office buildings. Beautiful suburbs such as Chateauguay, Delwood, and Spring Hill surround the city. Mobile is the home of Spring Hill College.

Industry and Commerce. Mobile is an important industrial and transportation center. Brookley Air Force Base, with more than 13,000 civilian employees, is Mobile's largest single employer. Paper and wood pulp used for paper is Mobile's largest single industry. Wood pulp is also the basic raw material for a large rayon fiber plant. Other important products include aluminum, lumber, rayon, roofing, cement, naval stores, chemicals, clothing, fertilizer, paint, and petroleum products. Shipbuilding and repair, and shipping itself, are other important industries. The Alabama State Docks can accommodate 30 ocean-going vessels at one time. The Port of Mobile handles over 17 million tons of cargo a year. Commercial fishermen in the area do a lively business in fish and oysters.

The city is served by four railroads and four bus lines. Four major airlines use Mobile's busy Bates Field. Bankhead Tunnel, the first underwater tunnel in the South, handles traffic under the Mobile River.

History. Founded originally in 1702 as Fort Louis de la Mobile, Mobile is one of the oldest cities in the United States. The settlers moved to the present site in 1711 because of flood waters. Mobile is often called *The City of Six Flags.* It has been ruled by the French, British, and Spanish, and has also flown the flags of the Republic of Alabama, the Confederate States, and the United States. The United States captured Mobile from the Spanish in 1813. Mobile was the last Southern stronghold to surrender to the Union forces at the end of the Civil War. Mobile received a city charter in 1819, and adopted commission government in 1910. It is the seat of Mobile County. CHARLES G. SUMMERSELL

For the monthly weather in Mobile, see ALABAMA (Climate). See also ALABAMA (pictures); IBERVILLE, SIEUR D'.

MOBILE BAY, BATTLE OF. See CIVIL WAR (Mobile Bay).

MAKING MOBILES

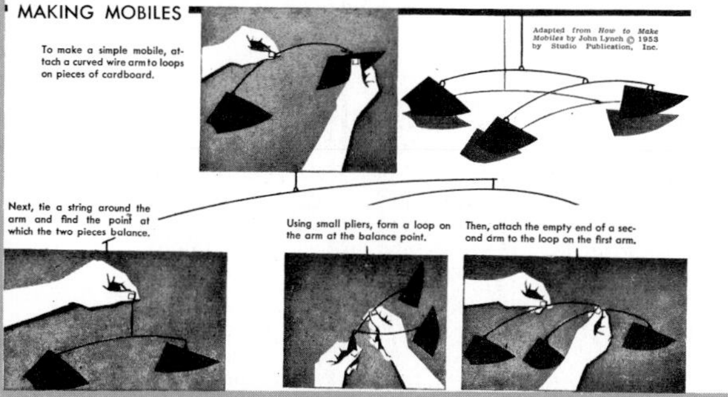

To make a simple mobile, attach a curved wire arm to loops on pieces of cardboard.

Next, tie a string around the arm and find the point at which the two pieces balance.

Using small pliers, form a loop on the arm at the balance point.

Then, attach the empty end of a second arm to the loop on the first arm.

Adapted from *How to Make Mobiles* by John Lynch © 1953 by Studio Publication, Inc.

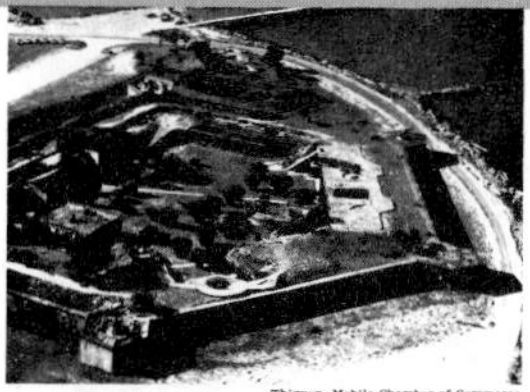

Thigpen, Mobile Chamber of Commerce

Fort Gaines, on Dauphin Island at the entrance to Mobile Bay, protected Mobile from the Union Navy during the Civil War.

MOBILE COLLEGE. See UNIVERSITIES AND COLLEGES (table).

MOBILE HOME. See TRAILER.

MOBILE RIVER is a short stream in southwestern Alabama. It offers transportation for cotton and other farm products of its valley. The Mobile was named for the Mobile, or Maubila, Indians who once lived along its banks. The Mobile River is formed where the Alabama and Tombigbee rivers meet in Clarke County. The Mobile flows southward for 38 miles before it empties into the Gulf of Mexico through Mobile Bay. For location, see ALABAMA (physical map). The port of Mobile lies at the mouth of the river. WALLACE E. AKIN

MÖBIUS, AUGUST FERDINAND. See MATHEMATICS (A Strange Twist).

MOBUTU, *mo BOO too,* **JOSEPH DÉSIRÉ** (1930-), seized control of the government in Congo (Kinshasa) in 1960 and again in 1965. In 1965, he declared himself president for five years.

Mobutu was born in a small village in what was then the colony called the Belgian Congo. He studied in Belgium and served in the colonial army. Trouble broke out among Congolese groups when the colony gained independence in 1960, and it threatened to destroy the nation. Mobutu headed a military government that restored order. He ruled for five months. Mobutu seized power again when new trouble broke out in 1965.

MOBY DICK. See MELVILLE, HERMAN.

MOCCASIN, *MAHK uh sin.* The American Indians called their slipperlike footwear *moccasins.* They made moccasins of animal skin and often decorated them with beads, and sometimes porcupine quills. Moccasins are soft, closely fitted, and have no heels. They may be ankle-length or extend to the hip. Hair is left on the skin of winter moccasins to serve as a lining. See also INDIAN, AMERICAN (color picture). LYNN FARNOL

MOCCASIN FLOWER. See LADY'S-SLIPPER.

MOCCASIN SNAKE. See WATER MOCCASIN.

MOCHA. See COFFEE (Kinds).

MOCK ORANGE, sometimes called *syringa,* is a bush covered with clusters of small, single or double, white or creamy flowers. The flowers of some kinds of mock orange have purple spots at the base of their petals. In most plants, the flowers are fragrant, but some are odorless. Some types of mock orange have leaves with toothed edges. The bush generally does not grow very high, although some species do reach 20 feet.

Gardeners in the United States and Mexico grow many different kinds of mock orange. A few kinds also grow in Asia and Europe. Almost all types of this hardy plant bloom in June. Breeders have produced many beautiful hybrids of mock orange. One of these hybrids, *Philadelphus virginalis,* is among the best and most fragrant of the mock oranges. Many mock orange plants escape from gardens and grow wild. The syringa is the state flower of Idaho (see IDAHO [color picture]).

Scientific Classification. Mock oranges belong to the saxifrage family, *Saxifragaceae.* They make up the genus *Philadelphus.* J. J. LEVISON

MOCK-UP. See AIRPLANE MODEL.

MOCKINGBIRD is an American bird famous for its ability to imitate the sounds of other birds. One naturalist reported a mockingbird in South Carolina

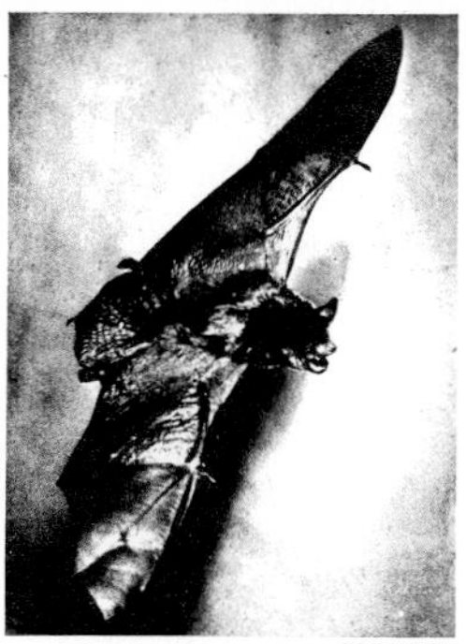

Harold E. Edgerton

The Little Brown Bat, above, uses the skin attached to its tail as flying equipment. To stop or turn, it bends its tail downward as a brake, much as an airplane does. The thin skin of the fruit bat's wings, below, is stretched like the silk of an opened parasol upon the long, slim bones of its forearms and fingers.

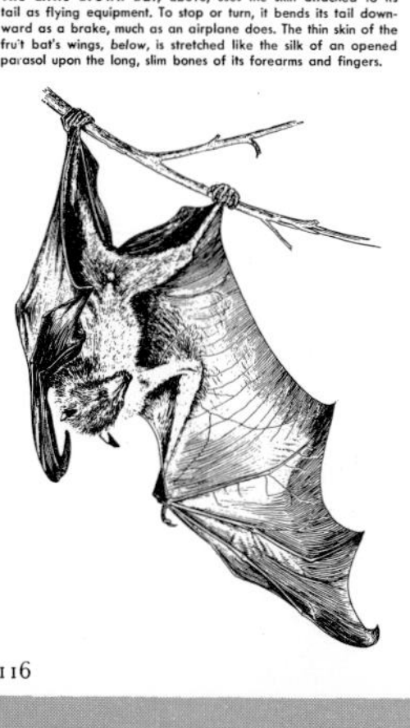

BAT is a small furry animal that flies. Its wings are thin skin that stretches from the arm-like front limb along the side of the body to the leg. Long bones allow the wings to stretch even farther. The bat's small body looks somewhat like a mouse's body. *Flittermouse* is an old-fashioned name for this animal.

Like mice, dogs, cats, and elephants, bats are *mammals.* That is, they feed their babies milk that is made in the body of the mother. But bats are the only mammals that can fly.

The world contains several hundred *species* (kinds) of bats. They are most common in warm climates, and the biggest bats live there. But there are about 40 species of bats in the United States. Four small kinds are even found in Alaska and northern Canada. Some of the northern bats fly south when winter begins. Others sleep through the winter in the hollow trees, caves, and buildings where they make their homes.

Most kinds of bats are useful to mankind. They eat vast numbers of harmful insects. Sometimes hundreds of thousands of insect-eating bats live together in caves or empty dwellings. The bat manure, or "bat guano," which collects on the floors of such places, is a valuable fertilizer for plants. Since prehistoric times, large populations of bats have lived for many years in caves. In some of these caves, the bat guano has formed layers many feet thick.

A few kinds of tropical bats are harmful. Among them are the large fruit-eating bats, or *flying foxes,* and the *vampire bats.* Flying foxes may gather in orchards and destroy fruit crops. Vampire bats live on the blood of other animals and human beings. The bite of a vampire bat and the bites of other kinds of bats may transmit rabies. But most bats do not harm human beings. Many people dread bats and have strange beliefs about them. This is probably because most bats fly at night and are not seen very often at close range.

The Bodies of Bats. Most bats are small. The little brown bat, which is common in the United States, has a body less than four inches long. It can spread its wings to a distance of 14 inches. One of the largest bats, the flying fox, lives in southeastern Asia. This bat's body is one foot long, and its wingspread may measure about five feet.

The heads of bats have many extraordinary shapes. Some of them look like the heads of tiny bulldogs, or like bears with long, pointed teeth. Other kinds, such as the *horse-headed bat* and the *long-tongued bat* of the tropics, have long snouts. Many have growths on their noses that look like horseshoes, leaves, or flowers. These growths carry *sensory* (feeling) nerve endings.

How Bats Navigate. Some insect-eating bats that feed on the wing have a keen sense of hearing that guides them in the dark. They produce twittering sounds so high-pitched that human beings cannot hear their full range. These sound waves strike objects in the path of flight and send back echoes to the bats' ears. The echoes tell the bats how they must turn in the air to avoid colliding with objects or with one another. By using their ears, bats can fly skillfully at night or in the utter darkness of caves. Experimenters, stringing threads across a room, have found that bats can find their way even with their eyes covered. But bats become nearly helpless in the dark if their ears or mouths are covered.

While they are flying, some bats catch large insects in their mouths. Some kinds of bats use their tail membranes to catch flying insects. Others use their wings to do the same job. During the day, bats sleep hanging from the ceilings of their homes by their hind feet. They usually hang upside down, with their wings draped around their bodies like cloaks. Bats are clumsy on the ground, because their wings get in their way and their knees bend backward. But in the air, few birds can fly as expertly as bats.

Scientific Classification. The bat belongs to the order of mammals called *Chiroptera,* meaning *hand-winged.* The most common bats in the United States are the red bat and the little brown bat. They belong to the family *Vespertilionidae.* The red bat is genus *Lasiurus,* species *L. borealis.* The brown bat is *Myotis lucifugus.* FRANK B. GOLLEY

See also ANIMAL (color picture: Animals of the Deserts); FLYING FOX; VAMPIRE BAT; GUANO.

BATA, *BAH tah* (pop. 27,024; alt. 7 ft.), is the capital of Río Muni, a province of Equatorial Guinea. Bata is a seaport on the Gulf of Guinea. For location, see EQUATORIAL GUINEA (map).

BATAAN DEATH MARCH. See WORLD WAR II (Burma and the Philippines).

BATAAN PENINSULA juts into Manila Bay from the southwestern coast of Luzon, largest of the Philippine Islands. On Bataan Peninsula, United States and Filipino troops held out for more than three months against much larger Japanese forces during World War II. Early in January, 1942, General Douglas MacArthur managed to withdraw his scattered troops into this hilly country. Once established on the peninsula, U.S. and Filipino forces found themselves hemmed in by the Japanese and cut off from any help.

For 98 days, this band of defenders beat back Japanese attacks. When an estimated 200,000 Japanese broke through their lines, the Americans and Filipinos withdrew to the very tip of the peninsula. MacArthur was ordered to report to Australia, and Lieutenant General Jonathan M. Wainwright took command of U.S. and Filipino forces in the Philippines. Major General Edward P. King, Jr. took command of U.S. and Filipino forces on Bataan Peninsula. On April 9, 1942, General King surrendered to the Japanese. The Japanese took about 75,000 Americans and Filipinos prisoner. Some men escaped to the fortress of Corregidor in Manila Bay, where they fought until May 6, 1942.

In February, 1945, troops under the command of MacArthur returned to Bataan. They landed on southern Bataan, captured points on Corregidor, and opened Manila Bay. Japanese forces surrendered, and surviving Americans and Filipinos were freed. In 1954, President Ramón R. Magsaysay of the Philippine Republic issued an order making the battlefield areas of Bataan and Corregidor national shrines. RUSSELL H. FIFIELD

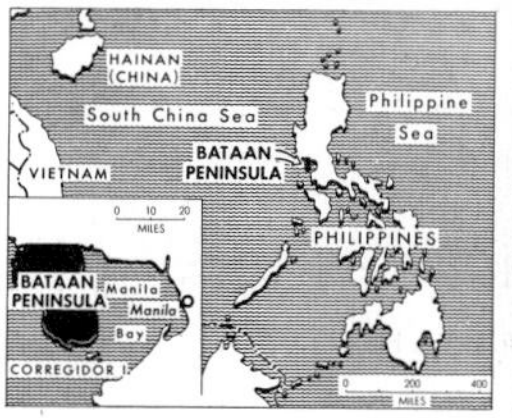

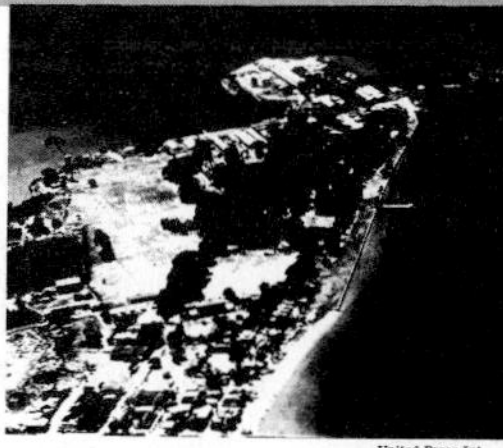

United Press Int.

Bataan Peninsula shelters Manila Bay from the South China Sea. Olongapo, above, lies on the northwestern part of the peninsula. In World War II, outnumbered U.S. and Filipino troops fought gallantly on the peninsula before surrendering to Japanese forces.

BATAVIA. See DJAKARTA.

BATES, KATHARINE LEE (1859-1929), an American poet and educator, wrote the words of the hymn, "America the Beautiful." She wrote short stories and books of travel, as well as poetry. Her hymn may be found in her *Selected Poems* (1930). *Fairy Gold* (1916) is a book of verse for children. Miss Bates was born in Falmouth, Mass. She graduated from Wellesley College and taught there from 1885 to 1925. PETER VIERECK

See also AMERICA THE BEAUTIFUL.

BATES COLLEGE. See UNIVERSITIES AND COLLEGES (table).

BATFISH. See SEA BAT.

BATH (pop. 85,870; alt. 405 ft.), is a health resort in England. It lies on the River Avon near Bristol in southwestern England (see GREAT BRITAIN [map]). The city is built on hills, and is famous for the Georgian architectural style of its houses. Some persons believe Bath's warm springs and mineral waters have health-giving qualities. The Romans founded Bath and used the springs. Baths the Romans built still stand. Bath became a resort for English high society in the 1700's. The *Wife of Bath* is a famous character in Geoffrey Chaucer's *Canterbury Tales.* JOHN W. WEBB

BATH, Me. (pop. 10,717; alt. 5 ft.), has been a shipbuilding center since the days of wooden ships. Today, it produces guided-missile destroyers for the U.S. Navy. Bath lies about 12 miles from the Atlantic Coast (see MAINE [political map]). The town is named for Bath, England. Founded in 1781, it was incorporated as a city in 1847. Bath has a council-manager form of government. ROBERT M. YORK

BATH, KNIGHTS OF THE. See KNIGHTS OF THE BATH.

Discussion

Help your class answer these questions:

1. Why are reference books good sources to use when you need to find information?
2. How do guide letters, key words, and guide words help you in locating information in an encyclopedia?
3. How do section headings help you to find quickly in an article the information that you want?
4. What do cross-references tell you?

On your own

Answer the following questions on a sheet of paper. Write the number and letter of each part of a question first (1a, 1b, and so on) and then your answer to it.

1. What key word or key words would you use to find information to answer each of these questions?
   a. How is a boomerang made?
   b. What does the Painted Desert look like?
   c. How does the moon affect the tide?
2. What is the number of the volume of the encyclopedia pictured on page 157 in which you would look for information to answer each of the following questions?
   a. During what years was William Howard Taft the president of the United States?
   b. When was San Diego first settled?
   c. Why is Yellowstone National Park an interesting place to visit?
3. In a long article about the planet Mars in an encyclopedia, the following section headings appear: Size, Movement and Distance, Moons of Mars, Life on Mars, and The Canals of Mars. In which section would you look to find information to help you answer each of the following questions?
   a. How far is Mars from the sun?
   b. Is there any plant life on Mars?
   c. Is Mars larger than our own planet Earth?
   d. Is there any positive evidence that there are canals on Mars?
   e. About how long would it take a space ship to travel from Earth to Mars?

Checking your work

If you are asked to do so, read aloud one or more of your answers. Then tell why you answered each question as you did. Listen while other boys and girls read their answers, and compare your answers with theirs. If you made a mistake, find out why it was a mistake.

Pierre and his horse
shared a special secret which
no one else knew.

A Secret for Two

by Quentin Reynolds

Montreal (mahn-tree-awl′) is a very large city, but, like all large cities, it has some very small streets. Streets, for instance, like Prince Edward Street, which is only four blocks long. No one knew Prince Edward Street as well as did Pierre (pee-yair′) Dupin, for Pierre had delivered milk to the families on the street for thirty years now.

During the past fifteen years, the horse that drew the milk wagon used by Pierre was a large white horse named Joseph. In Montreal, especially in that part of Montreal which is very French, the animals, like children, are often given the names of saints. When the big white horse first came to the Provincale Milk Company, he didn't have a name.

They told Pierre that he could use the white horse henceforth. Pierre stroked the softness of the horse's neck, he stroked the sheen of its splendid belly, and he looked into the eyes of the horse.

"This is a kind horse, a gentle and a faithful horse," Pierre said, "and I can see a beautiful spirit shining out of the eyes of the horse. I will name him after good St. Joseph, who was also kind and gentle and faithful, with a beautiful spirit."

Within a year Joseph knew the milk route as well as Pierre. Pierre used to boast that he didn't need reins. He never touched them. Each morning Pierre arrived at the stables of the Provincale Milk Company at five o'clock. The wagon would be loaded, and Joseph hitched to it. Pierre would call,

162

"*Bon jour, viel ami*" (Good day, old friend), as he climbed into his seat. Joseph would turn his head, and the other drivers would smile and say that the horse would smile at Pierre.

Then Jacques (zhahk), the foreman, would say, "All right, Pierre, go on," and Pierre would call softly to Joseph, "*Avance, mon ami,*" and this splendid combination would stalk proudly down the street.

The wagon, without any direction from Pierre, would roll three blocks down St. Catherine Street, then turn right two blocks along Roslyn Avenue, then left, for that was Prince Edward Street. The horse would stop at the first house, allow Pierre perhaps thirty seconds to get down from his seat and put a bottle of milk at the front door, and then go on, skipping two houses and stopping at the third. So it went, down the length of the street.

Then Joseph, still without any direction from Pierre, would turn around and come back along the other side.

Pierre would boast at the stable of Joseph's skill. "I never touch the reins. He knows just where to stop. Why, a blind man could handle my route with Joseph pulling the wagon."

So it went on for years—always the same. Pierre and Joseph both grew old together, but gradually, not suddenly. Pierre's huge walrus mustache was pure white now, and Joseph didn't lift his knees so high or raise his head quite as much. Jacques, the foreman of the stables, never noticed that they were both getting old until Pierre appeared one day carrying a heavy walking stick.

"Hey, Pierre," Jacques laughed. "Maybe you got the gout, hey?"

"*Mais oui,* Jacques," Pierre said, uncertainly. "One grows old. One's legs get tired."

"You should teach the horse to carry the milk to the front door for you," Jacques told him. "He does everything else."

Pierre knew every one of the forty families he served on Prince Edward Street. The cooks knew that he could neither read nor write, so instead of following the usual custom of leaving a note in an empty bottle if an additional quart of milk was needed, they would sing out when they heard the rumble of his wagon wheels over the cobbled street, "Bring an extra quart this morning, Pierre."

Pierre had a remarkable memory. When he arrived at the stable, he would always remember to tell Jacques, "The Paquins took an extra quart of milk this morning. The Lemoines bought a pint of cream."

Jacques would note these things in a little book he always carried. Most of the drivers had to make out the weekly bills and collect the money, but Jacques, liking Pierre, had always excused him from this task. All Pierre had to do was to arrive at five in the morning, walk to his wagon, which was always in the same spot at the curb, and deliver his milk. He returned some two hours later, got stiffly from his seat, called a cheery "*au'voir*" to Jacques, and then limped slowly down the street.

One morning, the president of the Provincale Milk Company came to inspect the early morning deliveries. Jacques pointed Pierre out to him and said, "Watch how he talks to that horse. See how the horse listens and how he turns his head toward Pierre? See the look in that horse's eyes? You know, I think those two share a secret. I have often noticed it. It is as though they both sometimes chuckle at us as they go off on their route. Pierre is a good man, Monsieur President, but he gets old. Would it be too bold of me to suggest that he be retired and perhaps given a small pension?" he added.

"But of course," the president laughed. "I know his record. He has been on this route now for thirty years, and never once has there been a complaint. Tell him it is time he rested. His salary will go on just the same."

But Pierre refused to retire. He was panic-stricken at the thought of not driving Joseph every day. "We are two old men," he said to Jacques. "Let us wear out together. When Joseph is ready to retire, then I, too, will quit."

Jacques, who was a kind man, understood. There was something about Pierre and Joseph that made a man smile tenderly. It was as though each drew some hidden strength from the other. When Pierre was sitting in his seat, and when Joseph was hitched to the wagon, neither seemed old. But when they finished their work, then Pierre would limp down the street slowly, seeming very old indeed, and the horse's head would droop and he would walk very wearily to his stall.

Then one morning Jacques had dreadful news for Pierre when he arrived. It was a cold morning and still pitch dark.

"Pierre, your horse Joseph did not wake this morning," Jacques said. "He was very old. He was twenty-five, and that is like seventy-five for a man."

"Yes," Pierre said, slowly. "Yes. I am seventy-five. And I cannot see Joseph again."

"Of course you can," Jacques soothed. "He is over in his stall, looking very peaceful."

Pierre took one step forward, then turned. "No . . . no . . . you don't understand, Jacques."

Jacques clapped him on the shoulder. "We'll find another horse just as good as Joseph. Why, in a month you'll teach him to know your route as well as Joseph did. We'll . . ."

The look in Pierre's eyes stopped him. For years Pierre had worn a heavy cap, the peak of which came low over his eyes, keeping the bitter morning wind out of them. Now Jacques looked into Pierre's eyes and he saw something that startled him. He saw a dead, lifeless look in them. The eyes were mirroring the grief that was in Pierre's heart and his soul. It was as though his heart and soul had died.

"Take today off, Pierre," Jacques said, but already Pierre was hobbling down the street. Had one been near, one would have seen tears streaming down his cheeks and have heard half-smothered sobs. Pierre walked to the corner and stepped into the street. There was a warning yell from the driver of a huge truck that was coming fast, and there was a scream of brakes, but Pierre apparently heard neither.

Five minutes later an ambulance driver said, "He's dead. Was killed instantly."

Jacques and several of the milk wagon drivers had arrived, and they looked down at the still figure.

"I couldn't help it," the driver of the truck protested. "He walked right into my truck. He never saw it, I guess. Why, he walked into it as though he were blind."

The ambulance doctor bent down. "Blind? Of course, the man was blind. This man has been blind for five years." He turned to Jacques. "You say he worked for you? Didn't you know he was blind?"

"No . . . no . . ." Jacques said softly. "None of us knew. Only one knew, a friend of his named Joseph. . . . It was a secret, I think, just between those two."

AUTHOR

Quentin Reynolds had a very interesting career. He started out as a sports writer on a newspaper. Then he was sent to Europe as a reporter for a news service. During World War II, he served as a news correspondent on battle fronts and also helped make two wartime movies in France and England. After the war, he wrote books and articles for adults and children until his death in 1965. He also appeared on television many times.

Among the topics he chose to write about in books for children are the Wright Brothers, the F.B.I., and Custer's Last Stand. Even though he wrote "A Secret for Two" in 1936 when milk was still delivered in horse-drawn wagons, he has instilled a special feeling for Pierre Dupin and his horse Joseph that is timeless.

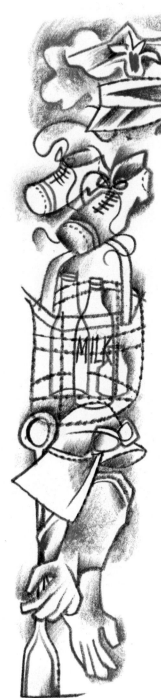

PSALM OF THOSE WHO GO FORTH BEFORE DAYLIGHT

The policeman buys shoes slow and careful; the teamster
buys gloves slow and careful; they take care of their feet
and hands; they live on their feet and hands.

The milkman never argues; he works alone and no one
speaks to him, the city is asleep when he is on the job;
he puts a bottle on six hundred porches and calls it a
day's work; he climbs two hundred wooden stairways;
two horses are company for him; he never argues.

The rolling mill-men and the sheet-steel men are brothers;
of cinders, they empty cinders out of their shoes after
the day's work; they ask their wives to fix burnt holes in
the knees of their trousers; their necks and ears are covered with a smut; they scour their necks and ears; they
are brothers of cinders.

Carl Sandburg

PICTURE PROVERBS

A proverb is an often-used short saying that expresses a well-known truth or fact. For example, "A stitch in time saves nine" is a proverb that you may have heard.

Look at the pictures below. Each one illustrates a common proverb. Try to guess each one, and then check your answers with the ones printed upside down at the bottom of the page.

1. 2. 3.

4. 5. 6.

6. Too many cooks spoil the broth.
5. Birds of a feather flock together.
4. A bird in the hand is worth two in the bush.
3. Half a loaf is better than none.
2. You can't teach an old dog new tricks.
1. The early bird catches the worm.

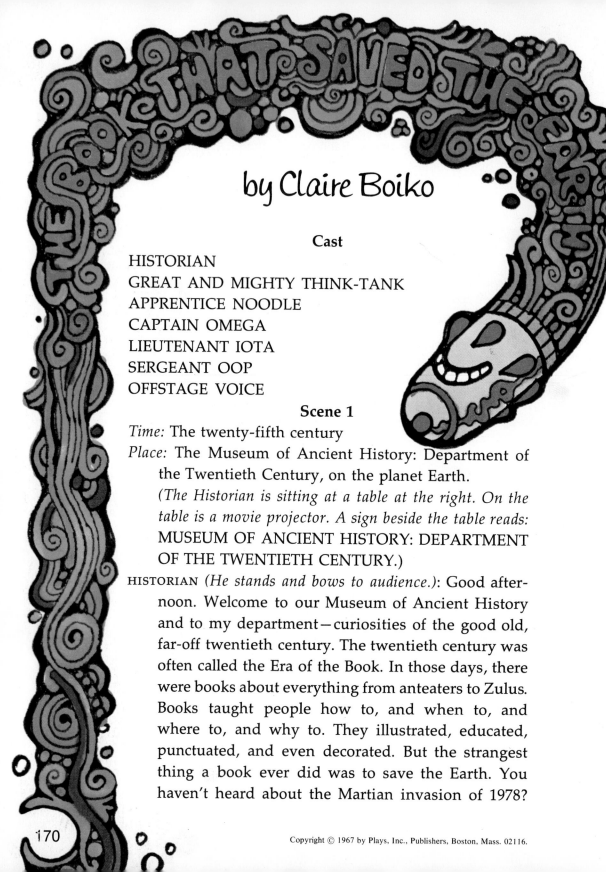

by Claire Boiko

Cast

HISTORIAN
GREAT AND MIGHTY THINK-TANK
APPRENTICE NOODLE
CAPTAIN OMEGA
LIEUTENANT IOTA
SERGEANT OOP
OFFSTAGE VOICE

Scene 1

Time: The twenty-fifth century

Place: The Museum of Ancient History: Department of the Twentieth Century, on the planet Earth.

(The Historian is sitting at a table at the right. On the table is a movie projector. A sign beside the table reads: MUSEUM OF ANCIENT HISTORY: DEPARTMENT OF THE TWENTIETH CENTURY.*)*

HISTORIAN *(He stands and bows to audience.)*: Good afternoon. Welcome to our Museum of Ancient History and to my department—curiosities of the good old, far-off twentieth century. The twentieth century was often called the Era of the Book. In those days, there were books about everything from anteaters to Zulus. Books taught people how to, and when to, and where to, and why to. They illustrated, educated, punctuated, and even decorated. But the strangest thing a book ever did was to save the Earth. You haven't heard about the Martian invasion of 1978?

Tsk, tsk. What *do* they teach children nowadays? Well, you know, the invasion never really happened, because a single book stopped it. What was that book, you ask? A noble encyclopedia? A volume about rockets and missiles? A secret file from outer space? No, it was none of these. It was — well, here, let me turn on the historiscope and show you what happened many, many centuries ago in 1978.

(*He turns on the projector and points it left. At the left is Think-Tank, who is seated on a raised box, arms folded. He has a huge, egg-shaped head, and he wears a long robe decorated with stars and circles. Apprentice Noodle stands beside him. A sign beside them reads:* MARS SPACE CONTROL. GREAT AND MIGHTY THINK-TANK, COMMANDER-IN-CHIEF. BOW LOW BEFORE ENTERING.)

NOODLE (*Bowing*): O Great and Mighty Think-Tank, most powerful and intelligent creature in the whole universe, what are your orders?

THINK-TANK (*Annoyed*): You left out part of my greeting, Apprentice Noodle. Go over the whole thing again.

NOODLE: It shall be done, sir. (*In a singsong voice*) O Great and Mighty Think-Tank, Ruler of Mars and her two moons, most powerful and intelligent creature in the whole universe, (*Out of breath*) what are your orders?

THINK-TANK: That's better, Noodle. I wish to be placed in communication with our manned space probe to that ridiculous little planet we are going to put under our generous rulership. What do they call it again?

NOODLE: Earth, your Intelligence.

THINK-TANK: Earth, of course. You see how insignificant the place is! But first, something important. My mirror. I wish to consult my mirror.

NOODLE: It shall be done, sir. (*He hands Think-Tank a hand mirror.*)

THINK-TANK: Mirror, mirror, in my hand. Who is the most fantastically, intellectually, gifted being in the land?

OFFSTAGE VOICE (*After a pause*): You, sir.

THINK-TANK (*Smacking mirror*): Quicker. Answer more quickly next time. I hate a slow mirror. (*He admires himself in the mirror.*) Ah, there I am. Are we Martians not a handsome race? So much more attractive than those ugly Earthlings with their tiny heads. Noodle, you keep on exercising your mind, and someday you'll have a balloon brain just like mine.

NOODLE: Oh, I hope so, Mighty Think-Tank. I hope so.

THINK-TANK: Now, contact the space probe. I want to invade that primitive ball of mud called Earth before lunch.

NOODLE: It shall be done, sir. (*He twists knobs and adjusts levers. Electronic buzzes and beeps are heard.*)

Scene 2

Time: Seconds later.

Place: Mars Space Control Center and the Centerville Public Library.

(*Captain Omega stands at center, opening and closing card catalogue drawers in a puzzled fashion. Lieutenant Iota is at the left, counting books in a bookcase. Sergeant Oop is at right, opening and closing a book, turning it upside down, shaking it, leafing through pages, and then shaking his head.*)

NOODLE (*Adjusting knobs*): I have a close sighting of the space crew, sir. They seem to have entered some sort of Earth structure.

CAPTAIN OMEGA

(Think-Tank puts on a pair of huge goggles and turns toward the stage to watch.)

THINK-TANK: Excellent. Make voice contact.

NOODLE: *(Speaking into a microphone)*: Mars Space Control calling the crew of Probe One. Mars Space Control calling the crew of Probe One. Come in, Captain Omega. Give us your location.

CAPTAIN OMEGA *(Speaking into a disc which is on a chain around his neck)*: Captain Omega to Mars Space Control. Lieutenant Iota, Sergeant Oop, and I have landed on Earth without incident. We have taken shelter in this *(Indicates room)*—this square place. Have you any idea where we are, Lieutenant Iota?

IOTA: I can't figure it out, Captain. *(Holding up a book)* I've counted two thousand of these peculiar things. This place must be some sort of storage barn. What do you think, Sergeant Oop?

OOP: I haven't a clue. I've been to seven galaxies, but I've never seen anything like this. Maybe they're hats. *(He opens a book and puts it on his head.)* Say, maybe this is a clothing store!

OMEGA *(Bowing low)*: Perhaps the Great and Mighty Think-Tank will give us the benefit of his thought on the matter.

THINK-TANK: Elementary, my dear Omega. Hold up one of the items so that I can view it closely. (*Omega holds a book on the palm of his hand.*) Yes, yes, I understand now. Since Earth creatures are always eating, the place in which you find yourselves is undoubtedly a crude refreshment stand.

OMEGA (*To Iota and Oop*): He says we're in a refreshment stand.

OOP: Well, the Earthlings certainly have a strange diet.

THINK-TANK: That item in your hand is called a "sandwich."

OMEGA (*Nodding*): A sandwich.

IOTA (*Nodding*): A sandwich.

OOP (*Taking book from his head*): A sandwich?

THINK-TANK: Sandwiches are the main food in the Earth diet. Look at it closely. (*Omega squints at book.*) There are two slices of what is called "bread," and between them there is some sort of filling.

OMEGA: That is correct, sir.

THINK-TANK: To confirm my opinion, I order you to eat it.

OMEGA (*Gulping*): Eat it?

THINK-TANK: Do you doubt the Mighty Think-Tank?

OMEGA: Oh, no, no. But poor Lieutenant Iota has not had his breakfast. Lieutenant Iota, I order you to eat this — this sandwich.

IOTA (*Doubtfully*): Eat it? Oh, Captain! It's a very great honor to be the first Martian to eat a sandwich, I'm sure, but — but how can I be so impolite as to eat before my Sergeant? (*Handing Oop the book and saying brightly*) Sergeant Oop, I order you to eat the sandwich.

OOP (*Making a face*): Who, sir? Me, sir?

IOTA and OMEGA (*Saluting*): For the glory of Mars, Oop!

174

SERGEANT OOP

OOP: Yes, sirs. *(Unhappily)* Immediately, sirs. *(He opens his mouth wide. Omega and Iota watch him breathlessly. He bites down on a corner of the book and pantomines chewing and swallowing, while making terrible faces.)*

OMEGA: Well, Oop?

IOTA: Well, Oop?

(Oop coughs. Omega and Iota pound him on the back.)

THINK-TANK: Was it not delicious, Sergeant Oop?

OOP *(Saluting)*: That is correct, sir. It was *not* delicious. I don't know how the Earthlings can get those sandwiches down without water. They're as dry as Martian dust.

NOODLE: Sir, sir. Great and Mighty Think-tank. I beg your pardon, but an insignificant bit of data floated into my mind about those sandwiches.

THINK-TANK: It can't be worth much, but go ahead. Give us your trifling bit of data.

NOODLE: Well, sir, I have seen our surveyor films of those sandwiches. I noticed that the Earthlings did not eat them. They used them as some sort of communication device.

THINK-TANK (*Haughtily*): Naturally. That was my next point. These are actually communication sandwiches. Think-Tank is never wrong. Who is never wrong?

ALL (*Saluting*): Great and Mighty Think-Tank is never wrong.

THINK-TANK: Therefore, I order you to listen to them.

OMEGA: Listen to them?

IOTA and OOP (*To each other, puzzled*): Listen to them?

THINK-TANK: Do you have marbles in your ears? I said, listen to them.

(*The Martians on Earth bow very low.*)

OMEGA: It shall be done, sir.

(*They each take two books from the case and hold them to their ears, listening intently.*)

IOTA (*Whispering to Omega*): Do you hear anything?

OMEGA (*Whispering back*): Nothing. Do you hear anything, Oop?

OOP (*Loudly*): Not a thing!

(*Omega and Iota jump in fright.*)

OMEGA and IOTA: Sh-h-h! (*They listen intently again.*)

THINK-TANK: Well? Well? Report to me. What do you hear?

OMEGA: Nothing, sir. Perhaps we are not on the correct frequency.

IOTA: Nothing, sir. Perhaps the Earthlings have sharper ears than we do.

OOP: I don't hear a thing. Maybe these sandwiches don't make sounds.

THINK-TANK: What? What? Does someone suggest the Mighty Think-Tank has made a mistake?

OMEGA: Oh, no, sir. No, sir. We'll keep listening.

NOODLE: Please excuse me, your Brilliance, but a cloudy piece of information is rolling around in my head.

THINK-TANK: Well, roll it out, Noodle, and I will clarify it for you.

176

GREAT AND MIGHTY THINK-TANK

APPRENTICE NOODLE

NOODLE: I recall that the Earthings did not listen to the sandwiches. They opened them, and watched them.

THINK-TANK: Yes, that is quite correct. I will clarify that for you, Captain Omega. Those sandwiches are not for ear communication, they are for eye communication. Now, Captain Omega, take that bright-colored sandwich over there. It appears to be important. Tell me what you observe.

(Omega picks up a very large copy of MOTHER GOOSE, *holding it so that the audience can see the title. Iota looks over his left shoulder, and Oop squints over his right shoulder.)*

OMEGA: It appears to contain pictures of Earthlings.

IOTA: There seems to be some sort of code.

THINK-TANK (*Sharply interested*): Code? Code? I told you this was important. Describe the code.

OOP: It's little lines and squiggles and dots. Thousands of them, next to the pictures.

THINK-TANK: Code. Perhaps the Earthlings are not so primitive as we have thought. We must break the code. We must.

NOODLE: Forgive me, your Cleverness, but did not the chemical department give our spacemen pills to break any Earth codes?

THINK-TANK: Stop! A thought of magnificent brilliance has come to me. Spacemen, our chemical department has given you pills to break Earth codes. Take them immediately and look at a sandwich. The meaning of the code will slowly unfold before you.

OMEGA: It shall be done, sir. Remove pill. (*Crew take pills from boxes on their belts.*) Present pill. (*They hold pills out in front of them, stiffly.*) Swallow pill. (*They pop the pills into their mouths and gulp all at once. They open their eyes wide, and their heads shake. They each take a book, open it, and study it carefully.*)

OMEGA (*Reading from a book*): "A simple closed surface formed by the union of six square regions is called a cube."

IOTA (*Reading also*): "When in the course of human events, it becomes necessary for one people to dissolve the political bands which have connected them with another, . . ."

OOP (*Reading*): "There is a change of pressure along a radius in curvilinear motion."

THINK-TANK: Excellent. Now decipher the code in that bright-colored sandwich.

ALL: It shall be done, sir. (*They frown over the book, turning the pages.*)

178

LIEUTENANT IOTA

Oho!

OMEGA *(Brightly)*: Aha!

IOTA *(Brightly)*: Oho!

OOP *(Bursting into laughter)*: Ha, ha, ha!

THINK-TANK: What does it say? Tell me this instant. Transcribe, Omega.

OMEGA: Yes, sir. *(He reads with great seriousness.)*

"Mistress Mary, quite contrary,
How does your garden grow?
With cockleshells and silver bells
and pretty maids all in a row."

OOP: Ha, ha, ha. Imagine that. Pretty maids growing in a garden.

THINK-TANK *(Alarmed)*: Stop! This is no time for laughter. Don't you realize the seriousness of this discovery? The Earthlings have discovered how to combine agriculture and mining. They can actually grow crops of rare metals such as silver. And cockleshells. They can grow high explosives, too. Noodle, contact our invasion fleet.

NOODLE: They are ready to go down and take over Earth, sir.

THINK-TANK: Tell them to hold. Tell them new information has come to us about Earth. Iota, continue transcribing.

IOTA: Yes, sir. (*He also reads very seriously.*)

"Hey diddle diddle! The cat and the fiddle,
The cow jumped over the moon,
The little dog laughed to see such sport,
And the dish ran away with the spoon."

OOP (*Laughing*): The dish ran away with the spoon!

THINK-TANK: Cease laughter. Stop! This is more and more alarming. The Earthlings have reached a high level of civilization. Didn't you hear? They have taught their domesticated animals musical culture and space techniques. Even their dogs have a sense of humor. Why, at this very moment, they may be launching an interplanetary attack of millions of *cows*! Notify the invasion fleet. No invasion today. Oop, transcribe the next code.

OOP: Yes, sir. (*Reading*)

"Humpty Dumpty sat on the wall.
Humpty Dumpty had a great fall.
All the King's horses and all the King's men,
Cannot put Humpty Dumpty together again."

Oh look, sir. Here's a picture of Humpty Dumpty. Why, sir, he looks like—he looks like—(*Turns large picture of Humpty Dumpty toward Think-Tank and the audience.*)

THINK-TANK (*Screaming and holding his head*): It's me! It's my Great and Mighty Balloon Brain. The Earthlings have seen me. They're after me. "Had a great fall!"—That means they plan to capture Mars Central Control and me! It's an invasion of Mars! Noodle, prepare a space capsule for me. I must escape without delay. Spacemen, you must leave Earth at once, but be sure to remove all traces of your visit. The Earthlings must not know that I know.

(*Omega, Iota, and Oop rush about, putting books back on shelves.*)

THE HISTORIAN

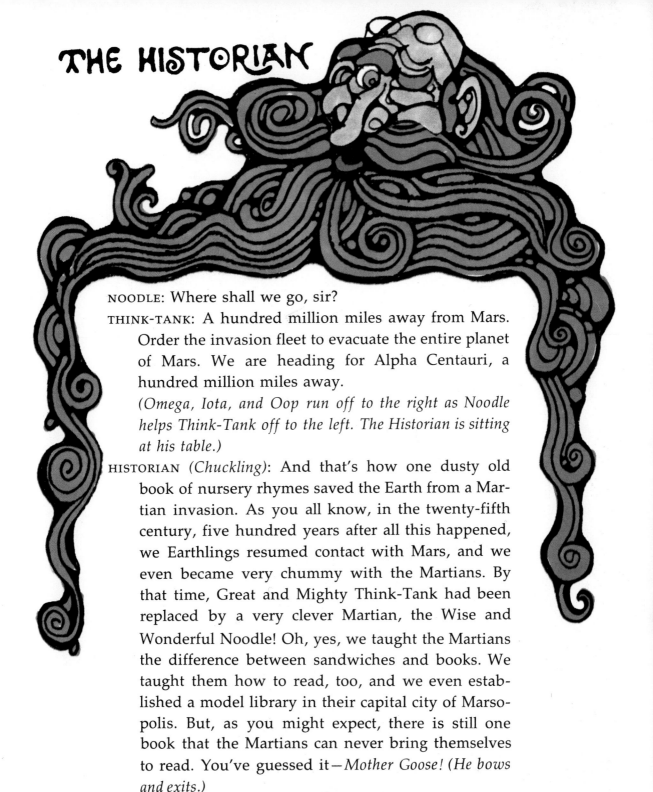

NOODLE: Where shall we go, sir?

THINK-TANK: A hundred million miles away from Mars. Order the invasion fleet to evacuate the entire planet of Mars. We are heading for Alpha Centauri, a hundred million miles away.

(Omega, Iota, and Oop run off to the right as Noodle helps Think-Tank off to the left. The Historian is sitting at his table.)

HISTORIAN *(Chuckling)*: And that's how one dusty old book of nursery rhymes saved the Earth from a Martian invasion. As you all know, in the twenty-fifth century, five hundred years after all this happened, we Earthlings resumed contact with Mars, and we even became very chummy with the Martians. By that time, Great and Mighty Think-Tank had been replaced by a very clever Martian, the Wise and Wonderful Noodle! Oh, yes, we taught the Martians the difference between sandwiches and books. We taught them how to read, too, and we even established a model library in their capital city of Marsopolis. But, as you might expect, there is still one book that the Martians can never bring themselves to read. You've guessed it—*Mother Goose! (He bows and exits.)*

TIME ON MARS

Fifty-five days hath September, March, June, and December —when you're keeping time on Mars. Since hours, days, months, and years have different meanings in space, today's scientists are preparing for our need to tell space time.

Time on Mars is getting earliest attention because astronomers know the most about Mars and that planet is the most likely to be visited first by man.

The first visitor to Mars will find that although its day is similar to ours, it is 39 minutes longer. And since Mars is about 49 million miles farther from the Sun than the Earth is, it takes nearly twice as long to make a complete journey around the Sun. Thus, there are about 687 Earth days, or 668 6/10 Mars days, in one Mars year.

To make calendar reading easier for the first Earthlings who explore Mars, scientists have broken the Mars year into twelve months, having the same names as our months even though they're twice as long. March, June, September, and December have 55 days; all the rest have 56.

On leap years (Mars has them too) December gets the extra day. However, a day is added every three out of five years, instead of one out of four.

The astronauts who blaze the trail to Mars will have to be able to know the times both on Mars and on Earth so that they'll know the exact second to begin their homeward journey.

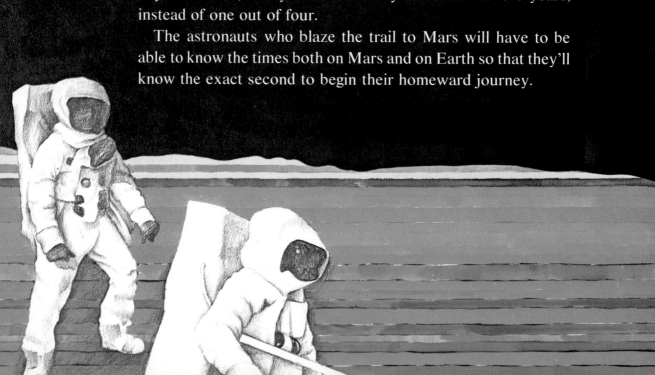

THE RAILROAD GHOST

by Murray Pringle

It was a spooky night. As the crack British express train raced through the chilly darkness, fog began to close in around it. It was just the sort of night anything could happen—a night one might even expect to meet a ghost.

Now, running a train isn't easy any time, but on this particular evening it was really hard work. Fog pressed in on the speeding train like folds of velvet. Even with the powerful headlight stabbing the darkness ahead, the engineer had to strain his eyes to see the track.

He was very much annoyed at the fog, because today of all days he wanted to make a record run. And the reason was that Queen Victoria herself was among the several hundred passengers on the train.

Suddenly a horrified gasp escaped his lips. Dead ahead, and outlined in the brilliant beam of the engine's headlamp, a figure in a black cloak stood in the middle of the tracks waving its arms frantically! The engineer made a desperate grab for the brakes and brought the express to a screeching halt.

After quieting the excited and frightened passengers, the trainmen got out to investigate. They searched and called, but there was no sign of the mysterious figure who had flagged their train.

Who had he been, and why had he stopped the train? The crewmen were puzzled. They decided someone had been playing a joke. Even the engineer was almost convinced that it had either been somebody's poor idea of a joke or his imagination playing tricks. But he wasn't absolutely sure.

Just to make certain, he swung down from his cab and walked up the tracks. Suddenly his face grew pale and his heart beat wildly. There, a scant two hundred yards ahead of the stopped train, he found a washed-out bridge! The whole thing had toppled into a swollen stream. If it had not been for the mysterious flagman, the train would have plunged into the stream, killing passengers and crew.

While the bridge and tracks were being repaired, the train

crew made another search, but they could not find the slightest trace of the strange figure who had saved the train.

Not until the train reached London safely was the mystery solved.

At the base of the locomotive headlamp, the engineer found a huge dead moth. He held the insect in his hand and frowned thoughtfully.

Then he did a strange thing. He wet the wings of the moth and carefully pasted it to the glass of the headlamp. Then he climbed back into the cab of his engine and switched on the light.

"Ah!" he cried triumphantly. "I thought so!" For as the bright beam stabbed ahead into the darkness, there appeared once again the "phantom" the engineer had seen earlier. But now the "arms" weren't waving wildly. They were still.

The mysterious rescuer had been this huge moth! Somehow, in the few seconds before the train reached the wrecked bridge, it had flown into the beam of the headlight. And because in the dense fog the trapped insect had resembled a cloaked figure waving its arms, many people— including the Queen of England herself—had been saved!

Did this really happen? Well, if you're ever in London, go to the Museum of Natural History and ask to see the "Victoria Moth." You will be shown a huge moth in a glass case—the moth the British call the Phantom Flagman!

the GRASSHOPPER

by David McCord

Down
a
deep
well
a
grasshopper
fell.

By kicking about
He thought to get out.
    He might have known better,
    For that got him wetter.
To kick round and round
Is the way to get drowned,
    And drowning is what
    I should tell you he got.

But
the
well
had
a
rope
that
dangled
some
hope.

And sure as molasses
On one of his passes
    He found the rope handy
    And up he went, *and he*

it
up
and
it
up
and
it
up
and
it
up
went

And hopped away proper
As any grasshopper.

This American Indian myth, retold by Henry Chafetz in his book, *Thunderbird and Other Stories,* is one Indian explanation of the cause of thunder and lightning.

When the earth was new, giants lived among the Indians. And the greatest of the giants that then walked the earth was Nasan. One hundred feet high Nasan stood, and each step he took was a mile long. Five feet wide was the space between his eyes, and his mouth when it was open seemed as large as a valley. His teeth looked like stumps of bright, white birch trees when he smiled.

Nasan's dwelling place was at one end of the earth on a very high mountain facing the Eastern Ocean, and his lodge was on the tallest peak of this mountain where the blue clouds met and passed one another. Nasan lived here all alone. He was a lonely giant.

One night, around the council fire of the giants, it was agreed that the Evening Star Lady was the fairest of all the women known to the great ones of the world. The Evening Star was lovely and bright to see, rising and shining in the sky each night.

The Indians respected and feared all the great beings—the Great Spirit, all the animal gods, all the bird gods, and the giants also—but they loved the Evening Star Lady.

She was many things to the Indians. Each night, the calendar men of the tribes looked to the rising of the Evening Star as the time to make another cut in their calendar sticks. The wanderer, the war scout, and the hunter returning home late at night always looked forward to the Evening Star to guide them on the trail. And to her only, the young Indian lovers sang happy songs and told the secrets in their hearts.

Now, Nasan was lonely.

"A pity it is," he said to himself, "that I have no wife to mend my moccasins, to keep my lodge in order, and to cook for me."

The giant looked at the Evening Star Lady up in the sky. His heart leaped with delight as he beheld her brightness, and at once he knew he had a great love for her. Nasan was determined to have the Evening Star Lady for his wife.

The giant called for the old Needlewoman.

Out of the cave where she made her home came the one-eyed Needlewoman. She came with her witching needles, her magic loom, and her buckskin bag of medicine.

"Make me wings, Grandmother," Nasan said to the Needlewoman. "I wish to go on a journey to the sky."

The Needlewoman was very old. Her hair was white and her one good eye was gray and deep. Old she was, but her hands were quick-moving and her fingers nimble.

In mid-forest by the light of the moon, while animal and Indian slept, the Needlewoman made the wings.

She took one thousand feathers from one hundred wild birds, and she obtained the finest and strongest thread from the

gray spiders who lived in the shadowy places of the Gloomy Hills where the mists linger. The Needlewoman stitched and stitched, and with the thread she bound the feathers together.

She deftly wove the silver of the moonbeams, the breath of a fleet deer, and the speed of a darting arrow into the wings.

The Needlewoman made a paint from the bark of a hemlock tree, and she colored the wings red.

She then dipped the wings in the waters of the Great Lake of Salt, and thus she made the wings strong.

Then the Needlewoman called for Nasan. Only a giant could carry these large and strong wings on his back. But Nasan was the greatest of the giants, and the wings fit him well.

Nasan soared like a big bird right up to the Evening Star Lady.

He brought her a buckskin bead bag and many white shells, and he dropped ermine skins and buffalo robes at her feet. Nasan promised the Evening Star Lady he would do anything she ever wished, if she would make her home in his lodge.

The Evening Star Lady smiled at the giant and put her arms around him. Off he flew with her to his mountain home.

The next night the Evening Star Lady did not appear in the sky. The night was gloomy.

The Indians looked and looked, but the Evening Star no longer shone in the sky at night. The night wanderers became lost, the calendar men could not keep the right time, and worst of all, the Indian lovers were dejected. Gone were their dreams, gone were their sweet songs, for gone was the Evening Star Lady, their star of love.

There was much sorrow among all the Indians. They assembled from near and far and cried out to the Great Spirit, who was the ruler of the sky:

"O Great Mystery, find and bring back for us the Evening Star Lady."

The Great Spirit looked over the edge of the sky and heard the cries of the Indians. The Great Spirit looked into his know-it-all medicine bag and saw that the Evening Star Lady had flown off with Nasan the giant.

The Great Spirit ordered Nasan to let the Evening Star Lady return to her place in the sky. But Nasan refused to give her up.

Now the Great Spirit was angry.

This was not good.

He swore an almighty oath to punish the giant.

The Great Spirit rattled his great war drum.

BOOM! BOOM! BOOM!

The Great Spirit sounded his war cry.

HI YI! HI YI! HI YI! YI! YI!

Now, Nasan, being a giant, was also a wizard who knew mighty magic.

When he heard the Great Spirit's war cry, Nasan pulled up a tall pine tree out of the ground. He used the tree, as he would a pencil, to draw a circle around his lodge. Four times he drew a ring around his home. Then, by placing a strong charm over the inside of the circle, he made it a magic zone where no harm could come to him.

The Great Spirit rode the winds to the mountain home of Nasan. With his hands he shook the mountain.

The grass flew and many trees fell as the mountain rocked. But the grass within the magic ring all around Nasan's lodge stood still, the trees were unshaken, and the giant's lodge did not fall.

The Great Spirit breathed upon the mountain.

His breath was fierce and burning, and out of it there came a roaring of fire and smoke that swept over the mountain, scorching all the land before it. But the fire crumbled to cold ashes at the edge of Nasan's charmed circle.

Truly, there was strong medicine in the giant's magic.

The Great Spirit sent five hundred dark shapes and weird forms to the home of Nasan. They could go no farther than the outside of the circle. The Great Spirit sent cold, and he sent floods. But these also failed to cross the edge of the ring. It was like a strong wall; nothing could pass it.

Now, the Great Spirit, who knew everything, knew that the Evening Star Lady desired above all things a robe of white deerskin. Through the Evening Star Lady, then, he would lure Nasan out from the protection of the magic circle.

The Great Spirit went to the Chief of the Ants and instructed him what to do and say.

The Chief of the Ants took his people to the mountain where Nasan lived, and the ants began to eat holes in the mountain. They dug and dug their way upwards until they came right underneath the floor of Nasan's lodge.

That night, as Nasan and the Evening Star Lady lay down to sleep, they heard voices beneath them. The giant and the Evening Star Lady, like all the great beings, knew the languages

192

of all creatures—whether human, bird, animal, or insect. Nasan and the Evening Star Lady put their ears to the earth floor of the lodge, and the words of the ants reached them from the ground underneath their sleeping blankets.

"One must see this wondrous white deer for himself," said an ant.

"Is it really all white?" another ant asked.

"Whiter than snow, silver, or clouds. White beyond all belief is this deer."

The ants talked in very loud voices to make certain that Nasan and the Evening Star Lady would hear.

"Where does this more than snow-white deer live?" asked one ant.

"This astounding white deer runs wild and free in the nearby forest of the hemlock trees."

"Surely," another ant said, "it is the only white deer in the world."

The Evening Star Lady could not sleep that night knowing there was a white deer nearby, and during the day she could not rest for thinking about the beautiful white robe its skin would make for her. The Evening Star Lady felt she could not live without such a robe.

"Husband," she said to Nasan, "I am most anxious for a white deerskin robe."

So great was Nasan's love for the Evening Star Lady, and so strong was her wish, that he agreed to go on a hunt for the white deer.

The giant set out down the mountain for the forest of the

hemlock trees. He moved cautiously, knowing the Great Spirit was still on the warpath against him.

The Great Spirit, who was hiding behind a gray cloud in the sky, watched Nasan leave his lodge. The Great Spirit was pleased that his plan had succeeded. He knew that no amount of caution could save Nasan from him once the giant left the protection of the charmed circle.

The moment Nasan stepped across the magic circle, the Great Spirit came out of his hiding place in the sky and seized him. With ten thousand phantom hands, the Great Spirit held Nasan. Sharper than spears were the Great Spirit's fingers. Stronger than the bull moose, stronger even than the oak tree, were his hands.

With a roar that echoed across the earth, Nasan tried to break away, but the Great Spirit's hands held the giant on all sides. Like ten thousand hammers, the fists of the Great Spirit beat pain against Nasan's bones.

Each way the giant turned and fought, he was beaten back by the phantom hands.

Nasan clutched at the hands he could not see and grappled fiercely with them. But for every hand he tore away from his body, ten more seized him.

The shouts of the Great Spirit and the giant were fearsome to hear, and the earth shook as they struggled with each other.

The fight continued from mountain to plain. Four suns, four moons, the Great Spirit and Nasan the giant fought each other.

Nasan crashed over mountains and staggered backwards into the great broad rivers. The Great Spirit marveled at Nasan's strength. Truly, he was the mightiest of giants.

But the giant fell to the earth at last, exhausted and beaten. The ground shook and crumbled and became a valley where he fell.

Thus, the Great Spirit captured Nasan and pulled him up to the sky.

The Great Spirit was not cruel or wicked, and he admired those who battled bravely and well. The giant, however, had disobeyed the Great Spirit's command, and brave or not, he must be punished.

The Great Spirit changed the giant into a large and awesome eagle.

"Your name shall be Thunderbird, ruler of the thunder and the lightning," the Great Spirit told Nasan. "Once the greatest of all giants, you are now the mightiest of all birds."

The Evening Star Lady was sent back to her place in the sky, and once more there was joy among the Indians.

Around the world Thunderbird now flies, the maker of the storm clouds and a wanderer of the dark skies. His voice is the noise of the thunder, and the flash of lightning is the flapping of his wings.

Indian children do not fear the thunder or lightning, not even at night when it awakens them from their sleep. They know it is Nasan the giant, who became the Thunderbird.

from

BEN *and* ME

A New and Astonishing *LIFE* of
BENJAMIN FRANKLIN
As written by his Good Mouse
AMOS
Lately Discovered, Edited
& Illustrated by
**ROBERT
LAWSON**

The manuscript for BEN AND ME, *a part of which is reprinted on the following pages, was sent to me by an architect friend. While altering an old Philadelphia house, workmen uncovered a small chamber beneath a bedroom hearthstone. This tiny room, for such it appeared to be, was about eighteen inches square. It contained various small articles of furniture, all of the Colonial Period. In one of these, a secretary desk, was found a manuscript book, the leaves of which, about the size of postage stamps, were covered with minute writing.*

With the aid of a powerful reading glass, the architect had managed to decipher the writing.

Scarce able to believe that such a remarkable document could be other than some ancient hoax, he sent it to various authorities for their opinions.

Scientists of the Brownsonian Institute have assured him that their analyses of the paper and ink prove them definitely to be of Early American manufacture, and that the writing was most certainly done with a quill pen of that period.

More startling still was the report from officials of the National Museum of Natural History, stating that, incredible as it might seem, there could be no possible doubt that the handwriting was that of a mouse!

Since the recent death of my lamented friend and patron Ben Franklin, many so-called historians have attempted to write accounts of his life and his achievements. Most of these are wrong in so many respects that I feel the time has now come for me to take pen in paw and set things right.

All of these ill-informed scribblers seem astonished at Ben's great fund of information, at his brilliant decisions, at his seeming knowledge of all that went on about him.

Had they asked me, I could have told them. It was ME.

For many years I was his closest friend and adviser and, if I do say it, was in great part responsible for his success and fame.

Not that I wish to claim too much. I simply hope to see justice done, credit given where credit is due, and that's to me — mostly.

Ben was undoubtedly a splendid fellow, a great man, a patriot, and all that; but he was undeniably stupid at times, and had it not been for me — well, here's the true story, and you can judge for yourself.

I was the oldest of twenty-six children. My parents, in naming us, went right through the alphabet. I, being first, was **A**mos, the others went along through **B**athsheba, **C**laude, **D**aniel — and so forth down to the babies: **X**enophone, (zen′oh-fohn) **Y**sobel, (iz′uh-bel) and **Z**enas (zee′nahs).

We lived in the vestry of Old Christ Church on Second Street, in Philadelphia — behind the paneling. With that number of mouths to feed, we were, naturally, not a very prosperous family. In fact we were really quite poor — as poor as church mice.

But it was not until the Hard Winter of 1745 that things really became desperate. That was a winter long to be remembered for its severity. Night after night, my poor father would come in tired and wet with his little sack practically empty.

We were driven to eating prayer books. When those gave out, we took to the Minister's sermons. That was, for me,

the final straw. The prayer books were tough, but those sermons!

Being the oldest, it seemed fitting that I should go out into
the world and make my own way. Perhaps I could in some
way help the others. At least, it left one less to be provided
for.

So, saying farewell to all of them—my mother and father
and all the children from Bathsheba to Zenas—I set forth
on the coldest, windiest night of a cold and windy winter.

Little did I dream, at that moment, of all the strange
people and experiences I should encounter before I ever
returned to that little vestry home! All I thought of were my
cold paws, my empty stomach—and those sermons.

I have never known how far I traveled that night, for, what
with the cold and hunger, I must have become slightly delirious. The first thing I remember clearly was being in a kitchen
and smelling CHEESE! It didn't take long to find it. It was only
a bit of rind and fairly dry, but how I ate!

Refreshed by this, my first real meal in many a day, I began to explore the house. It was painfully bare—clean, but
bare. There was very little furniture, and that was all hard
and shiny. There were no soft things or dusty corners where
a chap could curl up and have a good warm nap. It was cold
too, almost as cold as outdoors.

Upstairs were two rooms. One was dark, and from it came
the sound of snoring. The other had a light, and the sound
of sneezing. I chose the sneezy one.

In a large chair close to the fireplace sat a short, thick, round-faced man, trying to write by the light of a candle. Every few moments he would sneeze, and his square-rimmed glasses would fly off. Reaching for these, he would drop his pen. By the time he found that and got settled to write, the candle would flicker from the draft. When that calmed down, the sneezing would start again, and so it went. He was not accomplishing much in the way of writing.

Of course, I recognized him. Everyone in Philadelphia knew the great Doctor Benjamin Franklin, scientist, inventor, printer, editor, author, soldier, statesman, and philosopher.

He didn't look great or famous that night, though; he just looked cold—and a bit silly.

He was wrapped in a sort of dressing gown, with a dirty fur collar, and on his head was perched an odd-looking fur cap.

The cap interested me, for I was still chilled to the bone, and this room was just as bleak as the rest of the house. It was a rather disreputable-looking affair, that cap; but in one side of it I had spied a hole—just about my size.

Up the back of the chair I went, and under cover of the next fit of sneezes, in I slid. What a cozy place *that* was! Plenty of room to move about a bit, just enough air, such soft fur, and such warmth!

"Here," said I to myself, "is my home. No more cold streets, or cellars, or vestries. HERE I stay."

At the moment, of course, I never realized how true this was to prove. All I realized was that I was warm, well fed, and—oh, so sleepy!

And so to bed.

I slept late the next morning. When I woke, my fur-cap home was hanging on the bedpost, and I in it.

Dr. Franklin was again crouched over the fire attempting to write, between fits of sneezing and glasses-hunting. The fire, what there was of it, was smoking, and the room was as cold as ever.

"Not wishing to be critical—" I said. "But, perhaps, a bit of wood on that smoky ember that you seem to consider a fire might—"

"*WASTE NOT, WANT NOT,*" said he, severe, and went on writing.

"Well, just suppose," I said, "just suppose you spend two or three weeks in bed with *pewmonia*—would that be a waste or—"

"It would be," said he, putting on a log, "whatever your name might be."

"Amos," said I. . . . "And then there'd be doctors' bills—"

"*BILLS!*" said he, shuddering, and put on two more logs, quick. The fire blazed up then, and the room became a little better, but not much.

"Dr. Franklin," I said, "that fireplace is all wrong."

"You might call me Ben—just plain Ben," said he. "What's wrong with it?"

"Well, for one thing, most of the heat goes up the chimney. And for another, you can't get *around* it. Now, outside our church there used to be a Hot-chestnut Man. Sometimes, when business was rushing, he'd drop a chestnut. Pop was always on the lookout, and almost before it touched the ground, he'd have it in his sack—and down to the vestry with it. There he'd put it in the middle of the floor, and we'd all gather round for the warmth.

"Twenty-eight of us it would heat, and the room as well. It was all because it was OUT IN THE OPEN, not stuck in a hole in the wall like that fireplace."

"Amos," he interrupted, excited, "there's an idea there! But we couldn't move the fire out into the middle of the room."

"We could if there were something to put it in, iron or something."

"But the smoke?" he objected.

"PIPE," said I, and curled up for another nap.

I didn't get it, though.

Ben rushed off downstairs, came back with a great armful of junk, dumped it on the floor, and was off for more. No one could have slept, not even a dormouse. After a few trips, he had a big pile of things there. There were scraps of iron, tin, and wire. There were a couple of old warming pans, an iron oven, three flatirons, six potlids, a wire birdcage, and an anvil. There were saws, hammers, pincers, drills, nails, screws, bolts, bricks, sand, and an old broken sword.

He drew out a sort of plan and went to work. With the clatter he made, there was no chance of a nap so I helped all I could, picking up the nuts and screws and tools that he dropped — and his glasses.

Ben was a fair terror for work, once he was interested. It was almost noon before he stopped for a bit of rest. We looked over what had been done and it didn't look so bad — considering.

It was shaped much like a small fireplace set up on legs, with two iron doors on the front and a smoke pipe running from the back to the fireplace. He had taken the andirons out of the fireplace and boarded that up so we wouldn't lose any heat up the chimney.

Ben walked around looking at it, proud as could be, but worried.

"The floor," he said. "It's the floor that troubles me, Amos. With those short legs and that thin iron bottom, the heat—"

"Down on the docks," said I, "we used to hear the ship-rats telling how the sailors build their cooking fires on board ship. A layer of sand right on the deck, bricks on top of that, and—"

"Amos," he shouted, "you've got it!" and rushed for the bricks and sand. He put a layer of sand in the bottom of the affair, the bricks on top of that, and then set the andirons in.

It looked pretty promising.

"Eureka!" he exclaimed, stepping back to admire it—and tripping over the saw. "Straighten things up a bit, Amos, while I run and get some logs."

"*Don't* try to run," I said. "And by the way, do you come through the pantry on the way up?"

"Why?" he asked.

"In some ways, Ben," I said, "you're fairly bright, but in others you're just plain dull. The joy of creating may be meat and drink to you, but as for me, a bit of cheese—"

He was gone before I finished, but when he came back with the logs, he did have a fine slab of cheese, a loaf of rye bread, and a good big tankard of ale.

We put in some kindling and logs and lit her up. She drew fine, and Ben was so proud and excited that I had to be rather sharp with him before he would settle down to food. Even then he was up every minute, to admire it from a new angle.

Before we'd finished even one sandwich, the room had warmed up like a summer afternoon.

"Amos," said he, "we've done it!"

"Thanks for the WE," I said. "I'll remember it." And then I dozed off.

When I woke up, the room was sizzling warm. Ben was happily writing, as usual, and I went over to see what was going on. So far he had written, with a lot of flourishes:

An Account of the New Pennsylvania Fireplaces, Recently Invented by Doctor Benjamin Franklin, Wherein Their Construction and Their . . .

"Ben," I said, "we'll have to come to an understanding. Do you recollect your exact words when it worked?"

"Why yes, I do," he admitted, very prompt. He was always fair, Ben was, just overenthusiastic about himself. "As I remember, those words were, 'Amos, we've done it!'"

"Exactly," said I, "'We've done it!' 'We' means two: you *and* me. Now let's get things straight, Ben. Fame and honors are nothing to me—cheese is. Also there's my family to consider, twenty-five brothers and sisters in a cold vestry, and hungry. I can be a great help to you. I've proved that. Now what do you propose?"

He looked pretty thoughtful, and I could feel a quotation

coming on. Finally it did. *"THE LABORER IS WORTHY OF HIS HIRE,"* he said.

"I don't labor," I said, "I think. And maxims don't fill empty stomachs. That's not a bad one, itself. Be specific."

Well, we talked it over for some time, and Ben was very reasonable about the whole affair—generous too. I think that being comfortably warm, for once, helped that.

We finally made the following Agreement:

Twice a week, rain or shine, he promised to have delivered to the vestry:

> 1 two-ounce piece best quality CHEESE,
>
> 1 one-inch slice RYE BREAD, fresh,
>
> 88 grains unhulled WHEAT.

For myself I was to have as home or domicile to me and my heirs, to have and to hold forever without let or hindrance, with daily subsistence and clothing, in addition thereto:

> 1 FUR CAP.

On my part,
I was faithfully to give
and perform to him, Benjamin
Franklin, advice, aid, assistance, and succor, at all times
and under all conditions, and with him constantly to abide,
till death did us part, so help me . . . .

Ben wrote it all up neat with lots of flourishes, Latin
phrases, and seals. Then we both signed it and shook hands
on the bargain.

He was fine about the whole thing and never used a single
maxim. I must say he lived up to it, too. Not once in all the
rest of his life did that bread, cheese, and wheat fail to reach
the vestry twice a week, regular as clockwork.

After that we sat around for a while, basking in the warmth,
and I couldn't help thinking how my fortunes had changed
in a short twenty-four hours. Here I was in a snug, comfortable home, my family well provided for, with a good friend
and an interesting future.

I felt so much at peace with the world that when Ben fi-
nally asked, "Amos, what shall we call this affair?" I said,
"My friend, the credit is all yours. WE hereby call it the
FRANKLIN Stove."

ABOUT THE AUTHOR

Robert Lawson was trained as an artist and for years illustrated magazines, greeting cards, and books by well-known authors. He was forty-six before he himself wrote a book—*Ben and Me,* part of which you have just read. Encouraged by its success, he continued writing and eventually was author and illustrator of thirteen other books. Both his stories and his pictures reveal his sense of humor and love for animals, and much of the fascination of books like *Ben and Me* comes from seeing the world through the eyes of animals.

Until his death in 1957, Mr. Lawson and his wife lived in Westport, Connecticut. Their home, called Rabbit Hill, provided the setting and title for one of his award-winning books. Typical of Robert Lawson was this sign in his driveway: "Please drive carefully on account of small animals."

MORE BOOKS TO ENJOY

KANGAROOS AND OTHER ANIMALS WITH POCKETS,
by Louis Darling

This book describes animals that carry their young in pockets. It tells where these marsupial animals come from, how they are like other animals, and how they are different.

BRADY, *by Jean Fritz*

A boy makes a difficult decision and plays a heroic part in the Underground Railroad.

THE COMPLETE PETERKIN PAPERS, *by Lucretia Hale*

These are the ridiculous tales of the Peterkin family, who have many difficulties and very little common sense.

ON CITY STREETS, *compiled by Nancy Larrick*

This is a collection of poems about cities and their people. Many of the poems are thoughtful and sad, and some are humorous. Such familiar poets as Carl Sandburg and Langston Hughes are included, as well as many new poets.

MR. REVERE AND I, *by Robert Lawson*

Paul Revere's faithful horse, Scheherezade, tells about his master's exciting life and the famous ride.

LITTLE BURMA, *by Robert M. McClung*

An orphan boy runs away from the people he works for. He finds adventure in a job caring for Little Burma, the first elephant ever brought to the United States.

PATTERNS

Contents

PATTERNS

Indians and Eskimos, even the white men at the settlement of Unison, looked twice when they saw Nanook. He was more dog than any of them had ever seen, a giant Malemute (mal′uh-myoot) husky, with brute power in his firm body and long, rangy legs. There was speed in those legs, and he held his beautiful head so proudly and high that his silver-tipped ears came up to Rick Hale's hips.

Rick caught his breath the first time he saw the dog. It was chained behind the log trading post with twenty other new huskies and towering over all of them.

"Where did you get him?"

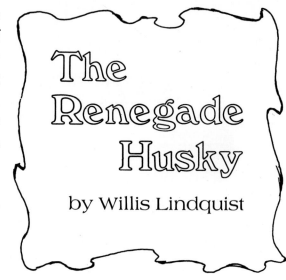

The Renegade Husky

by Willis Lindquist

Rick asked Mr. Twill, who ran the trading post.

"That's Nanook. Finest dog I ever laid eyes on," said Mr. Twill. "He's one of the lot the Eskimos brought in."

Rick nodded. In late summer the Eskimos brought in their spare dogs and traded them for supplies for the long Arctic winter. But they usually traded their poorest dogs. Nanook did not look like a spare dog, and that puzzled Rick.

"Why would they trade a beauty like Nanook?" he asked.

Mr. Twill shrugged. "I'm beginning to think they couldn't train him. Maybe he's a renegade," he grumbled. "I had to pay two prices for him."

Nanook was easily worth two prices, Rick decided. You couldn't compare a beauty like that with the other dogs. As Rick came closer, Nanook bared his fangs and uttered a low growl.

"Better not go too close," Mr. Twill warned. "He's a mean one."

A customer called from the back door of the post and Mr. Twill hurried away.

Rick smiled at the dog and spoke softly. "Nanook, now we can get acquainted," he said in quiet, soothing tones.

He held out his hand, palm up. It was an old trick one of the sourdoughs had taught him. "When you aim to make friends with a strange dog," he had said, "never raise your hand above his head, not at first. He might think you mean to strike him. Just hold your hand palm up and slide it slow and easy under his chin."

Rick took a step closer, his hand extended. Intelligent eyes looked up at him. "Sure," he said reassuringly. "We're going to be friends."

With a sudden snarl the big dog lunged for his throat. It was the leap of an enraged killer. White teeth snapped on empty air a scant six inches from their goal as the chain caught him up.

Rick fell back, dismayed. But after a moment he chuckled. "It was my fault," he said. "I was rushing you." He crawled as close as safety would permit and sat down. "You're lonely and puzzled. I can see it in your eyes. I'm going to sit here and talk and talk. You'll soon get used to me."

He went on and on in a low, soothing voice, and Nanook strained at his chain and listened. He listened for an hour or so every day for a week. It took that long before he finally relaxed enough to sit down.

It was a great moment for Rick. "That's the idea!" he said. "You can listen just as well sitting down. You're beginning to trust me, aren't you?"

But now that Nanook was finally down on his haunches, Rick made the most of it. He held out a piece of meat.

Nanook rose and sniffed. Then he took the meat gingerly between his teeth and snapped it up in a gulp.

Rick laughed. "You were careful not to bite my fingers, weren't you?"

Encouraged, he slid his hand beneath the massive jaws and stroked the heavy white fur of the throat. But he did so for only a few seconds. It was enough for a first lesson, and Rick almost burst with pride.

"Mr. Twill!" he cried, rushing into the post. "Guess what! I've been petting Nanook and he seems to like it."

The trader scowled. "He's a sly one," he muttered. "Don't trust him too far."

Up to that moment, Rick had never admitted that he wanted anything more than to be friends with the magnificent dog. To gain the dog's trust had been a challenge. But now that it seemed reasonably certain that Nanook liked him, he wanted to own Nanook, to have this kind of Malemute for his very own. He had to have him.

He wet his lips. "Mr. Twill," he began uncertainly, "how — how much do you want for him?"

"Nanook? Oh, I sold him to the sourdough on Balsalm Ridge. He asked to leave the dog here for a couple of weeks to get used to the whites."

"You mean Old Jake? Why— why he near beats his dogs to death."

Mr. Twill nodded. "It takes a strong hand with a killer like that."

"He'll kill him!" Rick choked. "You can't beat a dog like that. He's proud. He's got spirit. He'll die before he'll mind the whip."

Mr. Twill shrugged, making it clear that it was no longer his concern.

Rick walked out, dragging his feet. He felt sick, weak. If he'd been a little younger he would have cried, but he blinked back the tears and faced Nanook with a smile.

Personal danger seemed a thing of the past. It was the dog that was in danger now and, thinking of nothing else, Rick walked right up and began scratching his ear. The growl in Nanook's throat died as Rick continued, working both hands behind the ears and back along the shaggy neck until he was petting his back.

"You like that, don't you?" As he walked around the big beast, the dog watched every move with suspicion. Rick knew that one quick step, one quick motion with his hand, would have invited a death-dealing leap. But there was no fear in him. He was fighting now for the life of the animal he loved.

He sat down just within reach of the dog and began to talk. "We've got one week, Nanook. We've got to work fast. When old Jake comes for you, you've got to mind so he doesn't beat you. That's a good boy. Sit down. You know, I think I know what's wrong with you. You're not a killer. You're not a renegade. Someone beat you once, beat you bad, and you hated him so much after that that he had to get rid of you."

Rick became more and more convinced that he was right. His kindness and patience bore fruit with each passing day. He spent every spare moment with the dog, which meant almost all day, for he had little to do except help his father take observations at the weather station.

He came home for dinner glowing and breathless one evening. "I had Nanook on a leash almost all day," he boasted to his parents. "We walked all over the settlement and out over the tundra. If I can just make him behave so Jake won't beat him, he'll be all right."

"Just see that you don't get in Jake's way," his father warned. "He's a hard customer and he won't appreciate your telling him how to handle his dogs."

As it turned out, Jake didn't have to be told. He saw. Rick had the dog in his harness, dragging a rock about the backyard of the post when Jake came. The heavy-set, black-bearded sourdough let out a bellow of rage that brought Mr. Twill running.

"It's all right," Mr. Twill kept repeating. "The boy's been doing some wonderful things for the dog."

"I don't need any dim-witted boy to help with my dogs," raged Jake.

Rick left. He didn't want to be there when Jake led Nanook away.

The snow came a few days later. It was fine weather for dog teams, and business at the post was brisk. Jake came in several times, but Nanook was never in his team.

The great Malemute was a renegade, Jake reported. He said Mr. Twill had cheated him. The dog was useless in the harness, for he fought constantly with other dogs. He had even attacked Jake on several occasions, and Jake had beaten him to within an inch of his life.

"He's going to keep on beating him until he pounds some sense into him," Mr. Twill told Rick. "And if he can't do that, he'll shoot him."

"Oh, no!" blurted Rick. "Can't you do something to stop him, Mr. Twill?"

"It's his dog, Rick."

The blood rushed hot to Rick's face. "That's not so! Nanook's mine! I'm going out to see Jake. I'll — I'll pay anything."

"Don't get any foolish notions about going out there," said Mr. Twill. "Jake's in the habit of taking potshots at people who come too close. Anyone going to his place is headed for trouble."

"What's the matter with him?" asked Rick. "Gold?"

"Hate. People hate him for his low-down tricks. Someone burned his cabin several years ago to get even. He's not taking any chances on its happening again."

Rick clamped his jaw hard. Nanook's life was in danger. "Well, I'm not going to take any chance either," he said grimly. "I'm going out there."

He started before dawn next morning, snowshoes strapped to his back, and all his savings in his pocket to convince Jake he meant business. It was an eight-mile walk. The air was cold and still, and over the great lonely slopes of spruce and Norway pine, the northern lights flickered their last symphony of color. Then dawn squeezed them out.

Rick followed Jake's sled tracks over the balsam ridge into the valley. Looking down, he could see Jake's cabin in the distance. He hurried on, half waiting for the crack of a rifle. But the only sounds were the crunching snow and his hammering heart.

A movement on the far side of the valley caught his eye. A dog sled! He knew at once that it was Jake. Jake was going out the other side of the valley to check his traps. Rick started to run. He shouted. It was useless. Jake went on, unhearing.

As he stood undecided, he heard a low howl from behind the cabin. His heart leaped into his throat. Nanook was there, Nanook who had too much wolf in him to be able to bark.

He ran. The big Malemute leaped again and again at the end of his chain, snarled savagely, his eyes red with hate.

Rick bit his lips. The dog did not recognize him. But suddenly he knew why. The animal was half-starved.

Frantically, Rick searched until he found a box of frozen salmon. He tossed the dog two chunks, and he talked. He was still talking when he heard Jake's angry shouts.

The man leaped from his sled. He came rushing with his rifle.

"Stealing my dog, eh?" he screamed.

Rick had never seen such savage fury in a man's face. His blood turned to ice as he stood there, unable to move.

"I—came to buy—"

The huge fist struck the side of

his face and he went down. The man stood over him, roaring like a demon.

Then it happened. A gray blur flew at the man's throat. Jake screamed. Rick watched in horror.

"Nanook!" screamed Rick. He scrambled to his feet.

The great jaws closed over the fat neck as Rick hit with his full weight. Boy and dog rolled in the snow.

Rick threw himself over the prostrate Jake. Nanook crouched again, but he did not leap as Rick tried to quiet him with a steady flow of words.

The dog came closer. It nosed him. Rick slid his hand up along the neck and caught the collar. Then he drew Nanook away and held him fast while Jake got to his feet.

Jake felt the back of his neck. He was not hurt. There were only scratches. He stared at boy and dog, swaying a little. "You saved my life, boy. Why?"

From anyone but Jake, it would have been a strange question. But Rick understood. It was the first act of kindness the man had experienced in years.

"I came out here to buy Nanook." Rick dug out his money. "I'm the only master he knows."

Jake scowled fiercely. He fumbled in the snow for his gun and whip. "These," he growled, "are his only master. He's no good. Take him over to that tree, let him go. You go on up a ways and call him. I'll show you what I mean. And when he comes for me, he'll get a bullet between the eyes."

Nanook stayed by the tree where Rick told him to sit. Rick walked to the next tree, knowing it was an unfair test, not a test between masters. It was a test between the dog's love and hate, and Jake knew how strong hate could be.

"Come here, Nanook!" Rick cried, his voice muffled with emotion.

The whip cracked. Nanook stood up, looked from one to the other. Then the rifle spat and kicked up snow a few feet from the dog.

Nanook wheeled, ears flat and belly low, as he faced his enemy. His teeth bared with a snarl.

"Nanook!" Rick cried. "Come back!"

The terror in his voice brought the dog up sharp. He came in great loping bounds. Rick fell to his knees. He held out his arms and a moment later buried his face in the thick fur. And when he looked up, Jake was waving him away, his face showing a strange mixture of shame and sullenness.

"You can have him," the sourdough bellowed. "Take him away. It'll save me the price of a bullet."

With Nanook at his heels, Rick walked through the balsams and over the ridge as though he were walking on air. Nanook was his. And Jake wasn't so bad. He wasn't a renegade either.

AUTHOR

Willis Lindquist once sailed a four-masted sailing ship from Denmark to Australia in 102 days. Other travels have taken him to 40 different countries. He has written articles for *National Geographic Magazine* about some of these countries.

Born in Winthrop, Minnesota, he studied for three years at the University of Minnesota. After attending law school in Washington, D.C., he became a tax lawyer with the Bureau of Internal Revenue. During World War II, he spent two years at sea with the Merchant Marine.

Mr. Lindquist now lives in New York City where he has settled down to a life of writing. Many of his books are for boys and girls. Some of them are *Burma Boy, Call of the White Fox, Red Drum's Warning,* and *Alaska, the Forty-ninth State.*

You may not be a great sculptor, but that doesn't mean that you can't carve figurines, head-and-shoulder portraits, and any other small objects.

Oh, but you haven't any marble! Well, don't let that bother you. To carve in marble is hard work and takes a great deal of time. Soap, just white hand soap, is much easier and quicker to work with and less expensive. You will be surprised at the statues you'll be able to produce from it with a little effort and imagination. And you will be learning an old, old art.

To start your own sculpture, get a cake of white hand soap, a small knife, and an orange stick or nail file. Since this is your first experience with soap carving, it would be better to start with something simple, such as a fish.

FUN WITH SOAP SCULPTURE

by Pauline Rothrauff

First, draw a picture of whatever you want to make. Next, scrape all the lettering from your soap so that it is smooth and even. Now place the drawing on the soap and trace around it with a soft, fairly sharp pencil that will press through onto the soap, or trace your drawing over carbon paper. Some soap carvers transfer their designs by making pinpricks through it into the soap and then following the pattern made by the pinpricks.

After you have the design marked off on the soap, start cutting away the soap outside the outline of the object. Then round it out and carve the details. Don't hurry your carving. You will want to use an orange stick or nail file to carve grooves and lines. Very often a small penknife will work better for fine, intricate cutting.

When you have finished, you can smooth your sculpture by rubbing it with your fingertips or lightly washing it with your hands.

When your sculpture is dry, it can be painted with watercolors or poster paints. Or if you prefer to keep its marble-like finish, coat it with clear nail polish.

Witches and Onion Sandwiches
by Elaine Konigsburg

Jennifer said she was a witch disguised as a perfectly normal fifth grader. Perhaps she was, as she certainly called Elizabeth by her right name the first time they met, and she knew exactly how many chocolate-chip cookies Elizabeth had in her bag. She knew, too, that Elizabeth had just moved to town and was an only child. Being shy and lonely, Elizabeth jumped at the chance to be Jennifer's apprentice and to learn witchcraft. Of course, as an apprentice, she had to eat special foods. One week, for example, she had to eat one raw onion each day. Another special thing about witchcraft is that it is a very private affair, so the girls had to pretend they hardly knew each other. But it helped Elizabeth to know that Jennifer felt the same way she did about mushy school plays and gushy drama teachers and about that mean Cynthia whom all the adults thought was so perfect.

The minute we got back from Thanksgiving weekend, the whole school started getting ready for Christmas and the Christmas play — especially our grade. This year the fifth grade was to put on the play. The play is always presented twice, once for the whole school and once for the Parent and Teachers Association meeting at night. There are three fifth grade classes in William McKinley Elementary School, that's my school. Three fifth grades add up to about sixty kids. All the other classes of William McKinley Elementary School were to sing carols and recite poems.

That first Monday afternoon after Thanksgiving all the fifth graders met in the auditorium. Each classroom teacher had read the play in the morning. Mrs. Stuyvestant would direct the play, Mrs. Stuyvestant would choose the cast for the play, Mrs. Stuyvestant had written the play. The play was long. It had to be long so that all sixty kids could get a chance to act. Our school was democratic about Christmas. Here's the play:

There is a king who lives once upon a time (of course). He has a beautiful daughter (of course). He loves his beautiful daughter very much. (of course). She is very unhappy. No one knows why she is very unhappy. The king wants to make her happy, so he asks her what can he give her for Christmas. She doesn't know (of course). The king goes to Santa's workshop, and he asks Santa what can he give his beautiful, unhappy daughter for Christmas. Santa's workshop is full of merry elves who all love the princess like crazy. They are all hammering

and sawing and carrying on. Santa holds up all these dolls and things, but the king doesn't think they will make the princess smile. He shakes his head and walks away. Then the king goes to the queen's chamber, and he asks the queen what can he give their beautiful, unhappy daughter for Christmas. The queen's chamber is full of beautiful ladies-in-waiting who all love the princess like crazy. They are all singing and

dancing and carrying on. The queen holds up all these clothes and things, but the king doesn't think they will make the princess smile. He shakes his head and walks away. Then the king goes to the kitchen, and he asks the chef what can he give his beautiful, unhappy daughter for Christmas. The kitchen is full of cook's helpers who all love the princess like crazy. They are all stirring big pots and being jolly and carrying on. The chef holds up all these cakes and cookies and things, but the king doesn't think they will make the princess smile.

He shakes his head and walks away. He walks to his throne room. He sits down to think. He thinks and thinks. He thinks he has a real problem. Soon an old scrubwoman comes in. She looks so happy scrubbing that the king thinks she has an answer to un-

happiness. He asks her what can he give his beautiful, unhappy daughter for Christmas. She tells him that he should give the beautiful, unhappy princess a puppy because to be happy you have to love and take care of someone as well as be loved and be taken care of. She tells him that that is one of the lessons of Christmas. The king thinks this is a great idea. He gets his beautiful, unhappy princess a puppy (of course). She smiles happily (of course), and the play is over (at last).

Guess who was the beautiful princess? Cynthia (of course). Guess who was the little puppy? The smallest kid in the class—me (of course). Jennifer was a lady-in-waiting. I couldn't tell whether she enjoyed being a lady or not. She kept her eyes up the whole time Mrs. Stuyvestant was choosing the cast. No one knew that Jennifer and I had made a pact sealed in blood. No one knew that we were witch and apprentice or that we even knew each other. Witchcraft is a private affair— very private. It's secret.

Remember that my apprentice food that week was one raw onion per day. It was no problem because I love onion sandwiches. I loved onion sandwiches even before I was a witch's apprentice . . . when I was an ordinary, fussy eater. Here is my recipe for onion sandwiches: toast the bread, butter it, slice the onions, salt them, place them on the buttered slice of toast and cover with an unbuttered slice, cut off the crusts (of course), and eat. Delicious. On Sunday I had announced to my mother that I would be having an onion sandwich for lunch every day the next week.

"Every day?" my mother asked.

"Yes, *every* day," I answered.

"Hot dogs last week, onions this week. There must be some special reason," she said.

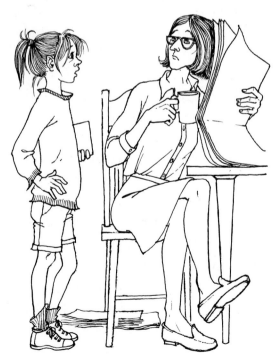

"There is," I said. My voice trailed because I was stalling for time to think of a reason.

"Tell me," my mother said. I could tell her patience was small because her voice was very slow and very patient. My father was home. That was the way she talked when she was angry if my father was home.

I thought fast. "I am conducting an experiment. I think I can keep from catching a cold for a whole year if I eat one onion a day for a whole week before winter officially begins."

"Well," my mother said, "you'll surely keep from catching cold for the week, if not for the whole year. No one will be able to get close enough to give you any germs." Her voice was still slow and low.

"Please, may I try it?" I asked.

"Thank goodness you don't know about asafetida," she said.

"What's asafetida?" I asked.

"I'll never tell," she answered.

I believe that if you like onions, you should love onions. Nice people love onions. If you love onions, you should find the odor of onions on someone's breath very pleasant.

Our first full rehearsal for the

Christmas play was on Friday afternoon. It was a long rehearsal. All the teachers except Mrs. Stuyvestant took coffee breaks. Everyone had to be prompted. Everyone stood in the wrong places. Mrs. Stuyvestant would bounce up on the stage and move the people around. She made chalk marks on the stage where they were to stand. By the end of the first rehearsal, the floor looked like our classroom blackboard just after Miss Hazen explained long division by the New Math. Mrs. Stuyvestant was the tallest woman I have ever seen. Everyone called her Mrs. Sky-high-vestant.

My part was toward the end of the play. The king brings me (the puppy) to Cynthia (the princess). I didn't have any lines to memorize. My role meant putting on an old doggie costume and crawling around on all fours and making bow-wow sounds. When the king gives me (the puppy) to Cynthia (the princess), Mrs. Stuyvestant said that I was to stand up on my hind legs and put my hands (paws) on Cynthia's lap, look up at her face, stick out my tongue, and pant. "Pant with excitement," Mrs. Stuyvestant said. "Frolic around," Mrs. Stuyvestant said. I was afraid that Mrs. Stuyvestant would ask me to wag my tail. Cynthia (the princess) was to snuggle her head up to mine and smile. Then everyone from Santa's workshop, from the Queen's chamber, and from the royal kitchen was to come back onstage and sing and dance and carry on.

Even though this was not a dress rehearsal for anyone else, I had to be in costume to get used to walking on all fours. Mrs. Stuyvestant said that, too. The puppy costume was made of some fuzzy black orlon stuff that was thick, heavy, and hot. Inside, it smelled like a small glue factory. We rehearsed the elves and the ladies-in-waiting and the cooks. Long before I had to walk onstage, I was so hot inside the costume that I was sure I was going to commit spontaneous combustion. But I had heard that the show must go on. Mrs. Stuyvestant said that. The only thing I did, the only thing I could do, was to unzip the head part of my costume and fling it back like a hood. I got some relief. Since this was only a rehearsal and no one else was in costume, I figured that it didn't make any difference.

Cynthia had been onstage almost the whole rehearsal. The king keeps visiting her during the play to see if she is smiling yet.

She smiled the whole time she was onstage. She was supposed to be unhappy, but she was grinning. She wasn't laughing, just grinning like the Mona Lisa. Mrs. Stuyvestant would say, "Be unhappy." Cynthia would frown, but soon the grin would creep back over her face. She was grinning when the king brought me in.

The king announced, "Princess, it is Christmas now, and it was Christmas then . . . when you last smiled. Here is our gift. We give you this puppy with our love for you to love." Then the king took me (the puppy) up to the princess. I put my hands (paws) on her lap. I stuck out my tongue. I panted. Cynthia, who had been grinning

when she was not supposed to, was now supposed to smile very large. Large enough for the audience in the back rows to see, Mrs. Stuyvestant said. Cynthia took a deep breath and began to snuggle her head up to mine. Instead of sighing and smiling, she stopped the sigh and the smile and puffed out her cheeks like the old North Wind and clamped her hands over her nose and mouth and ran from the stage. Mrs. Stuyvestant ran after her. I don't know what they discussed offstage, but Mrs. Stuyvestant came back to me and sniffed me and asked me to kindly take the puppy costume home and have my mother kindly launder it, and she asked me to kindly not eat raw onions before rehearsal. Since this was Friday, the end of my onion week, I kindly agreed.

Jennifer was offstage. As I walked away, I saw a Mona Lisa smile on *her* face. She winked. No one saw that but me.

We had rehearsals every gym period, every music period, and every art period. They didn't call it "rehearsal" during art period because we stayed in the art room and painted the sets and made cardboard crowns (covered with aluminum foil, glued, and sprin- kled with glitter dust). For the kitchen scene, we made a stove out of big cardboard cartons that we painted black. It looked nice from the back rows where the audience sat. It looked nicest from the very last row. Mrs. Stuyvestant asked each of us to bring in a cookie sheet or a pan or a kettle or a stirring spoon. We were to be sure to put our names on what we brought in so that we could get it back when the play was over. I brought in two cup- cake pans and put one letter of my name on the inside of each cupcake hole. It looked like this:

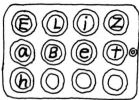

I hoped that the whole audi- ence, even the very last row, would see. Mrs. Stuyvestant asked me to kindly wash it off and kindly Scotch tape my name on the bottom — very small. She said, "In the theater one does not get top billing just because one can write one's name very large. One gets top billing because one has earned stardom." One always knew when Mrs. Stuyvestant was

scolding because she always called you *one* instead of your name.

Cynthia brought in her mother's electric mixer. She knew that she was the only kid in the whole U.S. of A. whose mother would let her carry the family's electric mixer to school. Mrs. Stuyvestant told her that it was very generous of her mother to lend it, and it was very generous of her to have car- ried it all the way from home. (I knew that Cynthia's mother had driven her to school that day, but Cynthia didn't mention it. An- other example of the way Cynthia was — two-faced.) But Mrs. Stuy- vestant didn't consider the mixer picturesque enough. In other words, in the days when there were kings and princesses, there just weren't any electric mixers. Cynthia didn't even have sense enough to be insulted. She sighed sadly and told Mrs. Stuyvestant that she would manage to get the mixer home, somehow, even though it was heavy.

Jennifer caused a small sensa- tion. She brought in a huge, black, three-legged pot. It would hold about twenty quarts of water. A little kid could swim in it almost. Jennifer didn't have to write her name on that pot to identify it. No one else had ever seen anything like it except in a museum. I happened to know that it was the pot we were going to cook our flying ointment in.

Mrs. Stuyvestant was overjoyed. She put her hands on her waist (with her elbows pointing out and her toes pointing out, too, she looked like a long, tall, five-pointed star) and exclaimed, "Oh, Jenny, how *won*-derful! It's *too* cute! A *three*-legged kettle!"

If you ever want to make Jennifer angry, call her what Mrs. Stuyvestant did. Call her Jenny instead of Jennifer, her rightful name.

Jennifer looked up, way up at Mrs. Sky-high-vestant, and said, "That makes one, two, three, doesn't it?"

Mrs. Stuyvestant looked down, way down at Jennifer, and said, "What do you mean, Jennifer?"

Jennifer answered, "*Won*-derful, *too* cute, *three*-legged. That's one, two, three." Jennifer didn't smile.

Mrs. Stuyvestant said, "I had no idea you were so clever." She smiled. I could tell that Jennifer wished that Mrs. Stuyvestant had not smiled. She wanted her to notice how angry she was at being called Jenny instead of Jennifer.

Everyone was a little surprised at how clever Jennifer was. She almost never spoke in class or during rehearsals. She never spoke to me; she would just slip me a note every now and then. I was worried that everyone would find out how clever Jennifer was. It feels wonderful to have a secret. Sometimes I thought I wanted our secret to be discovered accidentally, but I didn't want to share Jennifer with the entire fifth grade. It was lucky the kids of William McKinley Elementary School weren't ready to make the discovery. They were no longer paying any attention. Mrs. Stuyvestant walked all around the pot, pleased and smiling. She smiled over at Jennifer and asked, "By the way, Jenny, how did you get it here?" She was still feeling cozy toward Jennifer.

Jennifer pretended that she didn't hear the question. She was making herself very busy shaking a can of spray paint, and that little ball inside the can was rattling away. Mrs. Stuyvestant said, "Jenny. Oh, Jenny!" No answer from you-know-who. "Jenny. Oh, Jenny!" No answer from you-know-who again. Finally Mrs. Stuyvestant started walking to-ward Jennifer and said, "Jenny. Oh, Jennifer!" The minute she said *Jennifer*, you-know-who looked up.

"Yes?" asked Jennifer.

"I was wondering," Mrs. Stuyvestant said, "how you got that heavy kettle to school."

"Brought it in my wagon," answered Jennifer.

"Then your wagon is parked at school?" asked Mrs. Stuyvestant.

"Yes," answered Jennifer.

"Do you think that you can lend it to Cynthia to help her get her mixer home?"

Jennifer asked, "You want me to put the mixer in my wagon?"

Mrs. Stuyvestant said, almost sarcastically, "That's what I had in mind."

Jennifer replied, "I'll be happy to."

Mrs. Stuyvestant said, "Thank you." She smiled pleasantly at Jennifer and began to turn around.

Before she was completely turned around, Jennifer said, "Do you think I should tie my wagon to the bumper?"

Mrs. Stuyvestant spun around. "The bumper? Bumper? The bumper of what?"

Jennifer answered, "The bumper of their car."

But Cynthia's conversation had been just one shade on the safe side of lying. Mrs. Stuyvestant looked from Jennifer to Cynthia and then back again. She threw her arms in the air, turned around, and walked out of the room. Cynthia glared at Jennifer. Jennifer kept shaking the spray paint and kept looking up at the ceiling.

"Oh, Jennifer," I thought to myself, "how strong you are. Nerves of steel and the heart of a witch!"

No one noticed when Jennifer passed me a note later in the period. I was painting hinges on one of the oven doors. The note had only one word on it. It said:

ugh!

I knew what Jennifer meant, and I put my head inside the oven and laughed and laughed.

Mrs. Stuyvestant was too puzzled to get angry. She merely asked, "Why do that?"

Jennifer answered, "Because Cynthia brought the mixer here in their car, so I guessed that that was the way she would get it home, too." Somehow, Jennifer managed to look innocent.

Mrs. Stuyvestant looked at Jennifer. Mrs. Stuyvestant looked at Cynthia. Of course, Jennifer's conversation had been just one shade on the safe side of fresh.

The first two books Elaine Konigsburg wrote were published in 1967. One of them, *From the Mixed-up Files of Mrs. Basil E. Frankweiler,* won the Newbery Award as the best children's book of that year. Chosen as a runner-up for the Award was her other book, *Jennifer, Hecate, Macbeth, William McKinley, and Me, Elizabeth,* from which the story you have just read was taken. Such an unusual honor would make a veteran author proud, and yet Mrs. Konigsburg had been a writer for only about two years. But Mrs. Konigsburg is an unusual person. Before finishing her college studies as a chemist, she was at different times a bookkeeper, manager of a laundry, playground instructor, waitress, library worker, and laboratory researcher. She also taught science after her marriage to Dr. David Konigsburg. Later she studied painting and became an artist. Then, for several years, two sons and a daughter kept her busy at home. Not until all three children were old enough to go to school did she have time for writing. The youngsters played an important part in her success, though. They gave her helpful suggestions when she read to them what she had written each day, and they were the models she used in illustrating her stories. Little League baseball is the subject of Mrs. Konigsburg's third book, published in 1969 and called *About the B'nai Bagels.*

You can make up your own secret code by scrambling the letters of the alphabet in different ways. One simple way is to reverse the order of the letters in the alphabet like this:

Z Y X W V U T S R Q P O N M L K J I H G F E D C B A

Of course, in order to be able to write or read messages in an alphabet code, you will need to have a code key which tells you what letter in the regular alphabet each code letter in the coded message stands for. Here is a code key for the reverse-alphabet code. Notice that above each code letter is the letter in the regular alphabet for which it stands.

Regular Alphabet:

A B C D E F G H I J K L M N O P Q R S T U V W X Y Z

Code Alphabet:

Z Y X W V U T S R Q P O N M L K J I H G F E D C B A

How would you write the words **SECRET MESSAGE** in this code? The code key shows you that in writing the word **SECRET,** you would substitute the **H** for **S, V** for **E, X** for **C,** and so on. The words **SECRET MESSAGE** would be written **HVXIVG NVHHZTV.** Use the code key to read this message:

BLF PMLD SLD GL IVZW GSRH XLWV.

A more complicated alphabet code is one in which the alphabet is divided into two parts: **A** to **M** and **N** to **Z.** The order of letters in each half is then reversed. Here is the complete key for this code:

Regular Alphabet:

A B C D E F G H I J K L M — N O P Q R S T U V W X Y Z

Code Alphabet:

M L K J I H G F E D C B A — Z Y X W V U T S R Q P O N

Use the key to help you read this message:

AMCI SX MZ MBXFMLIT KYJI YH OYSV YQZ.
LI USVI TY QVETI M CIO HYV ET.

After you've done what the message says, you'll be able to write your own secret messages.

USING A CARD CATALOG

It had rained all day Sunday, but Kay didn't mind a bit. She had spent the afternoon reading *Mishmash,* which a friend had let her borrow. Kay hadn't laughed so much at a story in months, and she was sorry when she finally came to the end of it. She wondered whether the author had written other books about adventures of the big friendly dog called Mishmash. How could she find out?

That same afternoon, Tony had watched a science-fiction movie on television. In one exciting part, there had been a fierce battle between two enormous dinosaurs. Those strange-looking creatures had interested Tony, and he wanted to learn more about them. He felt sure that there must be many books telling about dinosaurs, but where should he look for them?

When you have questions like those raised by Kay and Tony, you can usually find the answers to them easily by using the card catalog in your school or public library. Knowing how to use the card catalog makes it possible for you to discover quickly what books are to be found in that library.

Almost every library has a card catalog, and all card catalogs provide the same kinds of information even though they may differ somewhat in size and appearance. Let us suppose that the card catalog in your library looks like the one pictured on the opposite page. Notice that there are twelve drawers and that each drawer has one or more letters on it. Cards inside the drawers are arranged in alphabetical order. The letters on each drawer show you what cards are in it, just as the letters on an encyclopedia indicate what topics are included in each volume. The card catalog can be used as a kind of index, an alphabetical list of all the books the library owns.

For every book in the library, two different cards are filed in the card catalog—an author card and a title card. For many of the books there is a third card—the subject card. The three cards filed for one book in the catalog in your library might look like those shown on page 239.

On the author card, the name of the author is most important, so it appears on the top line, with the last name listed first. Below it, other information is given about the book, such as its title, the location and name of the publisher, year of publication, number of pages, whether or not it is illustrated, and perhaps a sentence or two explaining what the book is about. An author card is filed alphabetically by the author's last name. If the library owns six different books written by one person, there will be six cards giving his name as author, one for each book. Kay, who enjoyed the book *Mishmash* by Molly Cone, could find out if her library has other books about the dog by looking at author cards filed under **Cone, Molly.**

On a title card, the title of the book appears on the top line. The information that follows it, as you can see from the illustration, is the same as on the author card. a title card is filed alphabetically by the first word in the title, unless that word is *A, An* or *The,* in which case the second word in the title is used for filing. To find the card for *A Bear Called Paddington,* for example, you would check under **B** for **Bear.** When you know nothing about a book except its title, you can get more information by reading the title card in the catalog.

The top line of a subject card tells the subject of the book, or what the book is about. From the first line of the bottom card on the opposite page, for example, you learn that the subject of the book is dinosaurs. Information below the top line is the same as that on the author card. Tony, who was interested in dinosaurs, could find the titles of books that have been written about them by looking at the different subject cards filed under **DINOSAURS.** If you are trying to locate information about subjects like satellites, hurricanes, or monkeys, use those words as key words and check the subject cards listed under them in order to learn what books your library has on those subjects. Or if you would like to read an adventure story about clipper-ship days or a detective story, you can locate what you want by looking through the subject cards filed under **SEA STORIES** or under **MYSTERY AND DETECTIVE STORIES.** When a subject has more than one word in it, the subject card is filed

Craig, M. Jean
    Dinosaurs and more dinosaurs, by M. Jean Craig. Pictures by George Solonevich. New York, Four Winds Press, 1968.
  96 p.   illus.

    A colorfully illustrated account of the monsters who roamed the earth millions of years ago. Explains what different dinosaurs looked like, where and how they lived, and why they died out.

AUTHOR
CARD

Dinosaurs and more dinosaurs
Craig, M. Jean
    Dinosaurs and more dinosaurs, by M. Jean Craig. Pictures by George Solonevich. New York, Four Winds Press, 1968.
  96. p.   illus.

    A colorfully illustrated account of the monsters who roamed the earth millions of years ago. Explains what different dinosaurs looked like, where and how they lived, and why they died out.

TITLE
CARD

DINOSAURS

Craig, M. Jean
    Dinosaurs and more dinosaurs, by M. Jean Craig. Pictures by George Solonevich. New York, Four Winds Press, 1968.
  96 p.   illus.

    A colorfully illustrated account of the monsters who roamed the earth millions of years ago. Explains what different dinosaurs looked like, where and how they lived, and why they died out.

SUBJECT
CARD

alphabetically by the first word. **SCIENCE FICTION** is under S, for example, and **GHOST STORIES** under **G.**

For subjects like **ANIMALS, COWBOYS, FOOTBALL,** or **FISHING,** there may be a great many subject cards. You will see that some of the books listed give facts about the subject while other books are made-up stories about the subject. Under **FOOTBALL,** for instance, you will find books that explain the rules of the game, the equipment needed, and how to play and coach the game. In other books authors tell stories that they have thought up themselves about football players and games. You can decide which of the books you want by reading the information that the various cards give.

Discussion

Help your class answer these questions:

1. How are cards arranged in a card catalog? In what way is a card catalog like an index?
2. What three kinds of cards are in a card catalog? What different information is on the first line of each? What information appears on all three cards shown on page 239?
3. How is each of the three cards filed alphabetically?
4. Give an example of when you might need to use each of the three cards.

On your own

On a sheet of paper, copy the number and letter of each of the following questions and then write your answer.

1. Which kind of card would you look for in the card catalog in order to answer these questions?
   a. What books have been written about snakes?
   b. Who wrote *Charlotte's Web?*
   c. What books by Herbert S. Zim does the library have?
   d. Has a woman written a book about Mark Twain?
2. In the illustration on page 237, what letter or letters are on the drawer in which you would expect to find the answer to each of these questions?
   a. Who is the author of *Viking Adventure?*
   b. How many Revolutionary War books are in the library?
   c. What are some books Carolyn Haywood has written?
   d. What makes a stamp collection valuable?
   e. Who wrote *The Noonday Friends?*
   f. What books by Beverly Cleary are in the library?

Checking your work

Read some of your answers aloud if you are asked to do so. Check your paper as others read their answers. If you made a mistake, be sure to find out why it was a mistake.

FROM SUPERCOLD

Remember the last wintry day you were out of doors when the temperature was zero? You may shiver just thinking of it. Imagine being in Siberia at 50 degrees below zero, on a windswept Himalayan mountain peak at 100 degrees below zero, or in the Antarctic on the day of the coldest temperature ever recorded: 126.9 degrees below zero.

These cold temperatures would be heat waves for a group of scientists who work in the strange world of *cryogenics* or "supercold." The temperatures they deal with are from minus 250 degrees to the coldest possible temperature, minus 459.7 degrees. At this temperature, called *absolute* zero, everything in the world would be frozen solid.

Scientists have found supercold to be a useful tool in space flight, medicine, and surgery. Supercold can turn oxygen and hydrogen gases into liquids. This reduces their volume and makes it possible for them to be used on spaceships as fuel. Supercold allows electricity to flow through wires with no friction to stop it. It enables doctors to store blood for many months instead of for just three weeks as in ordinary refrigerators. Surgeons can destroy a diseased spot in a human body with a cryogenic tool more quickly and safely than they can with a knife.

Cryogenics might be the answer to one of the problems in traveling to the distant stars. This problem is how to enable the passengers to endure trips that would take twenty years and even longer. One possible solution is frozen sleep.

Temperature Scale
Measured in degrees Fahrenheit

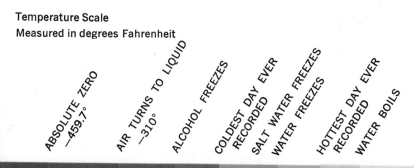

ABSOLUTE ZERO −459.7° | AIR TURNS TO LIQUID −310° | ALCOHOL FREEZES | COLDEST DAY EVER RECORDED | SALT WATER FREEZES | WATER FREEZES | HOTTEST DAY EVER RECORDED | WATER BOILS | TEMPERATURE OF A BAKING OVEN | LEAD MELTS

−459.7° | −310° | −170° | −126.9° | 28.5° | 32° | 136.4° | 212° | 500° | 621°

The passengers might be put into suspended animation with cold temperatures and brought back to consciousness when they reach their destination.

At the opposite end from cryogenics is the field of super-heat. At hot temperatures, like those on the sun, solid material turns into matter that is not a liquid, not a solid, and not a gas. It is so different from anything on earth that scientists call it the fourth state of matter and have given it the name *plasma*. Even though plasma does not normally exist on earth, most of the matter in the rest of the universe is plasma. The sun and the other stars are plasma.

It is difficult even to imagine how hot plasma is. The baking oven in the kitchen reaches about 500 degrees Fahrenheit. The gas burners on the kitchen stove will reach about 3,000 degrees. Gasoline burns in our automobiles at 3,500 degrees. Until the atomic bomb was developed, the hottest temperature that had been created on earth was 7,000 degrees. The atomic bomb produces 40,000 degrees.

No solid container on earth can hold plasma. It would melt anything you put it in. Scientists try to hold it in a "magnetic bottle." They surround it with magnetic forces to keep it from escaping. If scientists can learn to control plasma for a second or two, they will be able to use the waters of the oceans as a new type of nuclear fuel.

Arthur J. Snider

SUPERHEAT TO

ALUMINUM MELTS

HEAT OF A GAS STOVE FLAME

HEAT OF THE SURFACE OF THE SUN

HEAT OF AN ATOMIC BOMB EXPLOSION

1,220°

3,000°

11,000°

40,000°

FROZEN VICTORY

BY CHARLES COOMBS

It was a cold, crisp day on Miller Pond. Jimmy Benton was right in the middle of cutting a smooth figure eight, when a black-and-white dog came barking and slipping across the ice. At the last moment, both Jimmy and the dog tried to dodge out of each other's way. But the ice was too slippery. The wildly pawing dog crashed into Jimmy just below the knees. Both of them wound up in a heap on the wet ice.

"Ki-yi-yi-yi—" The dog scrambled away, losing its footing every few steps.

"Ha-ha-ha."

Jimmy knew that laughter. Even before he turned, he felt the anger rising in him.

"Bret!" Jimmy got his skates under him and faced the husky, sandy-haired skater who was getting so much pleasure from the mishap. "How about keeping that mutt of yours off the pond? One of these days he's going to get hurt, and . . ."

"Quit kidding," Bret laughed. "Spot can outskate you any day of the week. And he doesn't even have to wear skates to do it. Don't worry any about my dog. But you'd better start worrying about the big race tomorrow. I don't want to win it too easily, you know."

"You won't," Jim said hotly.

With Bret there, Spot had regained his courage. He kept just out of reach and yapped annoyingly at Jimmy.

Jimmy liked dogs. But Spot had been a constant source of trouble to him. First, he had chewed up the newspapers along Jimmy's route one morning. On another occasion, he had run out from behind a hedge and knocked Jimmy off his bike. Spot had meant to be friendly, in his clumsy way. But that didn't mend the seven broken spokes or straighten out the bent forks of the bike.

And now, after his hard spill on the ice, Jimmy felt a soreness creep into his hip—with the big race coming up tomorrow, too!

Sometimes he wished Bret's dog were a thousand miles away and still running. Oh, Spot was a good enough dog, Jimmy had to admit. But Bret just had never bothered to train him. He was always barking at people, jumping up on them, and making a general nuisance of himself.

It was Bret's fault, really. Any dog could be trained to behave itself, if its owner would take the time and patience. Bret seemed to get a big kick out of Spot's pranks.

The next morning, Jimmy rolled over in bed and was awakened by the soreness in his hip.

"It's just a bruise, son," his mother said as she looked at the tender patch of skin. "But perhaps it would be better if you didn't race today."

"But, Mom, I have to," Jimmy said quickly. "The winner at Willow Lake gets to race at the big Winter Festival next month. I . . . I'd rather race at the Winter Festival than be . . . well, be President."

"Well, since we already have a good President," his mother smiled, "I'll try not to stop you from racing."

"The soreness will go away, Mom," Jimmy said hopefully. "It's even getting better now. If it hadn't been for that blamed dog of Bret's . . ." He left the sentence unfinished. Every time he thought of that untrained dog, it made his blood fairly boil.

It was another clear day at Willow Lake, but it was a little too warm for the best skating. The ice was slightly mushy and wet. There were a few rather thin spots. In fact, warning flags marked a couple of places farther out on the lake where the ice had broken.

Jimmy was lacing his skates when he glanced up and saw Spot bounding in and out of the crowd. A quick chill went along Jimmy's spine. That dog was a jinx for sure. As soon as he saw Jimmy, Spot set up a wild yapping.

Trying to ignore the dog, Jimmy kept right on lacing his skates. Suddenly he was showered with water and ice shavings, as Bret braked to a stop in front of him.

"Hey!" Jimmy spluttered, "what's the big idea? If you're looking for trouble, I'll . . ."

"Oh, my," Bret mocked. "Were you sitting there, Jimmy? Here, let me brush you off."

"Just leave me alone," Jimmy bit out. Between Bret and his dog Spot, they sure had managed to make life miserable for him lately.

"I just wanted to warn you," the husky boy in the red-and-blue ski cap said. "Don't get in my way during the race. I'm counting on winning."

"Who isn't?" Jimmy said. "So am I!"

"You're just going to try," the bigger boy said. "I'm going to win."

"Phooey!" Jimmy stood up to test his skates. Spot lunged in, barking and nipping playfully at his ankles. It startled Jimmy. His skates went out from under him. Again he sat down hard on the wet ice.

Bret skated away, holding his sides laughing.

"You'd better tie that mutt up," Jimmy shouted after him. "Or there's going to be trouble!"

If Bret even heard, he didn't pay any attention.

The one-eighth-mile oval racing course was marked off with flags. The Junior Boys' race was to be a half mile, or four laps around the oval.

The ten young contestants crouched at the starting line. From the inside position, Bret grinned confidently over at Jimmy. "Don't forget," he called, "keep out of my way."

"Baloney!" Jimmy shot back. He found himself glancing around for Bret's dog. At least Spot didn't seem to be around. Maybe his paws had gotten too cold and he had decided to go back home. Jimmy hoped that was the case. He couldn't afford to have Bret's dog messing up his chances today.

The starter's gun cracked its sharp report across the wide expanse of ice that covered Willow Lake. The crowd that ringed the oval cheered as the ten skaters surged forward.

Bret sprinted ahead, taking an early lead. Then he eased off to a smooth distance-eating pace. Way back in sixth place, Jimmy knew that Bret would plan the race so that he would have plenty of strength left for a final sprint in the fourth lap.

Each time they hit a straightaway, Bret glanced back over his shoulder to see that no one was threatening his lead. When he needed to, he put on an added sprint.

By the end of the second lap, Jimmy had moved up into third place and was gaining a little on Bret with every yard. A feeling of confidence surged through him. His bruised hip barely bothered him now. His legs felt strong. Unless Bret was holding a lot of speed in reserve, Jimmy felt confident that he could catch him before the finish line was reached.

Then, as he glanced up for a moment, out of the corner of his eye Jimmy noticed a small dark object far out on the ice near the center of Willow Lake. In the brief flash of time that he saw it, before the view was screened out by the spectators lined around the oval, Jimmy realized that it was Bret's dog.

"Good thing," Jimmy thought happily. "At least, the troublesome little hound won't be ruining my chances to win the race."

Midway through the third lap, the skaters had spread out.

With a sudden burst of speed in the near straightaway, Jimmy surged ahead until he was in second place.

Only Bret was ahead of him — a scant ten yards ahead, at that. The larger boy's skates seemed slightly heavy on his feet. Jimmy figured that Bret had set too stiff a pace during the first half of the race and was tiring fast.

Then, going into the final straightaway of the third lap, Jimmy caught another glance off across the ice as he skated past a gap in the ring of spectators.

And what he saw in that one quick glance nearly made him lose his balance.

Far out on the frozen lake, his head barely visible above the surface, Spot was pawing frantically at the jagged edge of the ice.

Beads of sweat broke out on Jimmy's forehead. That dumb hound, to let himself fall through a hole in the ice! Well, someone was bound to see him, or hear him yapping. Besides a dog could keep his head above the water for quite a while. And he, Jimmy, had a race to win.

Trying to shake off the vision of the floundering dog from his mind, Jimmy turned on more speed. As they started on the final lap, he was almost up with Bret. Deep down, he knew that he was going to beat Bret. His legs felt good, and it was easy to see that Bret was tiring.

"Oh, boy," Jimmy thought happily, "Winter Festival, here I come!"

Bret glanced back over his shoulder. There was a frightened look on his face. He seemed to realize that Jimmy had enough power left to overtake him before the lap was finished.

Then, at a time when he should have been putting every thought into passing Bret, Jimmy's eyes jerked sideways, as though pulled by some unseen power. Off across the lake he saw Spot still struggling. But more slowly. No one seemed to have seen or heard the dog. Everyone was so intent upon the race, and there was so much yelling, that no one was paying any attention to what was taking place across the lake.

"Bret," Jimmy yelled at the back of the boy ahead of him. "Spot! He fell through a hole, and . . ."

But Bret merely attempted to put more speed into his skates. It was obvious to Jimmy then that Bret figured he was just trying to throw him off stride.

He was just swinging out wide to pass Bret when a sense of guilt surged over him, and Jimmy knew that, race or no race, there was only one thing that he could do.

At any moment, a tired Spot might sink below the surface of the icy water. It was no time to be thinking about winning the race, or about how much trouble the dog had caused him.

The thing that mattered was that the dog's life was in peril — extreme peril.

As the people watched with mouths agape, Jimmy suddenly swerved off the racecourse, sped through an opening in the crowd, and sprinted straight off across the frozen lake.

All thoughts of winning the race were gone now from his mind. Jimmy's only hope was that he hadn't waited too long in realizing where his real duty lay. He only hoped that he would reach Spot in time.

It seemed forever by the time Jimmy covered the two hundred yards across the lake. Nearing the jagged hole in the ice, he went down on his stomach and inched toward the edge.

"Easy, Spot," he soothed. "I'll have you out of there in a jiffy."

The dog's pleading eyes stared wildly at him. Spot could barely keep his head above the water.

"Give me your paw, Spot," Jimmy panted, lying flat and reaching far out. "Attaboy. Right here, boy. Good dog, Spot."

The dog yapped and pawed a little more frantically on the rough edge of the ice. Then Jimmy caught hold of one of the dog's feet. Hopeful that the ice wouldn't give way beneath him, Jimmy heaved on the dog.

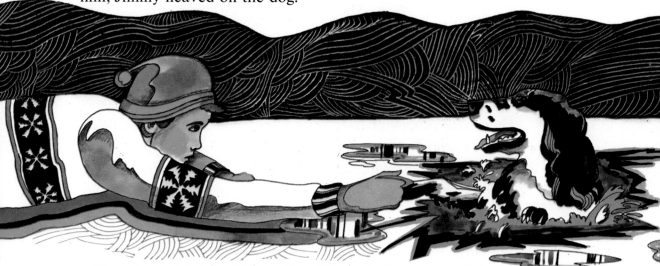

Then he got hold of his collar. With a hefty yet careful tug, Jimmy pulled the dog out onto the ice. Sighing his relief, and trying to control the sudden shivering of his body, Jimmy slid quickly back from the hole and got to his feet.

Bret came streaking across the ice. Some of the race officials were close at his heels.

"Jimmy!" Bret gasped. "Jeepers, guy, I thought you were just trying to pull a fancy one when you yelled at me about Spot. I thought you . . ."

"Yeah, I know," Jimmy said. "And I don't blame you. I'd have figured the same thing."

"I . . . I don't deserve winning the race," Bret said.

"Sure you do," Jimmy replied with a smile. "It doesn't matter to me, Bret. But I'm sure glad that I didn't wait any longer before . . . Well, I'm sure glad I got to Spot in time."

Jimmy knelt and snuggled the wet dog to him. Spot wagged his cold tail and licked Jimmy's hand. "He's a good dog, Bret," Jimmy laughed. "A real good dog."

He hadn't noticed that the race judges were huddled with their heads together over at one side. Then one of the judges walked over to him.

"Jimmy," he said, "everyone is agreed that this year Willow Lake can afford to enter two junior contestants in the Winter Festival. One for winning the race around the oval course; the other for winning a much more important race."

"Hurrah!" Bret cheered wildly.

". . . We, therefore, award to you, Bret, and to you, Jimmy . . ."

But the judge's words were drowned out by the loud cheers of the crowd.

Bret and Jimmy pounded each other happily on the shoulders, while a wet and cold black-and-white dog bounded joyously from one to the other.

AUTHOR

Before settling down to full-time writing for young people, Charles Coombs, the author of "Frozen Victory," worked at a number of jobs. He was a newsboy, a farmer, and a carpenter's helper. He also worked in various stores and in an airplane factory. Mr. Coombs's writing career began after graduation from college when, as he tells it, "I put up a card table in a tiny closet and began writing." An athlete in school

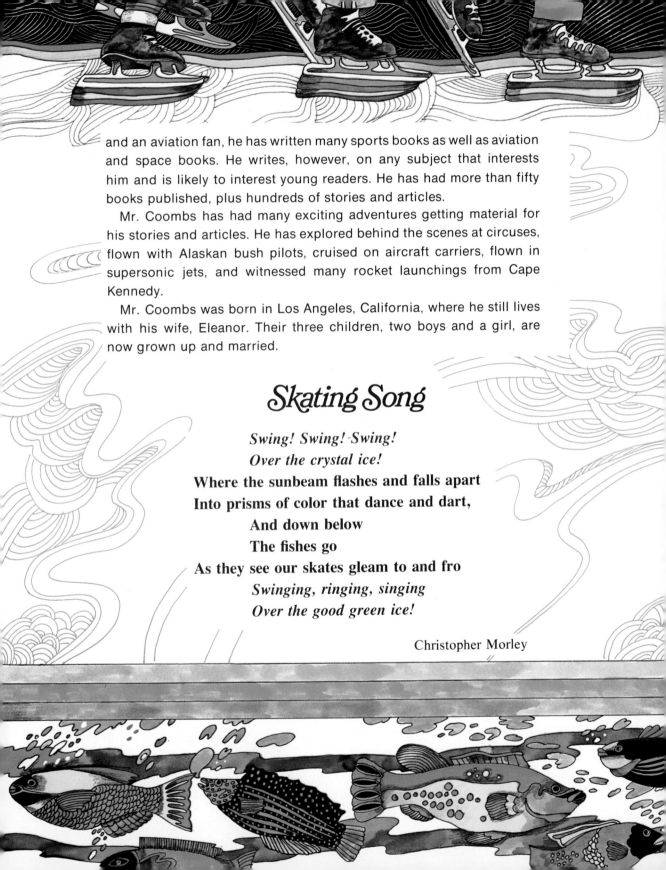

and an aviation fan, he has written many sports books as well as aviation and space books. He writes, however, on any subject that interests him and is likely to interest young readers. He has had more than fifty books published, plus hundreds of stories and articles.

Mr. Coombs has had many exciting adventures getting material for his stories and articles. He has explored behind the scenes at circuses, flown with Alaskan bush pilots, cruised on aircraft carriers, flown in supersonic jets, and witnessed many rocket launchings from Cape Kennedy.

Mr. Coombs was born in Los Angeles, California, where he still lives with his wife, Eleanor. Their three children, two boys and a girl, are now grown up and married.

Skating Song

Swing! Swing! Swing!
Over the crystal ice!
Where the sunbeam flashes and falls apart
Into prisms of color that dance and dart,
And down below
The fishes go
As they see our skates gleam to and fro
Swinging, ringing, singing
Over the good green ice!

Christopher Morley

THE VALIANT CHATTEE-MAKER

This folktale from India, retold by Christine Price, tells about
a man who lost a donkey and became rich as a result.

Long and long ago, in a terrible storm of thunder, wind, and rain, a mighty Tiger took shelter in a village. Wet and bedraggled, he lay down against the wall of an old woman's hut. The old woman was very poor, and the rain was coming *drip, drip, drip* through the thatch of her tumbledown house.

The Tiger could hear her moving about inside, dragging her belongings out of the way of the leaks in the roof and muttering to herself, "Oh, what shall I do? I'm sure the roof will come down! If an Elephant or a Tiger walked in, he wouldn't frighten me half as much as this Perpetual Dripping!"

The Tiger's tail began to twitch. "This Perpetual Dripping," he thought, "must be something very dreadful. Can it be an animal bigger and stronger than an Elephant?"

Just at that moment, through the darkness and the rain, a man came running down the road between the houses. He was the village Chattee-maker, a poor man who earned his living making earthen jars and waterpots. He had lost his donkey, and his wife had sent him out in the storm to hunt for it. "How can you carry your chattees to market without a donkey?" she cried. "Off with you, and don't come back till you find him!"

The Chattee-maker had almost reached the old woman's hut when suddenly, in a flash of lightning, he saw a large animal lying by the wall.

"My donkey!" he shouted, and charged up to the Tiger and seized him by the ear.

"You wretched creature!" he raged, beating the Tiger with a stick. "How dare you run away? Get up, or I'll break every bone in your body!"

The mighty Tiger staggered to his feet with all the breath knocked out of him. "So *this* is the Perpetual Dripping," he groaned, beginning to feel quite frightened. "No wonder the old woman was so afraid of it!"

Before the Tiger knew what was happening, the Chattee-maker had dragged him into the road and clambered on his back. In darkness as deep as the bottom of a well, the Chattee-maker forced the Tiger to carry him home, thumping him with the stick all the way.

Home at last, the man tied a rope around the Tiger's neck and another around his front legs and fastened him securely to a post in front of the house. Then he went indoors to bed.

Early next morning, the sun shone bright and clear, and when the Chattee-maker's wife got up and looked out the window, what did she see but a great big Tiger tied to the post in front of the house where they usually fastened the donkey!

She ran to wake her husband. "Do you know what animal you fetched home last night?"

"Why, the donkey, of course. I told you so!"

"Come and see!" she said.

When the Chattee-maker saw the Tiger, he gaped in amazement. He felt himself all over to find out if the Tiger had wounded him. But no! There he was, safe and sound, and there was the terrible Tiger securely tied to the post. His wife was so excited she forgot to scold him for not finding the donkey. Instead, she rushed out to tell the neighbors what had happened.

News of the Chattee-maker's exploit spread like wildfire through the village. All the people came to see him, to hear him tell his story, and to gaze at the mighty Tiger tied to the post. The Tiger had been the terror of their country. Now they had nothing to fear from him, and they danced and sang for joy. The wise men of the village sat down and wrote a letter to the Rajah (rah′juh) who ruled their country, telling him how the Chattee-maker had caught the Tiger with his bare hands and tied it to the post.

When the Rajah read the letter in his palace, he sent at once for his horses and elephants, his servants and courtiers, and they all set off together for the village.

As soon as he saw the Chattee-maker and the mighty Tiger, the Rajah decided to take the Tiger to the Royal Menagerie and to reward the man without delay.

So the Chattee-maker was carried away to the palace in a beautiful *howdah* on the back of one of the Rajah's elephants. The Rajah gave him houses and lands and enough money to fill a well. He made the Chattee-maker a great lord in the royal court and put him in command of ten thousand horsemen.

The Chattee-maker's wife was as proud as a peacock. She could dress in silks and jewels and have an army of servants to do her bidding. But the Chattee-maker was worried about the ten thousand horsemen. He wished he had his old lost donkey back again. He had never ridden a horse in his life, and he did not want to try.

He and his wife had only just settled into their fine house near the Rajah's palace when the ruler of a neighboring country, who was an old enemy of the Rajah, sent a

letter to say that he was preparing to make war. At the same time, news came to the palace that the enemy's army was already on the border and would invade the country at any moment.

The Rajah sent for his generals. "Which of you," he demanded, "is willing to take command of my forces and fight the enemy?"

They all replied that the country was not prepared for fighting. Not one of them wanted the job of Commander in Chief. The Rajah did not know what to do.

Then some of his people said to him, "You have just given command of ten thousand horsemen to the valiant Chattee-maker who caught the Tiger. Why not make him Commander in Chief? A man who could catch a Tiger and tie him to a post must be braver and wiser than anyone else."

So the Rajah immediately sent for the Chattee-maker and said to him, "In your hand I place all the power of the kingdom. You must put our enemies to flight."

The Chattee-maker was almost too startled to speak. "Very well," he stammered at last, when he had collected his wits, "but before I lead the whole army against the enemy, let me go by myself and examine their position, and find out, if I can, how many men they have."

The Rajah consented, and the Chattee-maker hurried home to his wife. "O wife," he said, "they have made me Commander in Chief! I shall have to ride at the head of the army, and you know I have never been on a horse in my life! But I have managed to gain a little delay," and he told her how he was to go out alone to find the enemy's camp and begged her to get him a nice quiet pony to ride.

But early next morning, before

the Chattee-maker had set out, the Rajah sent over to him a most magnificent charger, powerful and spirited, for the ride to the enemy's camp. The Chattee-maker did not dare refuse the Rajah's present and sent him back a message of thanks. Then he went to his wife in despair. "O wife," he said, "I cannot go on the quiet pony now that the Rajah has sent this fine horse, but how am I to ride it?"

"Oh, don't be frightened," she answered. "Just get on the horse, and I will tie you firmly to the saddle so that you cannot tumble off. If you start at night, no one will see that you are tied on."

That night the Chattee-maker's wife brought the great horse secretly to the door of their house.

"I can never get into the saddle," said the Chattee-maker. "It is so high up."

"You must jump," she said.

He tried to jump several times, but each time he tumbled down again until all the breath was knocked out of him.

"I always forget when I'm jumping," he panted, "which way I ought to turn."

"You must face the horse's head," said she.

"Of course! How silly of me!" he cried, and with one great jump he leaped into the saddle again—with his face toward the horse's tail.

"I always forget," he said, as his wife helped him down, "what to do with my right foot when my left one is in the stirrup."

"The right one must go in the other stirrup," she said. "Now try again!"

The horse was fresh and did not like standing still, but at last, after many tries and many falls, the Chattee-maker was safely in the saddle. "O wife, wife," he cried, "tie me on as quickly as you can!"

With strong rope she tied his feet firmly into the stirrups and fastened one stirrup to the other. Then she put another rope around his waist and another around his neck and fastened them to the horse's body, neck, and tail. When the horse felt all those ropes around him, he could not imagine what queer creature he had on his back. He began rearing and kicking and prancing, and finally, with a neigh like a trumpet call, he set off at a full gallop.

"Wife, wife!" cried the Chattee-maker, "you didn't tie my hands!"

"Hold on by the mane!" she called after him.

Away went horse, away went Chattee-maker, away, away, and away. They tore across fields of grain and of melons. They thundered through villages where people were sleeping, and they leaped over rivers at a single bound.

On they galloped under moon and stars, while the jackals yelped and the tigers prowled, and at last, when cocks were crowing for the dawn, the Chattee-maker sighted the enemy's camp. He was sure the enemy would catch him and kill him. The horse was racing straight for the camp, and the Chattee-maker decided to make a desperate effort to escape.

As the horse shot past a young banyan tree, the Chattee-maker seized hold of the tree with all his might, hoping the ropes that tied him would snap. But the horse was going too fast, and the soil in which the tree was growing was loose and sandy. When the Chattee-maker grabbed the tree, it came up by the roots, and on he charged, as fast as before, with the tree in his hand.

The soldiers in the enemy camp saw him coming. They had heard that an army was to be sent against them, and they were sure that the Chattee-maker must be one of the leaders. "Look!" they cried. "Here comes a man of gigantic stature on a mighty horse! He rides at full speed across the country, tearing up the very trees in his rage! The whole army must be at his back! If they are like him, we are all dead men!"

They ran to their Rajah in his tent and cried out again, "Here comes the whole force of the enemy! They are men of gigantic stature on mighty horses! As they come, they tear up trees in their rage! We can fight against men, but not monsters like these!"

The Chattee-maker was coming nearer and nearer to the camp, and more men rushed to the Rajah's tent. "The enemy is coming," they shouted. "Fly for your lives!"

They pleaded with their Rajah to write a letter to the ruler of the country he was about to invade. They begged him to propose terms of peace, to sign and seal the letter, and to leave it behind in his tent.

Meanwhile, the Chattee-maker was galloping on, the banyan tree still in his hand. He charged between the tents, and just as he reached the middle of the camp, the ropes snapped and he tumbled to the ground.

The horse stood still, too tired to go a step farther. The Chattee-maker picked himself up, expecting to fight for his life. But there was no one to fight with. The whole camp was deserted.

He went from tent to tent and stared at the rich clothes, weapons, and trappings that the army had left behind. At last he came to the biggest and grandest tent, made of shining striped silk and cloth of gold. The floor of the tent was spread with a magnificent carpet, and in the middle of the carpet lay a letter, sealed with an impressive seal. The Chattee-maker tiptoed across the carpet and picked up the letter. He looked at it this way and

that, and read the name of his Rajah written there.

"This must be a very important letter," he said, and grasping it in his hand, he hurried back to the horse.

Much too tired to jump into the saddle, the Chattee-maker set out to lead the horse all the way home. Off they went, through fields and villages, up hill and down valley, and taking the shortest road, they reached the city by nightfall.

The Chattee-maker's wife ran out of the house to meet him, overjoyed at his quick return.

"O wife, wife," he gasped, so weary he could hardly stand, "I have been all round the world and had many wonderful and terrible adventures. But never mind that now. Send this letter quickly to the Rajah by a messenger, and please

send the horse too, so that I shall not be obliged to ride him to the palace tomorrow morning."

Next day, when the Chattee-maker went on foot to the palace, the people had already heard the wonderful news of the flight of the enemy's army. They crowded into the streets to see the Chattee-maker pass by. "This man is as modest as he is brave," they said, staring at him in amazement. "After putting our enemies to flight, single-handed, he walks quite simply to the palace, instead of riding there in state, as any other man would do."

The Rajah came to the palace gate to meet the valiant Chattee-maker. The letter from the enemy's camp had proposed terms of peace. The war was over and the land was safe. The Rajah rewarded the Chattee-maker for all he had done by giving him three times as much wealth as before. "And now," said the Rajah, "is there anything else in the world you desire?"

"There is just one thing more, O King," said the Chattee-maker in a small voice. "You gave me a splendid horse to ride to the enemy's camp, but I am a peaceful man and not a warrior. Will you please permit me always to ride a donkey?"

The Rajah laughed aloud. "Is that all you want? You may have a thousand milk-white donkeys to ride!"

"I only need one, O King," said the Chattee-maker, "and that is the donkey I lost on the night I caught the Tiger. May I go to my village and look for him?"

What a day that was when the Chattee-maker and all his retinue went down to the village! How the people welcomed him!

To everyone he gave presents of gold and silver. Even the poor old woman had money at last to repair the leaky roof of her hut and stop the Perpetual Dripping when it rained.

But best of all on that wonderful day was the sight of the lost donkey, thin and scrawny, waiting patiently outside the Chattee-maker's old house for his master to come home. Instead of being beaten for running away, the donkey was loaded with garlands of flowers and taken in triumph to the city.

So the valiant Chattee-maker and his wife and the donkey lived happily together in their fine house near the Rajah's palace. The donkey was well cared for and grew sleek and beautiful, and the Chattee-maker never rode a horse again!

AUTHOR

Christine Price lives in Vermont in a house she designed herself. Her neighbors are the birds, the deer, and the woodchucks. She enjoys living in the country, because, as she puts it, "there is so much to see and to discover in the woods and fields at every season of the year."

Miss Price was born in England but has lived in the United States since she was in high school. After going to art school, she began illustrating children's books. Always having been interested in history, she wrote three historical stories for boys and girls and then several books on the history of arts and crafts, including *Made in the Middle Ages* and *Made in Ancient Greece.*

Miss Price has been fond of folktales for a long time. She especially likes the less well-known stories from Asian countries. "The Valiant Chattee-Maker" is a favorite of hers because it is humorous, unlike many tales from India.

WHAT DO YOU HAVE THERE, CHARLIE BROWN?

I'VE WRITTEN A POEM..

REALLY? READ IT..

ALL RIGHT.. IT ISN'T VERY LONG..

SOME DAYS YOU THINK MAYBE YOU KNOW EVERYTHING...SOME DAYS YOU THINK MAYBE YOU DON'T KNOW ANYTHING... SOME DAYS YOU THINK YOU KNOW A FEW THINGS...SOME DAYS YOU DON'T EVEN KNOW HOW OLD YOU ARE.

THAT'S THE WORST POEM I'VE EVER HEARD!

4-19

A POEM IS SUPPOSED TO HAVE FEELING! YOUR POEM COULDN'T TOUCH **ANYONE'S** HEART! YOUR POEM COULDN'T MAKE **ANYONE** CRY! YOUR POEM COULDN'T..

WAAH!

SOME DAYS YOU THINK MAYBE YOU KNOW EVERYTHING...SOME DAYS YOU THINK MAYBE YOU..

SNIF

GOOD GRIEF!

SCHULZ

265

THE WHALE HUNT

BY THE EDITORS OF AMERICAN HERITAGE

Driven by their hunger, whales roamed the world. The different kinds of whales—the bowhead, the humpback, and the right whale—searched for brit, the vast masses of tiny, shrimp-like sea animals that floated near the surface of the water. The sperm whale was even more of a traveler. It swam great distances seeking the giant squid, which it swallowed in huge chunks half the size of a whaleboat. And wherever the whales went, hungry for brit or squid, there went the whalemen, hungry for oil.

But before the whales could be killed, they had to be "raised," or found. Every day, from sunrise to sunset, on every ship cruising the whaling grounds, a lookout was on watch at the masthead. Each hand took his turn, staying aloft for two hours. The orders were always, "Keep your weather eye open, and sing out every time."

The lookout stood on the topgallant crosstrees, which were two narrow pieces of lumber nailed to

the mast. His only support was a pair of iron hoops at the height of his chest. Perched a hundred feet above deck, in fair weather or foul, he watched miles of sea for signs of whales. The most common sign was the spout, the plume or vapor caused by the whale's breath.

As soon as he saw a spout, the lookout sang out, "There she blows! Blo-o-ows! She blows!" If he saw a whale leaping up from the water, he added, "There she breaches!" Or, if the whale was falling back on the water with a foamy splash, "There she white-waters!"

"Where away?" the captain would call from the deck.

The lookout's reply would give the direction of the whale, such as, "Three points off the starboard bow," or "Two points off the lee beam."

"How far?"

"Mile and a half, sir."

"Call all hands! Stand by to lower."

At the captain's command, the ship seemed to shake itself and wake from sleep. The men came scrambling down the rigging and bursting from the forecastle. While the mates shouted orders, the men ran to the whaleboats, their feet thudding on the deck. For this was the real business of whaling; this was what the whalemen were here for—to kill whales and get oil.

Most whalers carried three or four small boats. Each boat had a crew of six men, with the captain or a mate acting as headsman. "Lower away!" the captain ordered, and they lowered the boats into the water. Then, climbing over the rail and down the side of the ship, they leaped into the boats.

The whaling ship itself was left in the care of the shipkeepers, a small group of men.

Sometimes, when the wind was right, the crews of the whaleboats raised their sails. Sometimes, to keep from frightening a nearby whale, they paddled their whaleboats like canoes. But usually they rowed.

As the actual chase began, a wild excitement ran through the men. Now they could forget the waiting and watching, the dreariness, the loneliness, the hardship. They would know these things again, of course, and soon. But during the chase they were more than sailors. They were kingly hunters, pursuing a monstrous beast over the rolling hills of the sea.

Part of the sport was racing the other boats. The crews fought to reach the whale first, even though, with every stroke of the oars, they pulled themselves closer to danger. It was a danger they could not see, for they rowed facing the stern. Only the headsman faced forward. Steering toward the whale, he would speak to his crew, shouting, roaring, swearing, joking, coaxing, commanding.

"Give way, lads! Give way! A long, steady pull does it. Pull, I say! Don't let those other boats beat ye! Pull harder, lads! That's

it, that's it! We're gaining! Pull, every mother's son of ye! Crack your backbones! Burst your hearts and your liver and your lungs! But pull! Merrily, merrily! Yes, we're gaining! We're gaining! I tell ye that whale is ours! Shall we take it? Aye! A dead whale or a smashed boat! Give way, my heroes, my hearties! Put your backs into it, ye rascals! Plum duff for supper if ye catch me that whale! Why, lads, I'll give ye anything I have! Thunder and lightning! Don't give up now, blast ye! Lay on, lay on! Are ye awake or asleep? Look alive! Smash your oars, double 'em up!

Oh, if ye could see that whale, maties, you'd pull till your eyes popped like buttons! She blows! She blows! And there she white-waters! Softly now! Steady, steady . . . . Easy, lads, easy. There! There! Harpooner! Stand up! Stand by your iron!''

Rushing toward the unknown terror behind him, a green hand might go crazy with fear. He might jump over the side, to be hauled back to life by one of the boats, or to drown before anyone could reach him.

Meanwhile, the harpooner balanced himself on the small platform in the bow. In his hand was a

harpoon, a line attached to the blunt end.

"Give it to him!" said the headsman, when the boat was within a few feet of the whale.

And the harpooner darted the harpoon, which struck deep into the monster.

"Give him another iron!"

And the harpooner flung a second harpoon.

"Stern all! Stern all, for your lives!" the headsman shouted, ordering the crew to back the boat away from the thrashing whale.

To keep the line from running out too fast, he had taken a turn of it around a small post called a loggerhead. Pulled by the whale, the line passed around the loggerhead, hot and smoking from friction. An oarsman wet the line. The headsman took a few more turns around the loggerhead, the line grew tight, and the boat sped after the whale.

The headsman signaled to the harpooner, and the two changed places. This was a tricky thing to do in a bouncing, rocking boat, and it killed more than one man. The headsman went forward to kill the whale with a lance; the harpooner went aft to steer. There was no good reason for it. But it was a custom, handed down over the years. All whalemen learned it, few dared to break it, and the exchange was made on almost every chase.

What happened next was decided by the whale. If the whale "sounded," or dived deep, the men bobbed about on the water, keeping an eye on the line, until the whale breached. If the whale "ran" across the surface of the water, the men were off on a "Nantucket sleigh ride," sliding over the waves in a shower of spray.

Whatever the whale did, the men waited for it to grow tired. They pulled on the line, drawing the boat close enough so that the headsman could use his lance. He dug the sharp weapon deep, trying to "reach the life" of the whale.

Mad with pain, the whale went

into its "flurry." It swam furiously, around and around, in smaller and smaller circles. Then it beat the water with its tail, gave a tremendous shudder, and turned over on its back, fin out.

And so the chase ended—when everything went well. But often things did not go well. The crews of the whaleboats might row all day and never get within striking distance of a whale. The harpoon might not score a clean hit, and

the whale would escape. Lines could become tangled. Boats could turn over in a storm. A whale could attack, crushing a boat in its jaws or smashing it with a flip of its flukes. A Nantucket sleigh ride might take a boat too far for the ship to ever find it again.

And even if the chase had ended, the work had just begun. Because of the winds, it was not always possible for the ship to sail to the whale, and the two had to be

brought together. The headsman
made a hole in the whale's head
with a cutting spade and attached
a line. Then the tired, hungry men
rowed again, towing the whale
behind them. The gigantic corpse,
the boats, and the men bending
over their oars made a strange
funeral procession under the evening sky.

And still the work was only
just begun. The whale was made
fast to the ship with heavy chains.
Early the next day, the crew rigged
a long, narrow platform over the
whale for the "cutting-in." There
was no time to lose. In southern
waters, sharks gathered around the
ship to feast on whale. With every
bite, they swallowed some of the

profits of the voyage, and the men
worked fast to keep from being
robbed.

Cutting-in was a butcher's kind
of job. The captain and the first
mate stood on the cutting stage,
as the long platform was called.
They hacked at the whale with
cutting spades, separating the head
from the body. The head, in turn,
was divided into three parts. The
twenty-ton "case" was full of the
purest oil, which could be bailed
out with a bucket. The "junk," the
lower half of the forehead, would
yield oil and spermaceti. Spermaceti was fatty matter, used for
making fine candles and ointments.
The jaw and teeth were saved for
ornaments.

The second mate, too, was on the cutting stage. He cut the blubber into long strips. As the strips were hauled up on the deck, the whale was turned around and around, while the blubber unwound like the peel of an orange. The strips were cut into "blanket pieces," weighing about a ton each. They were dropped through a hatch into the blubber room, where they were cut into blocks called "horse pieces."

Even dead, the whale was dangerous. Its juices made the deck and cutting stage slippery. A man could easily fall overboard to the sharks. Or he could be slashed by the sharp edge of a cutting spade, or crushed by a blanket piece swung through the air. The ship itself, rolling on the waves, swayed and creaked with the weight of the huge beast.

Pulling aboard the last of the blanket pieces, the crew sang out, "Five and forty more!"

Forty-five was the number of barrels of oil taken from the average whale. No matter what size the whale was, larger or smaller than average, the crew cried out, "Five and forty more! Five and forty mo-o-ore!"

The case and the junk were hauled up, and what was left of the whale was allowed to drift away.

Cutting-in was over. It was time for the trying-out, when the blubber would be melted down into oil. The crew was divided into two watches, each taking six-hour turns of duty through the day and night.

The first watch immediately went to work. Some of the men bailed out the oil from the case and tore the pulpy blubber from the sides. Other men lighted a fire under the big try-pots.

"Bible leaves! Bible leaves!" shouted the men at the try-pots.

The rest of the watch were carrying horse pieces from the blubber room to the cutting block. Here thin slices were cut into the blocks of blubber, so that they looked like the leaves of a book. Bible leaves was the name the whalemen gave them, and Bible leaves were what they tossed into the try-pots. For hours the whale cooked itself with the flames of its own cracklings. The ship had become a factory.

At last every bit of blubber was melted down, the oil cooled, poured into barrels, and stowed in the hold. The crew swarmed over the ship in a big cleanup. They washed, they scrubbed, they scraped, they polished. They washed themselves and put on clean clothes. Except for the masts and sails, darkened by the greasy, sooty smoke of the try-works, the ship shone like something new.

Again, lookouts were posted at the mastheads, watching for whales. Again would come the cry of "There she blows!" It might not happen for days, it might not happen for weeks—or it might happen within an hour. And so went life aboard a whaler, interrupted only by a school of whales, or storms, or visits ashore—the watching and waiting, the chase, the cutting-in, the trying-out, the cleanup, the watching and waiting . . . until the captain gave the order, "All hands, to get the ship under way for home!"

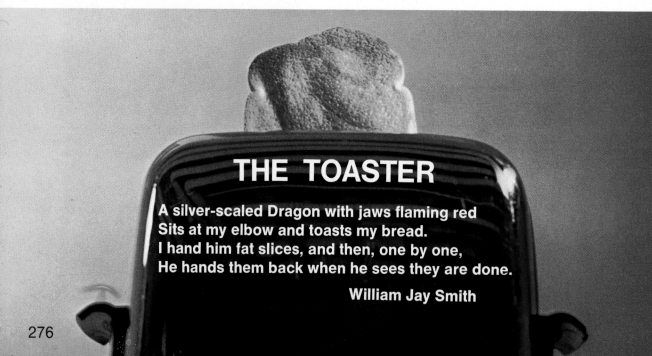

THE TOASTER

A silver-scaled Dragon with jaws flaming red
Sits at my elbow and toasts my bread.
I hand him fat slices, and then, one by one,
He hands them back when he sees they are done.

William Jay Smith

What Is the Last Number?

by Mary Elting

Suppose you were to start counting and did nothing but count, day and night, for the rest of your life. Would you get to the last number? The answer is *no*, because there is no last number. People who study mathematics tell us that we can never get to the end of numbers by counting. No matter how big a number we think of, there is always a bigger number. This idea is a very important one in science, and it has a name—the idea of infinity. Scientists write infinity this way: ∞

A million is a large number. A billion is larger. From there on, we don't very often use names for numbers, and some of them don't even have names. The largest number that has a name is a *googol*. It is a 1 with 100 zeros after it.

10,000,000,000,
000,000,000,000,
000,000,000,000,000,
000,000,000,000,000,
000,000,000,000,000,000,
000,000,000,000,000,000,
000,000,000,000

CROSSING

STOP   LOOK   LISTEN
as gate stripes swing down,
count the cars hauling distance
upgrade through town:
warning whistle, bellclang,
engine eating steam,
engineer waving,
a fast-freight dream:
B&M boxcar,
boxcar again,
Frisco gondola,

eight-nine-ten,
Erie and Wabash,
Seaboard, U.P.,
Pennsy tankcar,
twenty-two, three,
Phoebe Snow, B&O,
thirty-four, five,
Santa Fe cattle
shipped alive,
red cars, yellow cars,
orange cars, black,
Youngstown steel
down to Mobile
on Rock Island track,

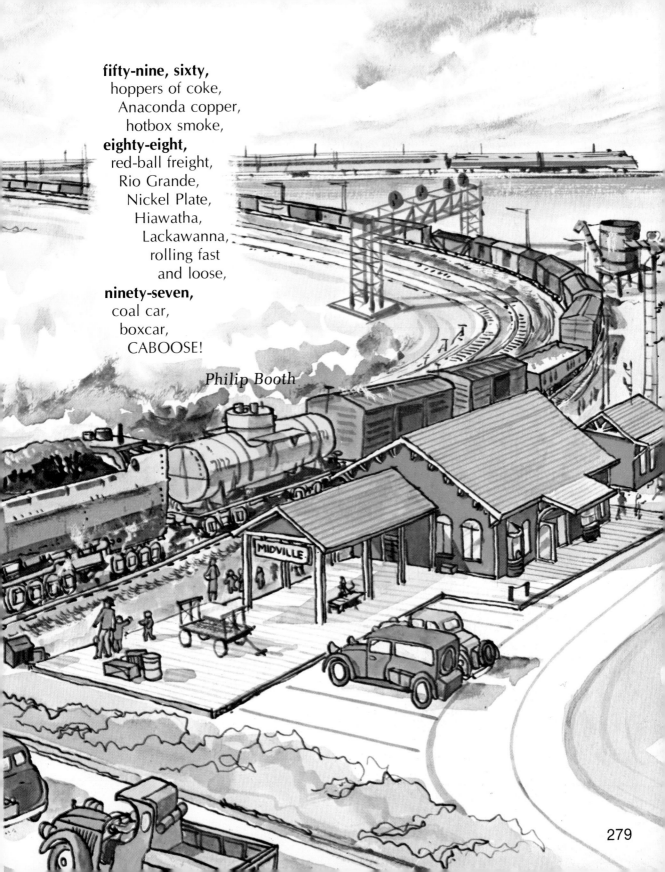

fifty-nine, sixty,
   hoppers of coke,
      Anaconda copper,
      hotbox smoke,
eighty-eight,
   red-ball freight,
      Rio Grande,
         Nickel Plate,
            Hiawatha,
               Lackawanna,
                  rolling fast
                  and loose,
ninety-seven,
   coal car,
      boxcar,
      CABOOSE!

Philip Booth

MAKING AND USING AN OUTLINE

PART ONE

What would you do to study an article so well that you remember the important points it gives and understand how those points are related to one another? Would you read that article two or more times? Would you make notes as you read, just one for each paragraph topic? Making and using a good outline that shows the important points in the article is a more helpful thing to do.

To make such an outline, first look to see whether the article has a title. If it does, you can use that title to start making your outline. If the article does not have a title, read the paragraphs quickly to decide what one thing they all talk about. Then use that one thing as the title for your outline.

After you have read the title of the article or have made one for your outline, think of a question which you expect the article to answer about that title. Your question may ask *How, What, When, Where, Which, Who,* or *Why,* and it can be your guide in deciding just which points in the article are the main ones. If an article had the title *Some Fire Hazards in the Home,* what question would you think of?

The next thing to do in making your outline is to read all the paragraphs to get answers to the question you have in mind. Do that now with the article which follows. You may want to use the question *What are those fire hazards?*

Some Fire Hazards in the Home

Different kinds of carelessness are a major fire hazard in the home. One kind is simply the mishandling of small flames. Throwing a burning match into a wastebasket, placing a lighted candle near curtains, or failing to screen a flaming or crackling fire in a fireplace are foolish things to do. Another kind of carelessness is the misusing of liquids that catch fire easily. Pouring kerosene on a smoldering fire in a fireplace is a dangerous act, and using gasoline to clean clothes in the house or the garage may lead to a bad fire.

Accumulated rubbish in the cellar, a closet, or the attic where it can be overheated or struck by sparks or a flame is a fire hazard. This rubbish may be paper such as old newspapers, empty cartons, or unused wrappings. Often it is old cloth, particularly oily rags, discarded clothing, or perhaps worn out bedding. All such rubbish can be good fuel for a fire.

Another hazard is the use of poor equipment. Some of this equipment is unsafe electrical parts. A worn or broken appliance cord, a damaged outlet, or wires which become overheated when trying to supply enough power for too many appliances should be replaced. Damaged or faulty parts of the central heating system are also poor equipment. A broken coal furnace chimney, with openings left by loose

bricks and crumbling mortar where it passes through the attic, should be repaired. On a gas furnace, poorly operating controls which fail to keep that furnace from becoming overheated should be replaced. Sparks, a small flame, or too much heat that poor equipment may create and send out can cause nearby rubbish to start burning.

What answers did you get to the question *What are those fire hazards*? They should be: (1) different kinds of carelessness, (2) accumulated rubbish, and (3) use of poor equipment. Those three ideas are the *main* points that the article gives about its title. In an outline of the article, they are called **main topics,** and they look like this:

Some Fire Hazards in the Home
  I. Different kinds of carelessness
 II. Accumulated rubbish
III. Use of poor equipment

You can see that the first word, the last word, and each important word in the title of an outline begins with a capital letter. The right Roman numeral and a period come before each main topic. Where is a capital letter used in each main topic? Is there a period at the end of that topic?

Often, but not always, a part or all of the topic of a paragraph in an article will be a main topic in an outline of that article. The topic of the first paragraph in the article about fire hazards can be stated as *Different kinds of carelessness as a fire hazard.* Is the first main topic in the above outline all, or just part of, that paragraph topic? Is each of the other main topics in the outline a part of the topic of a paragraph in the article?

When you are making an outline, try to find out whether the points you have chosen for main topics are good ones. To do that, see if you can use the *same word or words* in the title with each main topic to make a sensible statement. For example, in checking the main topics in the outline above, you could make these statements: (1) Different kinds of carelessness are a *fire hazard in the home,* (2) Accumulated rubbish is a *fire hazard in the home,* and (3) Use of poor equipment is a *fire hazard in the home.*

Usually an article you are studying gives points that tell about the main topic in your outline. To find those points for each main topic, think of a question you expect the article to answer about that topic. Then read all or part of the article again to get all the answers it gives. Do these things now with the article on fire hazards to get all the points that tell about the first main topic in the outline. Use the question *What are those kinds of carelessness?*

What answers did you get? They should be: (1) mishandling of small flames, and (2) misusing of liquids that catch fire easily.

To find points that the article gives about the second main topic, use the question *What is that rubbish?*

Your answers should be: (1) paper and (2) old cloth.

Can you find now answers that the article gives about the third main topic? Try using the question *What is this poor equipment?*

Your answers should be: (1) unsafe electrical parts and (2) damaged or faulty parts of the central heating system.

When we put into the outline the points that the article gives about the main topics, we call them **subtopics,** and they look like this:

Some Fire Hazards in the Home
I. **Different kinds of carelessness**
   A. **Mishandling small flames**
   B. **Misusing liquids that catch fire easily**
II. **Accumulated rubbish**
   A. **Paper**
   B. **Old cloth**
III. **Use of poor equipment**
   A. **Unsafe electrical parts**
   B. **Damaged or faulty parts of a central heating system**

Notice that the subtopics are indented under the main topics. The indenting shows that the subtopics under a given main topic tell about that particular main topic. The right capital letter and a period come before each subtopic. Where is a capital used in each subtopic? Is there a period at the end?

You can find out whether the points you have chosen to use as subtopics under a certain main topic are good ones. To do this, see if you can use the *same word or words* in that main topic with each subtopic to make a sensible statement. For example, in checking the two subtopics under the first main topic in the outline, you could make these statements: (1) Mishandling small flames is a *kind of carelessness,* and (2) Misusing liquids that catch fire easily is a *kind of carelessness.*

What statements could you make to check all the other subtopics in the outline?

Discussion

Help your class answer these questions:

1. In what ways can making and using an outline help you study an article?
2. Why is it important to have a question in mind when you read an article to choose points to use as main topics in an outline of that article? To choose points to use as subtopics?
3. What do the main topics in a good outline tell about? What do the subtopics tell about? Why are the subtopics indented?
4. How can you find out whether points you have chosen to use as main topics in an outline are good ones? How can you check the points you have chosen to use as subtopics?
5. What statements could be used to check the subtopics under the last two main topics in the outline about fire hazards in the home?
6. Where should capital letters be used in writing the title of an outline? In writing each main topic? In writing each subtopic? What should be placed before each main topic? Before each subtopic?

PART TWO

You already know how to find in an article good points to use as main topics and subtopics in an outline you are making of that article. Now you are ready to go on a little further.

Sometimes an article gives points that tell about one or more subtopics in your outline. To find out what those points are for a certain subtopic, think of a question you expect the article to answer about that subtopic. Then read part or all of the article again to get all the answers it gives to your question.

To get the points that the article on fire hazards in the home gives about the first subtopic in the outline on page 283, use now the question *What is the mishandling of small flames?*

What answers did you get? They should be: (1) throwing a burning match into a wastebasket, (2) placing a lighted candle near curtains, and (3) failing to screen a fire in a fireplace.

To get the points that the article gives about the next subtopic in the outline, use the question *What is the misusing of liquids that catch fire easily?*

The answers should be: (1) pouring kerosene on a smoldering fire in a fireplace and (2) using gasoline to clean clothes.

Now try to find by yourself the points that the article on fire hazards gives about all the other subtopics in the outline on page 283. Remember to think of a question about each subtopic to use as a guide in deciding which points are good ones.

When we put into an outline of an article the points which that article gives about the subtopic, those points are called **details.** What are the details in the complete outline of the article on fire hazards shown on the next page?

Some Fire Hazards in the Home

I. **Different kinds of carelessness**
   A. **Mishandling small flames**
      1. **Throwing burning match into wastebasket**
      2. **Placing lighted candle near curtains**
      3. **Failing to screen fire in fireplace**
   B. **Misusing liquids that catch fire easily**
      1. **Pouring kerosene on smoldering fire in fireplace**
      2. **Using gasoline to clean clothes**

II. **Accumulated rubbish**
   A. **Paper**
      1. **Old newspapers**
      2. **Empty cartons**
      3. **Unused wrappings**
   B. **Old cloth**
      1. **Oily rags**
      2. **Discarded clothing**
      3. **Worn out bedding**

III. **Use of poor equipment**
   A. **Unsafe electrical parts**
      1. **Worn or broken appliance cord**
      2. **Damaged outlet**
      3. **Wires which become overheated**
   B. **Damaged or faulty parts of central heating system**
      1. **Broken coal furnace chimney**
      2. **Poorly operating controls on gas furnace**

In the outline you just read, notice that each detail is indented under the subtopic to which it belongs. The right Arabic number and a period come before each detail. Where is a capital letter used in writing each detail? Is there a period at the end?

How can you find out whether the points used as details under a certain subtopic in the outline about fire hazards in the home are good ones? Just try to make sensible statements that use the *same word or words* in that subtopic with each detail. Such statements for the first subtopic in the outline could be: (1) Throwing a burning match into a waste basket is *mishandling a small flame*, (2) Placing a lighted candle near curtains is *mishandling a small flame*, and (3) Failing to screen a fire in a fireplace is *mishandling a small flame*.

What statements could you use to check the details under the subtopic *Old cloth?* Under *Unsafe electrical parts?*

After you have made an outline that shows many of the points an article gives, use that outline to test yourself. See if you can use each main topic with its subtopics and the details to make statements that give clear information about that main topic. For example, in testing yourself with the first main topic in the outline about fire hazards, you could make statements like these: (1) One kind of carelessness is the mishandling of a small flame by throwing a burning match into a waste basket, placing a lighted candle near curtains, or failing to screen a fire in a fireplace; and (2) Another kind of carelessness is the misusing of a liquid that catches fire easily, such as pouring kerosene on a smoldering fire in a fireplace, or using gasoline to clean clothes. Making such statements will help you understand and remember the important things the article says.

Discussion

Help your class answer these questions:

1. Why should you have a question in mind when you read an article to get points to use as details in an outline of that article? What should that question ask about?
2. What do the details in an outline tell about?
3. How can you find out whether points you have chosen for details in an outline you are making are good ones?
4. What statements could you use to check the details under the subtopic *Old cloth?* Under *Unsafe electrical parts?*
5. Where should each detail in an outline be written? Why should it be indented? What should come before each detail? Where should a capital letter be used?
6. How can you test yourself with an outline you have made?

On your own

On a clean sheet of paper, make an outline of important points that the following article gives. To help you choose good points to use as main topics, subtopics, and details, you may need to use questions that ask *What, How,* and *For what reasons.* Be sure to leave space between main topics so that you can write subtopics there, and between subtopics for the details you will need to write.

Some Small Fires That Help Us in the Home

Have you ever thought how a fireplace fire helps us? It provides warmth to take the chill off a room on a raw day late in the spring or early in the fall when the furnace is not running. On a very cold day, we sometimes use that warmth to add to the heat from the furnace. The pleasure that a fireplace fire gives may be simply a feeling of coziness, the sight of colored flames, or the sound of wood crackling as it burns.

In some homes gas flames provide heat for keeping the house warm, for cooking, and for heating water. A few small gas flames, called pilot lights, start the burners in gas appliances. Some of these appliances are cooking stoves, water heaters, and incinerators that burn trash.

Candle flames supply light for emergencies, and sometimes they offer us pleasure. The failing of electric power at night and needing to find something in a dark and unfamiliar room are two such emergencies. The soft glow that candle flames cast on a dinner table and the gayness they add to a room on special occasions, such as a birthday or Christmas Eve, are two of the pleasures those small fires offer.

Checking your work

If you are asked to do so, read part of your outline aloud. Find out why any mistake you may have made in choosing a point for a main topic, a subtopic, or a detail is a mistake.

THE SWAN OF STORYTELLERS:
HANS CHRISTIAN ANDERSEN

BY RAFE GIBBS

If you have ever read "The Ugly Duckling," you already know much about its Danish author, Hans Christian Andersen, because that fairy tale is really the story of his life.

When Hans was a boy, playmates would cry jeeringly, "Hello, Long Legs." Indeed, he seemed to be almost all legs. In addition, his nose was much longer than necessary. But like the homely and awkward baby swan in the Andersen fairy tale, he changed greatly in growing up.

True, even as a man Hans was far from handsome, but he had an inner beauty which came from great determination and courage. And he handled words so beautifully that they continue to delight readers today, a century after his death in 1875.

Hans was born on April 2, 1805, the son of a poor cobbler in the village of Odense on the little Danish island of Fýn. As he grew up, people in the town referred to him as that "strange Andersen boy." He seldom went to school or played with other children. He was a dreamer. Serious and sensitive, only on rare occasions did he thrill to being a boy.

Odense's big event of the year was a parade on the Monday before Lent. One of these parades, when Hans was small, haunted him all his life. As the procession came down the cobblestone street, Hans watched shyly from the doorway of his father's shop in the family home. At the head of the parade was a huge ox, with chains of daisies draped over its neck. Riding the ox was an "angel," a blond-haired boy wearing golden wings of cloth. Behind him came horn-tootling bandsmen and dancing clowns.

Suddenly Hans was out in the street, too, flinging his long, spindly legs this way and that in time to the music. His wooden shoes were too big as usual, and one sailed off, clattering over the cobblestones. Hans did not mind. He sent the other flying after its mate and jerked his legs as if he wanted them to fly off also.

The crowd roared with laughter. Hans bowed and blew kisses. He was having a wonderful time until. . .

"Look at that Andersen boy," said a woman. "Crazy, crazy!"

Hans heard. Shame, then terror, gripped him. His dancing stopped. He could only stand and stare wildly at the laughing crowd. Finally his legs began to move again, and he scuttled home with lowered head. Neighborhood boys followed, teasing and calling to him through the open doorway of his house.

Then, just as the mother duck spoke to the other ducks when they pecked at the Ugly Duckling, Hans's mother scolded the boys and said, "Leave him alone now. He's not bothering you." After that day, Hans kept very much to himself and became even more of a dreamer.

Rivers — because they flow to far places — are to dream by, and Fyn Island has a lovely river. The bank of the Odense, which wound north through the meadows and woods of Hans's village, was his favorite spot for dreaming.

As he sat with chin resting on bony knees, he told himself over and over again the folktales he had learned from his grandmother, until he himself became part of the tales. Old Grandma, who thought she no longer served any purpose in life, did not realize that in passing the ancient island lore on to young Hans, she was planting seeds that someday would grow and grow.

Hans would sit quietly for hours beside the river. Often he sang, in a voice that was unusually clear and true. One afternoon

a woman who was washing clothes in the stream turned and spoke to him. "Do you know, boy, that beneath this very river lies the empire of China?"

Hans nodded silently and went back to his dreaming, but now his dream was about a Chinese prince. . . . Hearing Hans sing, the prince became enchanted by his voice and appeared from under the river, wearing a black silk robe decorated with golden dragons. He grasped Hans by the wrist and took him down, down to China, where Hans became noble, rich, and famous. Years later, the prince let him return to Odense, and there Hans built himself a palace like that of the Chinese emperor.

Many times Hans dreamed this dream, and he even spent several evenings making drawings of his castle.

Hans was sure he would become famous one day, and he longed to see the great world beyond his island home. Hans grew more restless after the death of his father when the boy was eleven, and three years later, like the Ugly Duckling, he said, "I think I had better go out into the wide world."

On September 6, 1819, after traveling two days and nights by ferry and horse-drawn coach, Hans finally arrived in the busy capital city of Copenhagen. At fourteen he was taller than most men. But gangly and awkward, a stranger to everyone he saw, with many dreams but almost no education, he was truly a frightened boy. In his pocket he had scarcely ten Danish dollars, and under his arm he carried a pitifully small bundle of clothes.

As Hans looked around him, however, it was excitement, not fear, that made him tremble. Copenhagen was all he had imagined it would be and more. He gazed up at buildings that were three and even four stories high. Fine carriages, with handsomely dressed ladies and gentlemen, whirled by him. Everywhere street sellers were calling attention to their newspapers and playbills, fish and cheese, fruit and chestnuts. Copehagen was alive. It was a city in which to make one's fortune.

Pinned inside his jacket pocket, Hans had a letter of introduction from one of the leading citizens of Odense to Madame Schall, the famous ballet dancer at the Royal Theater of Copenhagen. Hans had been so fascinated by the few plays he had seen at the small theater in Odense that he yearned to go on the stage. He could not decide whether he should be a dancer, an actor, or a singer. He only knew that all his hopes now centered on the Royal Theater, and he had no doubt that Madame Schall would help him begin a career in it.

As soon as he had found lodging in an attic room, Hans presented himself at the home of Madame Schall. The dancer was surprised to see him, but gracious.

"What would you like to do for me?" she asked.

Hans gulped. He had seen *Cinderella* performed in Odense by the Royal Theater Company, and this came to mind now.

"A—a bit from *Cinderella*," he stammered. "May I take off my boots, the better to do it?"

Madame Schall nodded.

Then, with hat for tambourine, Hans began to dance and sing. He could control his long legs fairly well now, and he had an excellent voice. But he also had a weakness. He did not seem to know when he had reached the mountaintop—in other words, when he should quit.

His dancing grew wilder and his singing louder. Madame Schall became amused, then alarmed, and finally ran from the room, leaving the boy without an audience. As at the Odense parade years earlier, he scuttled away in shame.

With no more letters of introduction, the fourteen-year-old boy was now entirely on his own. The next morning, calling on the manager of the Royal Theater, he tried again.

"You are too thin for the theater," said the manager, not even letting Hans through the stage door.

"Oh," replied the boy, "if you will only engage me, I will soon get fat on the salary you pay me!"

The manager smiled but waved Hans away, calling after him, "We engage only people with education."

In the tale "The Ugly Duckling," the young swan, alone on a pond in the wide world, swam "round and round in dizzy circles." Now Hans walked round and round in the city. He, too, was traveling in dizzy circles. Finally, after days of hopelessness, he remembered having read in an Odense newspaper about a man named Siboni, the director of the Academy of Music in Copenhagen.

That evening a desperate Hans, who had not eaten for two days because he had no more money, rapped at the door of Siboni's home. A maid answered and explained that the master could not receive callers because a dinner party was in progress

for some important people of the city. She started to close the door, but Hans pleaded with her. "I must sing for the great Siboni. He can train me, and I will become great, too. If he won't help me, I'll have to find a ship captain to take me back to Odense because I— I—" Hans ended by pouring out the story of his life in Odense and of his coming alone to Copenhagen.

"Wait out here on the steps," said the maid when he had finished. After what seemed like hours to Hans, the door opened again and there stood Siboni and all his distinguished guests— among them, the well-known poet Jens Baggesen.

"You wish to sing for us?" asked Siboni. "Then come in."

No aspiring artist ever had a more critical audience than Hans had that night, but fortunately he did not realize this. He sang beautifully, acted out some scenes from a Danish play, and recited two poems. He might have gone on and on as he had at Madame Schall's home, but the hunger that gnawed at his stomach and his fear of having to return in defeat to Odense would not let him. At the end of the second poem, he hesitated and suddenly burst into tears.

The audience applauded.

"Well done, lad!" said Siboni. "You will indeed be my pupil. But now we must see if there is any food left in the kitchen."

"Food—food—what is food? But a fine voice—ah, *that* is something!" exclaimed Poet Baggesen. "Someday, Hans, you will become a great singer, but do not grow vain when the public applauds you. You have true naturalness—a rare quality that is found in very few people."

Hans only half understood what Baggesen was saying. Later, however, he was to remember the poet's words with gratitude.

Supported by Siboni and his friends, Hans began his training with the master. For six months, Siboni seemed more and more pleased with Hans's singing, but then he became increasingly discouraged. One morning, with sadness in his eyes, he said gently to the boy, "You are growing up, and your voice is changing. The clear notes are gone." Siboni slowly shook his head and continued, "There is no hope now of your becoming a fine singer. You must return to Odense, Hans—learn a trade."

No, no, thought Hans, now seeking comfort from Poet Baggesen's words. Even if he could not become a great singer as the poet had predicted, might not that "true naturalness" which Baggesen had spoken of eventually win him fame in some other way? But how?

As Hans, in the next few years, clung to Copenhagen, he frantically sought the answer. Always short of money, usually hungry, he managed to survive with the help of kind citizens. He even received a little schooling—not much, but enough to convince him that he was now ready to try another of the arts: writing. Hans's interest in the theater had never faded, and although he had been denied a career as an actor or singer, perhaps he could succeed as a playwright.

At seventeen, he wrote a play and submitted it to the Royal Theater. Long weeks, six of them, passed. Finally the manuscript was returned to Hans. One critic had written stingingly across it: "He needs more education before he can hope to write a play."

That might have been the end of Hans's climb to fame except for his determination and a man named Jonas Collin. Never one to give up easily, Hans wrote a second play and submitted it to the Royal Theater. When Collin, the director of the theater, read it, he saw in Hans's writing what Poet Baggesen had seen in his singing and acting—naturalness. What the boy lacked was elementary knowledge, and Collin set about trying to help him acquire it. He spoke highly of Hans to King Frederick VI of Denmark, and the king granted the boy some money to be used for his education.

Now Hans was more eager than ever to make good, not just for himself but for king and country and for Mr. Collin. So at the age of seventeen he began grammar school, starting in the lowest grade and sitting beside much younger and smaller boys who knew more than he did and often teased him. He later said that this was the darkest and bitterest period of his life, but he

worked hard for six years and did extremely well in his studies.

In 1829, when he was twenty-four, Hans had his first taste of success. He wrote a humorous book about a walking tour through Copenhagen that sold well and was praised by many. Later that year he had a play produced at the Royal Theater. Still, the real fame he dreamed of did not come, and the numerous poems and plays he wrote in the years that followed were not widely read or well received. Impressed by his work, however, and hoping to broaden Hans's outlook, the king gave him a further grant which enabled him to travel in Europe for more than a year.

After Hans returned at last to Copenhagen, several months passed before he completed a novel he had begun in Italy. By the time the manuscript was ready to go to the printer, once more he had no money. Knowing he must write something else immediately in order to earn enough to buy food and clothing, he planned to dash off a new novel which he could sell quickly. But Hans soon made a shocking discovery — words simply would not flow from his pen. No matter how long or hard he tried, he could not seem to get the novel started.

One day, as he stared at the blank sheets on the desk before him, Hans let his mind wander. He thought about his boyhood back in Odense and, especially, about his grandmother and the folktales she had told so easily, so entertainingly. He had often recounted these tales to the children of friends, and the young people had been captivated by them and had begged for more. Hans decided he would write down a few of his grandmother's stories and perhaps think up some tales of his own. If they were published, they would bring him the money he needed.

So the fairy tales of Hans Christian Andersen came into being. Three of those included in the first slim volume, published in 1835, were his retellings of stories he had heard as a child. The fourth, however, was a tale he made up himself, and it proved to be the one his readers liked best. Consequently, Hans relied more and more on his own imagination, and most of the stories in later volumes he invented himself.

Because Hans considered these tales rather unimportant, he turned repeatedly to more serious writing and produced some excellent novels, travel sketches, and poems. But it was the fairy tales that had captured an audience, and the public kept wanting more. In them, Hans's naturalness was revealed in abundance, and it touched adult as well as juvenile minds and hearts.

Hans continued creating these well-loved tales until his death, writing 168 in all. With them, his fame was assured. People throughout the world were charmed, as they are today, by the simplicity and freshness of such stories as "The Emperor's New Clothes," "Little Claus and Big Claus," "The Princess and the Pea," "The Little Mermaid," "The Nightingale," and that reflection of Hans's early life, "The Ugly Duckling."

On December 6, 1867, when Hans was sixty-two, the town of Odense held the grandest celebration in its history. It was Hans Christian Andersen Day.

Houses, shops, the cathedral, and the Guild Hall were gay with red and white flags. Schools had been closed for the public holiday. The weather was cold, but the hearts of the people thronging the streets were warm with welcome for Odense's greatest native son in his triumphant return.

Smiling and waving a high silk hat, the beloved writer rode

in a stately carriage to the Guild Hall. Parading behind him came school children, craft guilds with colorful banners, community singers, and a band much larger and better than the one Hans remembered from that pre-Lenten parade of his childhood.

And the singing. . . It brought a great swelling where Hans's heart was, because the words the children sang were those of a hymn he had written for Denmark.

Inside the Guild Hall, where the speechmaking was to be held, all the important people of Odense were assembled. They clapped and cheered wildly when Hans entered and took his place on the platform beside the mayor. No one's eyes left the face of the cobbler's son, this man who had brought so much honor to Odense and who was now being honored by the town. A hush fell over the audience as the mayor started to speak.

"About fifty years ago, a poor boy left his native town to begin the struggle of life. His departure was quiet and unnoticed. Only two women, his mother and grandmother, accompanied him a

little way on the road, but their wishes and prayers followed him the whole journey. His first object was to reach the capital; there would he struggle to attain the great end of his life.

"In the awesome city, he stood alone, but he began his struggle and he had in it two powerful supports—trust in Providence and confidence in his own strength. . . .

"The boy has now become a man, and his name has in these latter days been upon all men's lips. He stands here honored by kings and princes, but—what is more—esteemed by his fellow townspeople who have elected him an honorary citizen. . . .

"However much he has wandered, he never has forgotten that he is a Dane and that his cradle stood here in our town. So, then, a *hurrah* for our honorary citizen, Hans Christian Andersen!"

The applause was thundering.

Later, in his autobiography, Hans wrote, "It was, on that day, as if one sunbeam after another shone into my heart. I could not comprehend it."

But the world comprehended it—Hans Christian Andersen, the "Ugly Duckling" of Odense, had become the "Swan of Storytellers."

AUTHOR

Rafe Gibbs decided to be a writer when he was about the age of eleven. At thirteen, he wrote and sold his first short story for $35.00. He wrote his stories while sitting between boxes of canned goods in the storeroom of his father's grocery store in Yakima, Washington.

Mr. Gibbs studied writing at the University of Idaho. While in college, he had many articles published in magazines. He paid for much of the cost of his college education with the money that he earned.

After graduating with honors, Mr. Gibbs worked for five years for a newspaper in Milwaukee, Wisconsin. During World War II, he rose to the rank of colonel in the Air Force. Since 1946, he has been Director of Information at the University of Idaho and teacher of a course in magazine writing.

THE NIGHTINGALE

A
Chinese Fairy Tale

by
Hans Christian Andersen

In China, where the Chinese live, even the emperor is Chinese, as you well know. Now, what I am about to tell you happened many years ago, but for this very reason it is all the more important that you should hear the story before it is forgotten.

The Emperor's palace was the most magnificent mansion in the world. It was made entirely of the finest porcelain, but so very costly and fragile that it was dangerous even to touch it. The choicest flowers were to be seen in the garden. To the most gorgeous flowers, little silver bells were fastened so that their tinkling might prevent anyone from passing by without noticing them. Everything in the Emperor's garden was most cleverly arranged. The garden itself extended so far that even the gardener did not know where it ended. Whoever walked beyond it, however, came to a beautiful wood with very high trees and deep lakes. That wood extended as far as the wide blue ocean. Large vessels could sail close under the branches. Among the branches there dwelt a nightingale, who sang so sweetly that even the poor fisherman, who had so much else to do, would stand still and listen to her song. "How beautifully this bird sings," he would say, but then he had to attend to his work and forget the bird. Yet the following night, if the nightingale sang again and the fisherman heard it, he would again exclaim, "How beautiful!"

Travelers came from all parts of the world to the Emperor's city. They admired the city, the palace, and the garden, but when they heard the nightingale, they said, "This is the best of all." They talked about it after they got home. And learned men wrote books about the city, the palace, and the garden, but they never omitted mention of the nightingale. And poets wrote beautiful verses about the nightingale in the wood near the sea.

These books were translated into every language of the

world. One of them fell into the hands of the Emperor of China. As he was sitting in his golden chair, he read and read and nodded his head, for the splendid descriptions of the city, the palace, and the garden pleased him greatly.

"But there is nothing like the nightingale" was written in the book.

"What is this?" said the Emperor. "The nightingale? I never heard of it. Can there be such a bird in my empire, even in my garden, without my knowing? And do I have to learn of it from books?"

So he called his chamberlain. Now the chamberlain was so grand a person that no one of inferior rank presumed to speak to him. If anyone dared do so, he only answered "pish," which has no particular meaning.

"They say there is a remarkable bird here, called the nightingale," said the Emperor. "Her song, they think, is worth more than anything else in my dominion. Why has nobody told me?"

"I have never heard any mention of her," said the chamberlain. "She has never been presented at court."

"I wish her to come and sing before me this evening," said the Emperor. "The whole world seems to know what I have, and I do not know it myself."

"I have never heard any mention of her," repeated the chamberlain, "but I shall find her."

But where was she to be found? The chamberlain ran up one flight of stairs and down another, through halls and through passages. Nobody he met had ever so much as heard of the nightingale. So the chamberlain returned to the Emperor and said that the nightingale was a figment of the book-writer's imagination.

"Your Imperial Majesty must not believe all that is written in books. Much in them is pure invention and belongs in the realm of black magic."

"But the book in which I have read it," returned the Emperor, "has been sent to me by the high and mighty Emperor of Japan, and, therefore, it cannot be untrue. I wish to hear the nightingale. She must be here this evening. If not, the whole court will be flogged after supper."

"Psing-pe!" said the chamberlain, and again he ran upstairs and downstairs, through halls and through passages, and half the courtiers ran with him, for no one relished the idea of a flogging after supper. They all asked about the wonderful nightingale, whom the whole world talked of, and whom nobody at the court knew.

At last they asked a poor little girl in the scullery, who said, "Oh, the nightingale. Yes, I know her very well. Oh, she can sing! Every evening I carry the leftovers to my sick mother who lives by the shore. When I walk back and stay to rest a little in the wood, I hear the nightingale sing. It is so beautiful that it makes tears rush into my eyes. It is just as if my mother were kissing me."

"Little scullery maid," said the chamberlain, "I shall get you a permanent appointment in the kitchen, together with permission to see His Majesty the Emperor dine, if you will conduct us to the nightingale. She is commanded to sing at court this very evening."

They went to the wood where the nightingale used to sing. Nearly half the court went with them. While they were on their way, a cow began to low.

"There she is," shouted the court-pages. "Now we have her. It is certainly an extraordinary voice for so small an animal. But we have heard it somewhere before."

"No, those are cows you hear lowing," said the little scullery maid. "We are still far from the place."

The frogs were now croaking in the pond.

"That's wonderful," said the famous court preacher. "Now I hear her. It sounds just like small church bells."

"No, those are frogs," said the little scullery maid, "but now I think we shall soon hear her."

Then the nightingale began to sing.

"There she is," said the little scullery maid. "Listen! She is sitting up there." And she pointed to a little gray bird in the branches of a tree.

"Can it be possible?" said the chamberlain. "I should never have thought so. How plain she looks. She seems to have lost her color at the sight of so many distinguished people."

"Little nightingale," called the scullery maid, "our gracious Emperor wishes you to sing something to him."

"With the greatest pleasure," replied the nightingale, and she sang quite delightfully.

"It sounds like glass bells," said the chamberlain. "And look at her little throat, how it moves. It is surprising that we should never have heard her before. She will be a great success at court."

"Shall I sing again to the Emperor?" asked the nightingale, because she thought the Emperor was among her audience.

"Most excellent nightingale," said the chamberlain, "I have the great honor to invite you to a court festival which is to take place this evening. His Imperial Majesty will doubtless be enchanted with your delightful song."

"My song would sound far better among the green trees," said the nightingale. However, she followed them willingly when she heard that the Emperor wished it.

There was a general cleaning and polishing at the imperial palace. The walls and the floors, which were all of porcelain, glittered with a thousand gold lamps. The loveliest flowers with the merriest tinkling bells were placed all round the passages. People were running to and fro excitedly. This caused all the bells to ring, and there was such a din that nobody could hear himself speak.

In the middle of the grand hall, where the Emperor had his throne, a golden perch was erected on which the nightingale was to sit. The whole court was present. The little scullery maid, who had now been given the rank and title of Imperial Court Cook, received permission to stand behind the big folding door leading to the hall. Everybody wore his best clothes, and all eyes were fixed upon the little gray bird to whom the Emperor now nodded kindly as a signal for her to begin.

The nightingale sang so sweetly that tears came into the Emperor's eyes and rolled down his cheeks. And now the nightingale sang more sweetly still, and that touched the hearts of all who heard her. The Emperor wanted to present her with a golden slipper which she was to wear round her neck at all times, but she thanked him and said she was already sufficiently rewarded.

"This is the most amiable way to win hearts," said the ladies present. They put water into their mouths and tried to move their throats as the nightingale did, whenever somebody spoke to them. That way, they thought, they would become nightingales too. Even the footmen and chambermaids declared that they were satisfied. That meant a lot, because they were always the most difficult to please. Yes, indeed, the nightingale's success was complete. She was now to remain at court, and to have her own cage with permission to fly out twice a day and once a night. Twelve attendants were to accompany her on her excursions, and they held her by a silken band that was fastened round her foot. And since they kept good hold, there was no pleasure for the nightingale in such an excursion.

All the city was talking of the wonderful bird. When two people met, one would say 'night' and the other 'gale', and then they sighed and understood each other. Eleven newborn babies were named Nightingale, but so far all they could do was cry.

One day, a large parcel arrived for the emperor at the palace, on which was written NIGHTINGALE. "Here we have another new book about our famous bird," said the Emperor.

However, it was not a book. It was a small piece of machinery, carefully packed in a box—an artificial nightingale, which was intended to look like the living one. The plaything did not look gray and modest like its model. It was covered all over with diamonds, rubies, and sapphires. When this artificial bird had been wound up, it could sing one of the tunes that the real nightingale sang. Its tail, glittering with silver and gold, went up and down all the time.

A little band was fastened round its neck on which was written, "The nightingale of the Emperor of Japan is poor compared with the nightingale of the Emperor of China."

"How delightful!" exclaimed everybody, and the bearer was immediately given the title of Chief Imperial Nightingale Bringer.

"Now they shall sing together," they all said. "What a wonderful duet that will be."

And so they had to sing together, but it was not a success, for the real nightingale sang in her own natural way, whereas the artificial bird produced its tones mechanically. The Master of the Emperor's Music took the side of the artificial bird and said, "It is not his fault. He keeps exact time, quite in accordance with the method I teach."

So the artificial bird sang alone. He was just as successful as the real nightingale, and he was much prettier to look at.

Thirty-three times he sang the same tune, and yet he was not weary. People wanted to listen to him again, but the Emperor thought it was now time the real nightingale sang once more. But where had she gone to? Nobody had noticed that she had flown out of the open window and back to her own green wood. "What is the meaning of this?" said the Emperor angrily, and all the courtiers called the nightingale an ungrateful creature.

"Anyway, we have the better bird," they consoled themselves, and the artificial bird had to sing his song for the thirty-fourth time. The audience still had not learned it because it was so difficult. The music master praised the bird inordinately and declared he was superior to the real nightingale, not only in his exterior appearance but also in his voice. "You see, Your Majesty and my noble lords," he said, "with the real nightingale, one never knows what is coming, but everything is settled with the artificial bird. He can be taken to pieces, and the works can be examined to discover how the wheels fit into each other and how the sound is produced."

"That is perfectly true," everybody agreed, and the music master received permission to show the bird to the people the next Sunday.

"They should also hear him sing," commanded the Emperor. And so it happened. The people were as pleased as if they had been drinking tea, for it is tea that makes the Chinese merry. They all said, "Oh," and raised their forefingers and nodded their heads. But the fisherman who had heard the real nightingale said, "It does sound quite pretty, almost like the real bird, but yet there is something missing, heaven knows what."

The real nightingale, however, was exiled for disobedience.

The artificial bird had his place on a silken cushion next to the Emperor's bed. All the presents he had received, gold and precious stones, lay around him. He had obtained the rank and title of High Imperial Nightingale Singer, and was allotted the number one seat at the left side. For the Emperor thought the left-hand side was the noblest, because one's heart is on the left-hand side, even an Emperor's heart.

The music master wrote twenty-five volumes about the artificial bird, using the longest and most difficult words contained in the Chinese language. It was much too Chinese even for the Chinese, but they all said they had read it. Otherwise, they would have been considered stupid.

Thus it went on for a whole year. The Emperor, the court,

and the whole of the Chinese people now knew every note of the artificial bird's song by heart. That was the very reason they liked it so much, they could now sing with him. The street urchins sang "Cluck, cluck, cluck," and even the Emperor sang the song. Yes, it was charming!

One evening, when the bird was in full song and the Emperor was lying in bed listening, there was a sudden bang and then a "surrrrr", and all the wheels were running about, and the music stopped. The Emperor jumped out of bed and called his chief physician, but what use could he be? Then the best clockmaker was fetched. At last, after much trial and error, the bird was in some measure put to rights again. But the clockmaker said he must be spared much singing, for the pegs were almost worn out and could not be renewed in such a way that the music would still be correct. There was great grief.

Once a year only, therefore, the artificial bird was allowed to sing, and even then there were difficulties. The music master made a speech full of his favorite long words and said the singing was as good as ever.

When five years had passed, a great affliction visited the land. For the people had heard that the Emperor was ill and could not live very much longer. They thought highly of him in their hearts, although they had already elected a new Emperor. But they stood in the street outside the palace and asked the chamberlain how the Emperor was.

"Pish," said he and shook his head.

Cold and pale the Emperor lay in his magnificent bed. All the court believed him to be already dead, and everyone had hastened away to greet the new Emperor. The footmen were standing in the corridors gossiping about the new Emperor, and the maids were having a grand tea party.

The floors in all rooms and passages had been covered with thick cloth in order that no step should be heard, and all over the palace silence and stillness reigned.

But the Emperor was not yet dead. Stiff and pale he lay in his splendid bed with the long velvet curtains and heavy gold tassels. A window was slightly open, and the moon shone down on him and the artificial bird.

The poor Emperor, who could hardly breathe, felt as though something were sitting on his chest. He opened his eyes and saw that it was Death, who had put on the Emperor's crown and was holding the golden scimitar in one hand and the splendid imperial banner in the other. From under the folds of the thick velvet hangings, the strangest-looking heads were seen peering forth, some with an absolutely hideous expression, others with an extremely gentle and lovely aspect. They were the bad and the good deeds that the Emperor had done, and were now fixing their eyes upon him, while Death was sitting on his heart.

"Do you remember this?" they whispered one after another. "Do you recollect that?" They were telling him so much that sweat broke out upon his forehead.

"I cannot stand it," he said, "Music, music! Beat the great Chinese drum to drown the sound of it."

But the voices went on, and Death nodded his head in Chinese fashion to everything they said.

"Music, music," cried the Emperor. "You dear little artificial bird, sing! Oh, do sing! I have given you gold and precious stones. I have even hung my golden slipper round your neck. Sing, do please sing."

But the bird was silent. There was no one who could wind him up, and he could not sing of his own accord. Death continued to stare with his great hollow eyes at the Emperor, and everywhere it was still, fearfully still.

All at once the sweetest song was heard from the window. It was the little living nightingale who was sitting on a branch outside. She had heard of her Emperor's severe illness and had come to comfort him with her song and to give him new hope. As she sang, the spectral forms became paler and paler, the blood flowed more and more quickly through the Emperor's feeble limbs, and even Death listened and said, "Go on, little nightingale."

"Yes, I will if you give me the splendid gold scimitar and the gay banner and the Emperor's crown," answered the nightingale.

And Death gave her all these treasures, each for a song. And the nightingale sang on. She sang of the quiet churchyard where white roses blossom, the lilac sends forth its fragrance, and the fresh grass is bedewed with the tears of the sorrowing friends of the departed. Then Death was seized with longing for his garden and flew out of the window like a cold, white shadow.

"Thank you, thank you, you heavenly bird," said the Emperor. "I have recognized you. I banished you from my realm, and yet you have returned and sung away those evil faces from my bed and Death from my heart. How can I reward you?"

"You have rewarded me," said the nightingale. "I saw tears in your eyes when I sang to you for the first time. Those I shall never forget. They are like jewels to a singer's heart. But sleep now and awake fresh and healthy. I will sing you to sleep."

And the nightingale sang, and the Emperor fell into a deep slumber. When he awoke strong and healthy, the sun was shining in at the window. Not one of his servants had returned, for they all believed him dead. Only the nightingale was still sitting there and singing.

"You must always stay with me," said the Emperor. "You need only sing when you wish, and I will break the artificial bird into a thousand pieces."

"Don't do that," said the nightingale. "He has done his best for as long as he could. Keep him and take care of him. I cannot stay and build my nest at your palace, for I need my freedom and the green wood. But I shall come when I like. I shall sit on a branch close to this window in the evening and will sing to you to make you joyful and pensive. I shall sing to you of the happy people and of the sorrowful ones. The good and bad in the world, which are concealed from you, I will reveal to you, for I get around in the country. I fly to the fisherman's hut, to the peasant's cottage, to all who are far distant from you and your court. I know your heart and love it better than your crown. I will come and I will sing, but you must promise me one single thing."

"Anything," said the Emperor. "Anything you like." And now he stood in his imperial robes which he had put on himself, and held the scimitar to his heart. The sword was heavy with gold.

"One thing only I ask of you," said the nightingale. "Let no one know that you have a little bird who tells you everything. Let them all think you are wise."

And with that the nightingale flew away.

Quietly the attendants came in to look at their dead Emperor. And, lo, there he stood! "Good morning!" he said.

MORE BOOKS TO ENJOY

SEABIRD, *by Holling Clancy Holling*

Seabird, a carved model of a gull, brought luck to four generations of men on whalers, clipper ships, steamships, and airplanes. The story is full of adventure and facts.

BIG RED, *by James A. Kjelgaard*

This exciting story is about seventeen-year-old Danny and Big Red, an Irish setter. Together the boy and the dog face such dangers as blizzards and a bear.

THE LION, THE WITCH, AND THE WARDROBE,
by C. S. Lewis

Four children discover the way into a strange land through an old wardrobe. They meet up with a lion and an evil witch.

PIPPI LONGSTOCKING, *by Astrid Lindgren*

Pippi is a very independent tomboy who lives alone with a horse and a monkey. She has fantastic adventures and invents a few, too.

MATTHEW HENSON: ARCTIC HERO, *by Sheldon Ripley*

Matthew Henson, the only man to accompany Admiral Peary on all his polar expeditions, was a man of courage and determination. His dream was to stand at the North Pole.

THE FEARSOME INN, *by Isaac Bashevis Singer*

This is a tale full of enchantment and spells about three girls and three young men and a witch who makes them her prisoners.

MOSAICS

Contents

MOSAICS

One Night at Dead End Bluff

Quig Smith had been blind since birth. But despite his handicap, he was an excellent swimmer and could do many other things as well as his friends. One thing his father would not permit him to do, however, was to go near the steep bluff, called Dead End Bluff, that led down to the river near his home. Quig's friends often went down the side of the bluff, because it was a shortcut to the river. But this was much too dangerous for a blind boy.

This story from the book *Dead End Bluff* tells what happened one night at the bluff. Quig and his neighbor Peg Bradford were baby-sitting for Quig's younger brother Tommy and two other small children. Suddenly they discovered that the three children had started down the bluff to go frog hunting. It was up to Quig and Peg to get them back.

by Elizabeth Witheridge

"Tom Smith," Quig commanded sternly, "you come back up that bluff this minute, do you hear? Pete and Marcy, you come back *immediately!*"

"We're coming, Quig," Pete responded meekly. "We only went halfway down. We're coming right up."

Quig heard them puffing, and the sound of their feet scrambling on the rock steps. In a minute they were at the top, and Peggy was pulling them over the barricade.

"Tommy," Quig shouted furiously, "if you aren't on your way up by the time I count to ten, I'm coming down after you." Even as he said the words, the familiar thrill of fear and anticipation tingled through him.

"Ho, ho!" laughed Tommy at the bottom of the bluff, "You've never been down Dead End in your life. Daddy won't let you. I'm gonna stay down here till I get my big old frog. He's here. I can see him with my flashlight, and I'm gonna get him."

Above the swishing of the rapids and the remote murmur of the low falls, Quig heard Tommy's feet slithering around on the rocks at water's edge. He sucked in a big breath of air and began to count.

"I'm at nine, Tommy," he called. At the same time he began to take off his shoes. He could feel the way better with his bare feet.

"You can't go down there, Quig," Peggy wailed. "You'll break your neck. If it weren't so dark, I'd go, but I can't go in the dark. I just can't, Quig. You know I can't go down Dead End in the dark!"

"Ten!" counted Quig and threw his leg over the barricade.

"Don't you come down here!" screamed Tommy. "I'm getting my frog. He's sitting on the next rock. I'm getting him with my net."

Quig was over the edge now, fumbling for the first foothold. He was going down with his stomach flat against the bluff, feeling for support with his fingers and toes. He tightened his muscles, trying desperately to still the trembling in his body. There was a sudden silence from below, then a hoarse croak from the enormous bullfrog, and the clatter of metal against stone. Simultaneously

Tommy's voice rose in a high thin shriek of pure terror.

"Quig, I've dropped my flashlight. It's pitch dark. I can't see! I've got my frog, but he's trying to get away."

"Don't move. I'm on the way," Quig called. His voice sounded more confident than he felt. Then he smiled to himself. It was a lucky thing Dad wasn't here. The thought somehow braced his nerve. He could do it.

Peggy was standing at the top, making distressed, helpless noises. Tommy below was moving on the rocks, and there was the thud, thud, thud of the frog's heavy body struggling to get out of the net. Suddenly he heard Tommy lurch. There was the sound of sliding stones, a frightened, panic-stricken yelp, and a splash into the water.

"Quig, I fell in! The current's pulling me out. I can't touch bottom!"

"Grab a rock and hang on!" Quig ordered. "I'm coming. Peg, go for help, quick!"

Peggy was evidently too terrified to answer. Pete and Marcy were squealing, though. He heard the sound of racing feet as Peg rushed down Bluff Road. Quig continued his slow, painful descent. He had always planned to explore Dead End Bluff some day, but never like this. It was to have been a great, triumphant moment, the symbol of victory over his blindness. But this wasn't like that. It wasn't something anticipated safely and calmly from the other side of the barricade. It was something he had to do and he was doing it even though he was scared stiff.

"Tom, are you hanging on?"

"Uh-huh, I found a place. Hurry!"

Tommy was down there, alone in the dark, fighting to hang on in the turmoil of the rapids. Quig was going down to save him from drowning, not to prove anything to himself or his father or anybody else. The noise of the rushing water was much louder now, as he dropped with desperate slowness

down the face of the steep bluff into the miniature gorge.

"Hurry, Quig! Hurry! I can't hang on much longer!" Tommy's voice was terribly frightened above the confusion of the water.

Quig couldn't hurry, he didn't dare hurry. If he fell and hurt himself, if he rolled into the water and was swept beyond his depth by the strong current, that would be all for both of them. There was no one else to do it.

"You *can* hang on, Tommy. You've *got* to, just a little longer!"

Quig forced all the strength he had into his voice, all the assurance. He hoped he sounded strong to the little boy waiting in the darkness, because at that moment he felt anything but strong himself. It was one thing to think about doing this, and another to do it. What had become of Peggy?

He slipped and fell a few feet, scraping his knees and his arms on the rough face of the cliff. He clutched wildly at a jutting rock, held still for a moment, and then moved on toward the bottom. He couldn't have far to go now. Suddenly the child called out, "I see you, Quig. You're down."

Quig reached cautiously with his foot and felt water. He found that he was on a flat ledge of rock. He had done it, after all these years he had done it. But strangely, there was no sense of elation. He just snatched off his slacks and shirt and sat down, gingerly sliding off into the river. The current caught him and he knew what was coming. Somehow he must find Tommy in the welter of tumbling water, and he must find him in time. He must wade as far as he could on the rocky bottom and pray that he wouldn't lose his balance and be flung down against the rocks. Also he must be constantly on guard against the deep holes that he knew were there.

"Here I am, Tommy," he called in as calm a voice as he could manage. "Hang on. Tell me which way to go."

Now that Tommy had caught a glimmer of his brother's body through the darkness, he began to cry. With Quig actually in the river, coming toward him, all of his bravery seemed to fade away. "I-I can't tell you," he sobbed. He snuffled mightily. "I've got water in my nose. I can't hang on any longer. I'm going to drown!"

The fear that had gripped Quig all the way down the bluff was transformed into blazing anger. "You sure are if you let go now, and you're going to drown if you don't keep talking to me so I know where to go. Stop that blubbering and *talk to me,* I tell you!"

"Come straight ahead," Tommy gulped, shocked back to control.

Quig saved his breath for struggling with the current and inched his way over the rocks toward the sound of Tommy's voice. Once he slipped on a slimy stone and floundered into a deep hole, but a powerful kick sent him spinning to the surface.

"Here I am," Tommy squeaked in a very small voice, so close to Quig that he almost slid into another hole in astonishment.

"Let's go," Quig commanded, the strength generated by his anger still upon him.

The water where Tommy was clinging to the rock was indeed over his head, but Quig was so much taller that he could easily stand on the bottom. The water swirled around them dangerously, though, and Quig was anxious to get out of the rapids. He knew that the hardest part of the task lay ahead. Coming out by himself hadn't been so bad, but returning with a heavy, frightened child would be another thing. Quig braced himself against the current, supporting Tommy. His lifesaving instruction came back to him quickly.

"Now, Tommy," Quig said urgently, "you listen to every word I say and do exactly what I tell you."

"O.K., Quig, I will." The panic was gone from Tommy's voice now, and Quig felt sure he could count upon obedience. He floated him on his back, squatted down in the water himself, and flung Tommy across his shoulders. In a moment they were on their slow, perilous way to shore. As Quig had feared, the going was very rough. His brother was a solid, muscular seven-year-old, and Quig was bearing his whole

weight, with no water to lighten the load. The footing was so precarious and the current so strong and erratic in the little rapids that Quig wondered if he could manage even the few yards he must go. Without Tommy to steer him straight, it probably would have been impossible. There was no sign of Peggy and the Munson children. He and Tommy were all alone in the emptiness of Dead End Bluff, struggling to get out of the water.

Far away in the village, Quig heard the wail of a siren and wondered wearily where the fire was. He slid into a hole and dunked Tommy. They both came up spluttering. He heard the siren of the village squad car mingled with the sound of the fire engine. They seemed to be coming closer, and Quig thought vaguely, as he made the last part of his trek, that the fire must be somewhere on Bluff Road. Right now he didn't care. All he wanted in the world was to set Tommy down safely at the bottom of Dead End Bluff.

The water was shallower, the current pulled at him less savagely. A few more steps and he would have it made. Tommy had been unbelievably quiet all the way, but now he wriggled on Quig's shoulders and cried, "We're almost back!"

"Hold still," Quig ordered. "Don't upset the works now."

The wail of the sirens seemed to pierce the air above them, and then they were still, and Quig could hear the sound of excited voices, shouting at the top of the bluff. Above them all came Peggy's familiar, high call, "Quig! Are you all right? I've got help!"

She certainly had. As Quig's foot struck the shore and he crawled up onto the narrow little ledge, it seemed to him that half the village must have come to the rescue. He heard the voices of Officer O'Brien and Officer Barry, plus the men of the volunteer fire department. He recognized Mike's deep voice and the higher pitched ones of Joe and Don. Liz and Joy must have come, too—he could hear their squeals.

"We're all right!" Quig called. "We're out of the water."

His first reaction was frustrated anger. Why did she have to call out the police and the fire department, too? This was his problem, and he had solved it himself. Somehow, having all these people around took something away from him. In the first relief of getting back all alone, without help, he forgot that he had sent Peggy flying for aid, and that a little while before in the rapids he had wondered frantically what was taking her so long.

"Shine that spotlight right down the bluff, Mac," called Officer O'Brien to the captain of the fire department. "Now let's set your ladder up, and we'll get those kids up here in no time."

It remained for Tommy to set everybody straight as far as Quig was concerned. Standing in the glare of the spotlight, looking up at the dark bluff above them, he shouted in his high, childish voice.

"Nobody needs to come down here. I fell in the river, that's all, and my brother came down to get me and he carried me out. We can come up the bluff by ourselves."

There was a consultation at the top. Quig could hear them talking in low tones. What to do? He didn't really know, either. His inclination was to finish the job, to climb back up the face of the bluff with Tommy in front of him as he would have had to do if Peggy hadn't arrived with her rescue operation. On the other hand, his anger had cooled, and he realized that Tommy was very tired and certainly wasn't used to climbing around the bluff in the dark. He'd hate to insist upon bringing him up alone, just to look big, and have him fall and break a leg, or worse. There were chances you had to take, and chances you didn't.

While everybody stood pondering, there was the sound of a car rushing toward them on Bluff Road. The driver slammed on the brakes, and Quig heard the door flung open and numerous pairs of feet running to the top of the bluff. He heard his mother's voice with a frantic question, and Peggy explaining. Then his father's voice joined the conversation. Quig relaxed. They were home, and this was the time to leave the decision to them.

In a minute his father came to the edge of the bluff and called down.

"Quig, we've decided that the men will put the ladder down and bring Tommy up. As long as they're here, they might as well do it, and it'll be a lot easier."

The long ladder was lowered carefully over the edge of the bluff, and Mac came down. He settled it firmly at the bottom and said, "Come on, young one, let's go up. Quig, hold it for me, just to make sure, eh?"

He started up the ladder carrying Tommy, who protested every inch of the way. Quig waited, beginning to shiver in the cool of the August evening. Mac had reached the top. Quig knew his mother had gathered her child into her arms when he heard her say, "Oh, Tommy!"

Quig began to search hastily around on the ledge for his pants and shirt, now that the crisis was over. He couldn't be sure where he had come ashore. To his great relief, he came upon them and quickly scrambled into them. In the excitement of the moment, he had forgotten that he was standing in the full glare of the spotlight in his underclothes, soaking wet. At any other time, he would have been terribly embarrassed, but now it struck him as being hilariously funny and he began to laugh in fatigue and reaction to his ordeal.

"I'm coming down for you, Quig," Mac called.

"Oh, no, you aren't," Quig called back, suddenly serious. He would not accept help he didn't need. "If I can drag Tommy out of the rapids all alone, I guess I can climb this ladder by myself. Here I come!"

He climbed the ladder, slowly, carefully, but with perfect confidence. It was his father who waited at the top with firm hand to help him off.

"Well done, Quig!" he said.

"Thanks, Dad," Quig responded. "Next time I'll climb the bluff without the ladder."

AUTHOR

The schools in Minneapolis, Minnesota, where Elizabeth Witheridge and her family live, have an excellent program for blind children. Before she wrote *Dead End Bluff,* Mrs. Witheridge spent almost a year visiting these schools to observe the blind children in their classrooms.

Quig, the main character in the story, is really a combination of two blind boys with whom Mrs. Witheridge became acquainted during her visits. These two boys, plus identical twin girls who had been blind since birth, provided much of the inspiration for the book.

If you enjoyed *Dead End Bluff,* you may also enjoy *Never Younger, Jeannie* or *Jim Penney's Golden Nugget,* two other books written by Mrs. Witheridge. She says that whenever she writes a book, her whole family gets into the act. According to Mrs. Witheridge, her husband and two sons are her best critics.

Mrs. Witheridge was born in Saginaw, Michigan, where she also attended school and later taught kindergarten. After her marriage, she lived in Chicago for several years before moving to Minneapolis.

IN TIME of SILVER RAIN

by Langston Hughes

In time of silver rain
The earth
Puts forth new life again,
Green grasses grow
And flowers lift their heads,
And over all the plain
The wonder spreads
    Of life,
    Of life,
    Of life!

In time of silver rain
The butterflies
Lift silken wings
To catch a rainbow cry,
And trees put forth
New leaves to sing
In joy beneath the sky
As down the roadway
Passing boys and girls
Go singing, too,
In time of silver rain
    When spring
    And life
    Are new.

READING TABLES

Have you ever looked at a timetable to see when you could get a bus from one place to another? Or have you ever checked the box score in a newspaper to find out how your favorite major-league baseball player performed in the game the day before? Bus schedules and baseball-game summaries are tables, and if you have used them, you know that the way facts are arranged in a table makes it possible for you to get the answer to a question quickly.

Many different kinds of information can be presented most effectively and understood most easily when they are given in the form of a table. A series of sentences containing a number of city names and departure and arrival times of dozens of buses would be extremely confusing. This same information seems clear and uncomplicated, however, when it is set up in columns and rows. Reading a table is not the same as reading a story, of course, but it is a skill that you can acquire quickly and one that will save you time and effort.

The table on the opposite page is a simple one, but note how much information it gives you. From the caption, as the title of a table is called, you can usually tell at once whether the table will be useful or of interest to you. For example, if you needed to know what the largest continent is, you could expect to get the answer from a table which has the caption: **Size and Population of the Continents.**

The headings above the columns in a table are also helpful to you because they tell just what kind of information is in each column. In most tables, solid lines are used to set off the headings and to separate columns. Sometimes the rows of items are also separated by solid lines.

Table 1.   Size and Population of the Continents

Name	Area in Square Miles	Population
Asia	16,988,000	1,850,949,000
Africa	11,506,000	303,948,000
North America	9,390,000	290,978,000
South America	6,795,000	161,733,000
Antarctica	5,500,000	—
Europe	3,745,000	614,449,000
Australia	2,975,000	11,251,000

From the table above, you can learn immediately the total number of continents, their names, how large each one is, and how many people live there. If you wanted to know the population of Europe, you would first look down the column with the heading **Name** until you came to *Europe*. Then you would look along that row to the right until you found the figure 614,449,000 in the column headed **Population.**

In the same way, you could compare the size or population of two continents. That is, to learn whether North America or South America is larger, you would find the name of each continent in the first column and, after it, the figure in the same row in the column headed **Area.** Comparing the two figures would tell you which is the larger continent.

In the first two columns of the table above, you can see that the continents appear in decreasing order of size. In other words, the largest continent is listed at the top and the smallest at the bottom. This arrangement cannot be carried out in the third column, however, because the size of a continent does not necessarily determine its population. Look, for instance, at the population figures for Europe and Antarctica. Europe is listed sixth in the first column because it is the next to smallest continent, but it has the second largest population. Antarctica, on the other hand, which is fifth in size and larger than Europe, has no permanent inhabitants at all. If you were interested in comparing the population, but not the size, of the seven continents, you could easily put the third-column figures into numerical order in your mind or on paper. When reading a table like this one, it is important to pay attention to the order in which items are listed in the various columns.

In using a table, you will not always start with the first column. If you wanted to know the name of the smallest continent, for instance, you would begin by looking down the column headed **Area.** Seeing that each figure in that column is smaller than the one above it, you would know that the smallest must be at the bottom and would then look to the left in that row to find the name of the continent.

Did you notice that the figures in the table on page 335 are rounded off to the nearest thousand? It would be impossible to give totals for area or population that are exact to the last square mile or person, and the approximate figures are accurate enough for most purposes.

When there are several tables in a book or an article, they are usually numbered so that they can be referred to without difficulty. Because the table on the preceding page is the first one in this lesson, it is numbered **Table 1.** The second table in the lesson, on the next page, is **Table 2.**

Notice how much the caption of Table 2 tells you. From it you learn that the table gives the names of scientists and inventors only and that it lists only American Negroes. And the word **Some** lets you know that, because of limited space, not every outstanding person in this category has been included.

Notice, too, that from the headings of Table 2 you know what four kinds of facts are given in the four columns. If you wanted

Table 2.
Some Outstanding American Negro Scientists and Inventors

Name	Born	Died	Important Contributions
Banneker, Benjamin	1731	1806	Author and surveyor. Helped map out Washington, D.C.
Carver, George Washington	1864	1943	Researcher. Derived over 300 products from peanut and soybean.
Drew, Dr. Charles R.	1904	1950	Researcher. Perfected modern blood-bank system.
Julian, Dr. Percy	1898	—	Chemist. Created drugs used to treat arthritis and glaucoma.
Lawless, Dr. Theodore K.	1892	—	An internationally known skin specialist.
Matzeliger, Jan	1852	1889	Inventor of lasting machine that revolutionized shoe industry.
McCoy, Elijah	1844	1928	Inventor of devices used to lubricate machinery in motion.
Morgan, Garrett A.	1877	1963	Inventor of gas mask and automatic traffic light.
Williams, Dr. Daniel Hale	1856	1931	Surgeon famous for pioneering in open-heart surgery.
Woods, Granville T.	1856	1910	Inventor of air brake on trains and of electrical equipment.

to see how far back in time the table goes, you would read down the second column for the earliest date. By looking for dashes in the third column, you could discover which of these individuals are still living. In a table like this, you might be most interested in finding out who has been included and what contribution each person has made. In that case, you would probably read only the first and last columns. Suppose, however, that you had heard of Garrett A. Morgan and wanted to know when he lived and what made him famous. You would look for his name in the alphabetical list in the first column and then read the information given in that same row in the other three columns.

If there are many columns in a table and the rows of items are quite close together, it is often difficult to keep your eye on one particular row as you read from left to right. This is especially true of a table like the following one, where there are ten columns containing nothing but figures. Working with such a table is easy, however, when you lay a ruler, a pencil, or even a piece of paper under the row you are looking at, or when you use your finger as a kind of pointer and move it across the row or down the column of figures you are reading.

Table 3 below shows the mileage by airplane between ten large cities. Notice that in this type of table the cities listed alphabetically in the first column also appear alphabetically as headings of the other ten columns. In a mileage table, you must use one city name from the first column and one city name from the headings in order to get the information you want.

Table 3.
Mileage by Air Between Some Major Cities in the United States

City	Boston	Chicago	Cleveland	Detroit	Houston	Los Angeles	New York	Phila.	St. Louis	Wash. D.C.
Boston	—	851	551	613	1,605	2,596	188	271	1,038	393
Chicago	851	—	308	238	940	1,745	713	666	262	597
Cleveland	551	308	—	90	1,114	2,049	405	360	492	306
Detroit	613	238	90	—	1,105	1,983	482	443	455	396
Houston	1,605	940	1,114	1,105	—	1,374	1,420	1,341	679	1,220
Los Angeles	2,596	1,745	2,049	1,983	1,374	—	2,451	2,394	1,589	2,300
New York	188	713	405	482	1,420	2,451	—	83	875	205
Philadelphia	271	666	360	443	1,341	2,394	83	—	811	123
St. Louis	1,038	262	492	455	679	1,589	875	811	—	712
Washington, D.C.	393	597	306	396	1,220	2,300	205	123	712	—

Try finding the distance between Detroit and New York in the following way. First, run the index finger of your left hand down column 1 until you locate *Detroit,* and run the index finger of your right hand across the column headings until you locate **New York.** Then move your left hand along the row in which *Detroit* in column 1 appears, and move your right hand down the column which has **New York** as its heading. Your two fingers should meet at the figure 482, which is the mileage between those two cities.

It doesn't matter which of the two cities you work from in the first column as long as you locate the second city in the headings. To prove this, find the distance between Detroit and New York again, but this time locate *New York* in the first column and **Detroit** in the headings. What figure do you arrive at? It should be 482, the same figure as before. This won't surprise you, because you know that you would travel exactly the same distance whether you went from New York to Detroit or from Detroit to New York.

Discussion

Help your class answer these questions:
1. Why are tables numbered? How are they numbered?
2. What does the caption of a table tell you?
3. How are column headings in a table helpful to you?
4. According to Table 1, Antarctica has the smallest population—none. Which continent has the second smallest population?
5. From Table 1, is North America or South America the larger continent?
6. What contribution made by Dr. Daniel Hale Williams did you learn about in Table 2?
7. From the dates given in Table 2, who was born earlier, Granville T. Woods or George Washington Carver?
8. Using the figures in Table 3, what is the distance by air between St. Louis and Los Angeles?
9. From Table 3, which city is farther from Houston by air, Washington, D.C., or Detroit?

On your own

On a sheet of paper, copy the number and letter of each question that follows and then write your answer to it.

1. According to Table 1:
   a. What is the area of Africa?
   b. Which continent has only a slightly smaller population than Africa?
   c. How does Australia compare in size with the other six continents?
   d. How many continents have a smaller population than South America? Which continents are they?
2. According to Table 2:
   a. What made Dr. Daniel Hale Williams outstanding?
   b. Of the individuals who are listed, two are still living. What are their names?
   c. Which of the men listed was born in the most recent year? What year was it?
   d. What was the name of the person who invented a lasting machine that revolutionized the shoe industry?
3. According to Table 3:
   a. How far is it by air from Boston to Cleveland?
   b. What is the air mileage between Washington, D.C., and Los Angeles?
   c. Which city is closer to Detroit by air, Chicago or Philadelphia?
   d. Which plane trip is longer, from Houston to Cleveland or from St. Louis to Boston?

Checking your work

If you are asked to do so, read one or more of your answers aloud, and explain why you answered as you did. As the other members of the class read their answers, check what you wrote on your paper. Be sure to find out why any mistake you made was a mistake.

HERBERT'S CHEMISTRY SET

*Herbert gets some shocking
results from a chemistry experiment
in this story by Hazel Wilson.*

Herbert had wanted a chemistry set for a long time before his Uncle Horace gave him one for his birthday. "A boy needs to be old enough to follow rules with absolute accuracy before he is old enough for a chemistry set," Uncle Horace told him, and made Herbert promise to make only the experiments described in the booklet that came with the chemistry set. Since there were six hundred and eighty-six experiments described, Herbert could keep busy experimenting quite awhile.

It was a wonderful chemistry set. It had a laboratory-style cabinet with built-in test tube racks, scales to weigh chemicals, a mortar and pestle for pounding things up, an alcohol-lamp blowtorch, several flasks, four beakers, a Bunsen burner, funnels, and all the chemical elements that are not actually dangerous to handle, from actinium to zirconium. When set up, the

chemistry set took up one whole side of the recreation room. Herbert spent many happy hours sitting on a high stool in front of his chemistry cabinet mixing, pounding, heating, cooling, pouring, and having a fine time.

He made perfume for his mother. When she put some on her handkerchief before going to the movies with his father, he asked her if she had spilled some of his hair tonic on her dress. It was a good hair tonic but it smelled terrible, he said. And Herbert made ink that was even harder to wash out of his clothes than real ink. At various times he performed chemical experiments that filled the house with the smells of rotten eggs, a house on fire, a glue factory, a hospital, and a garbage-disposal plant. Herbert learned to make

marvelously strong smells with his chemistry set. Mr. Yadon, Herbert's father, never knew just what he would find his house smelling like when he came home from work at night.

Herbert was not selfish about his chemistry set and invited the members of his club over often. When Pete, Donny, and Chuck helped Herbert perform chemical experiments, the house was so full of fumes of this or that or something else that Mrs. Yadon would go to the grocery store even when she did not need to, just to draw a breath of fresh air.

But Herbert kept his promise to Uncle Horace about performing only the experiments described in the booklet that came with his chemistry set. It was not at all his fault that something most unusual happened to him one afternoon. He was busy pounding up a bit of this, that, or something else in his mortar when he heard the rumble of distant thunder. Herbert was not at all afraid of thundershowers. He rather liked looking at lightning if it was good and bright, and he thought that a good strong crash of thunder was nearly as enjoyable as a cannon cracker during a

Fourth of July celebration. So, although he was working near an open window, which his mother had asked him to do so that some of the smells would go outside, Herbert saw no need of closing the window right away. Then the storm increased and crash-banged like everything, and slanting rain came in the window and began to trickle down the back of the chemical cabinet. Of course, Herbert could not have that. He put down his pestle and was just going to the window to close it when the lightning struck. The crash of thunder that accompanied it shook the house.

It was a flash of freak lightning.

It ran like mischievous fingers over Herbert's chemistry set, breaking a few vials and test tubes, and smashing the mortar in which Herbert just a minute before had been pounding a bit of this, that, and something else. Then the lightning ran around an electric-light cord and went out of the house, leaving a tingling sensation in the air, a strong smell of something burning, and Herbert quite unharmed although considerably stunned.

Mrs. Yadon came running to the recreation room crying, "Herbert, are you all right? Herbert, did you get struck? Speak to me, Herbert."

"Hello, Mother," said Herbert. "Naw, I didn't get struck. Just about got singed though," he said rubbing his arms, which still prickled. "But look what the lightning did to my chemistry set," he mourned, half crying. "If it felt like smashing dishes, why didn't it go up into your china closet and leave my test tubes alone? See, it spoiled all these. And my mortar's smashed to bits. Say, just look at that. It turned the stuff I was mixing bright blue. What do you think of that? It was white powder and now it is blue. That lightning performed a chemical experiment of its own."

Herbert touched the blue powder with his finger. "Ouch, it's still hot," he cried, and put his burned finger into his mouth.

A second later, his mother gave a terrible shriek.

"What's the matter?" asked Herbert, quite bewildered, for his mother was sobbing and taking on so that he knew that something dreadful must have happened. "Did the lightning hurt you? What's the matter with you?"

"Thank goodness you can speak," gasped Mrs. Yadon. "Thank goodness I can at least touch you and you are there," she cried, groping strangely about and catching hold of Herbert so near his right eye that he had to dodge or she would have poked her finger in it.

"Mother, did the lightning blind you?" asked Herbert. "Can't you see me, Mother?"

"Oh, my poor boy, my poor boy," Mrs. Yadon kept saying over and over. "I would have rather been struck blind a dozen times than to have such a dreadful thing happen to my only son."

"I'm all right. Nothing has happened to me," declared Herbert stoutly.

"My poor, poor boy," Mrs. Yadon repeated and led Herbert to a mirror. "I can't believe my eyes," she moaned.

Herbert looked in the mirror. For a few seconds he could not believe his eyes either, for what he saw there, or rather what he did not see there, was so astonishing that it was hardly believable. He saw his brown tweed suit reflected in the glass, his necktie—the green and yellow striped one, and his moccasin-toed shoes. Herbert's clothes looked as usual. The amazing and different thing that Herbert beheld in the mirror was that there was no sign of him in his clothes.

It was like seeing a headless dummy in the glass, a suit of clothes with no boy inside, just a suit of clothes standing upright with one empty sleeve upraised to touch a head that was not there with a hand that was not there.

"Holy cats!" breathed Herbert. "Where am I? What's become of me?"

He looked for a hand and there was no hand to be seen. Yet when he felt one hand with the other, it was there, only out of sight, quite out of sight. "Why, what do you know!" cried Herbert, not knowing yet whether to feel pleased or sad. "I'm invisible. I bet I'm the only invisible boy in the whole world."

"How could such a dreadful thing have happened?" sobbed his mother.

"Aw, don't feel so bad," said Herbert. "It could have been a lot worse. I might have been struck dead."

"Heaven forbid!" sighed Mrs. Yadon.

"Say, I bet I can figure out what happened," said Herbert excitedly. "I was still visible right after the lightning struck. It wasn't until I burned my finger on that blue powder and put it into my mouth that I became invisible. That powder was struck by lightning and I must have tasted a little of it. I remember now that I had an awfully bitter taste in my mouth and I had a funny feeling, just as if I had been hit on the head, only it didn't hurt. Well, what do you know about that?" And Herbert pinched himself a little anxiously to see if he really was still there and had not evaporated entirely while speaking. He was still there all right, only none of him showed. None of him showed at all, even in the brightest sunlight.

Mrs. Yadon telephoned to Herbert's father, but he would not believe her until he came home and saw Herbert's animated, yet apparently empty, clothes. Then Mr. Yadon telephoned three doctors to come at once, and he talked to Uncle Horace by long distance. Uncle Horace usually knew what to do about everything, but this time he said he was not sure what remedy he would advise immediately. He would come just as soon as he could be excused from an important committee meeting of which he was chairman.

Meanwhile, Dr. Brown, Dr. White, and Dr. Gray had arrived. They examined Herbert separately and in consultation. They all agreed that this was the first case of its kind in medical history, but they had quite an argument about which of them was to write it up for the American Medical Society. Finally they had to draw lots, and Dr. Gray won.

Of course, the three doctors prescribed stuff for Herbert to take, and they gave him X-ray treatments, Z-ray treatments, electric shocks (mild, of course), Turkish baths, Swedish massage, and assorted powders and pills that nearly all tasted bitter. But none of the remedies made Herbert the least bit visible again. Dr. Gray, who wore spectacles and had original ideas, even had an electric eel shipped to him. He had Herbert come to his office and pat the eel twelve times every ten minutes for an hour. Nothing happened except that Herbert's arm tingled and by the end of the hour the electric eel seemed much less electric. It even looked quite dim. Dr. Gray was afraid that if Herbert kept on patting it, the eel might catch Herbert's invisibility, which the doctor did not want to happen because the eel was just rented by the day.

Of course, the news of Herbert's invisibility caused an immediate sensation. Town reporters and those from out of town rushed to the Yadon house for interviews. Photographers arrived with cameras. So many of them came that Mr. Yadon had to forbid their entering the house. Yet they still hung around, hiding in the shrubbery. Every time Herbert's tweed suit appeared at the door, there was a click of cameras. This rather pleased Herbert, for he always did like to have his picture in the newspapers. Of course, now none of him showed in the pictures except his clothes, but they were good pictures of his tweed suit.

As fast as they could get there—on foot or by auto, train, or plane—people began to come to see the boy who could not be seen. Mr. Yadon had to refuse to let anyone in the house without a special appointment, or Herbert would have been pinched black and blue by the more skeptical visitors. His father could have made a fortune charging admission to see Herbert, but, of course, Mr. Yadon did not want to do that. Herbert would not have minded being on exhibition for a few hours a day, because he found it exciting to have so much fuss made over him.

When Uncle Horace arrived, he found the Yadon yard full of people packed as thick as sardines in a can. Some of them had been there all night in order to get a good look at the little boy who was not there. Two policemen were stationed in the yard to keep order. At intervals, Herbert would come out on the front porch and wave what looked like an empty sleeve at the waiting people. "How do you do?" he called politely. "I feel very well, thank you. It doesn't hurt at all to be invisible. Good-by, now." Herbert apparently was enjoying the excitement he created when he made one of his appearances.

Uncle Horace put a stop to these personal appearances. He had barbed wire put around the yard and a police guard outside to keep curious visitors from entering. "We must treat this astounding thing in a dignified manner," he said, and he answered only the letters and telegrams from eminent scientists and doctors, except that Herbert insisted that the circus manager be allowed an interview.

Herbert was glad to see the circus manager, who made Herbert a very generous offer if he would join the circus as a performer. "I won't put you in the sideshow with the other freaks—I mean the other attractions like the skeleton man and the bearded lady. You would have a tent of your own with a barker spieling outside to get the folks in to see you—pardon me, I mean to *not-see* you. Folks will fall over each other to hear the world's only invisible boy say a few words and go through a few simple gymnastics. To see an apparently empty pair of black satin tights doing the knee bends would be sensational. You'll be the highest-paid performer in the circus if you come with me, Herbert," said the circus manager.

Herbert was all for accepting the offer, but Uncle Horace agreed with Herbert's parents that he was too young to join the circus.

Of course, Herbert received many other offers of employment. The head of the F.B.I. sent one of his top men to ask Herbert to come to Washington to work for the F.B.I. "Being invisible would be a tremendous advantage in capturing criminals," the F.B.I. man explained, but when Herbert learned that for work of this kind he would have to go about with no clothes on, he refused. Herbert did not think he would be comfortable, especially in cold weather.

And he said no to the diplomat from the State Department who tried to get him interested in Intelligence work for the same reason, even though the diplomat promised that Herbert would be sent only to warm countries. "I'm afraid the mosquitoes would bother me," said Herbert. "Unless the time comes when my country is in great peril, I must refuse your offer."

Two weeks went by. Herbert thoroughly enjoyed the first week of his invisibility. He always did like having a fuss made over him. Yet before the end of the second week, Herbert had had more than enough of being a celebrity. It was like having nothing to eat but cake all the time. At first it seemed wonderful, but after a while he was sick and tired of being so different from other boys. Why, he could not even go to school without a police escort, which he rather enjoyed, especially the sirens. But even that got to be an old story, and the policemen, though pleasant enough, were not Herbert's age and, therefore, not much company for him.

Even in his classroom, Herbert was not safe from sightseers. A special guard had to be kept at all the school entrances, or tourists would come in and stand outside the door of Herbert's classroom, ready to make a rush for him when school was dismissed. One day he lost his necktie and all but two buttons off his suit before he could be rescued from people anxious to grab a souvenir.

And in the classroom, although the teacher kept telling the children to keep their eyes on the blackboard instead of on Herbert's tweed suit, they did not mind her for long. They watched Herbert's clothes so much that nobody learned any lessons. It was partly Herbert's fault, for he could not resist the temptation to wave his coat sleeves and get a laugh by making motions. Whenever he got up to recite, the children all clapped, for he was like a show to them. Finally Herbert's teacher wrote a note telling his parents that his invisible presence was disrupting the whole school and that, for the present, it would be best to let him stay home from school. So Herbert didn't have to go to school. Strangely enough, now that he did not have to go, he found that it wasn't much fun to stay home from school.

All this time, eminent scientists and physicians in the United States and foreign countries were working on the problem of how to make Herbert visible again. Because nothing like this had ever before happened to anybody, nobody knew what to do. Uncle Horace chartered a plane and visited every famous chemical laboratory in the world, carrying a sample of the blue powder that had made Herbert invisible. Chemists experimented with the powder, did all to it that they knew how to do, and still could not account for what it had done to Herbert. One thing they did prove. The blue powder no longer possessed the power to make any man or beast invisible, for when a few grains were fed to a rat and to a man who volunteered to experiment for the sake of science, both rat and man were not affected in any way.

"The mixture of chemicals that the boy had in his mortar had to be tasted immediately after having been struck by lightning in order to cause invisibility," the scientists finally concluded, which was no help at all in bringing Herbert back in sight again.

Uncle Horace came back from visiting the scientific laboratories a little discouraged and fed up with eminent scientists, although he did consent to allow a very few of the most eminent ones to come to interview Herbert. Herbert was always glad to show just what he had been mixing in his mortar that afternoon, but no matter what the scientists did to the this, that, and something else that Herbert had been using in his chemical experiment that afternoon, they could not turn the mixture blue, nor could they change the blue powder back to white. "Apparently there is still a lot that scientists do not yet know about science," Uncle Horace said to Herbert after they had been visited by the most eminent scientists in the country. "I am beginning to suspect that you can be made visible again only through our own efforts, Herbert."

Busy man though Uncle Horace was, he now devoted his entire time to his nephew. He kept the chartered plane and took Herbert for airplane rides, for only in the air could Herbert be rid of autograph hunters.

Every rainy or windy day, when an airplane ride would not be either safe or pleasant, Uncle Horace encouraged Herbert to play with his chemistry set. At first, Herbert was a bit reluctant to conduct any more experiments, for fear that something else might happen to him. But when Uncle Horace promised that he would be on hand, Herbert felt safe to resume his chemical experiments. With Uncle Horace's help, Herbert performed all the experiments from 448 to 637 in his chemical manual, and nothing happened except smoke and smells and an occasional small bang.

One afternoon, Herbert was busy doing experiment 642 when he heard a loud clap of thunder. Looking out the open window, he saw black thunderheads rolling up, and even as he looked, torrents of rain began to fall. Quickly Herbert stopped working on experiment 642. "I'm getting out of here," he told Uncle Horace. "I'm not afraid of thundershowers, but after what happened to me I'm not going to conduct any chemical experiment during a shower. Can you blame me?"

"I certainly can't," said Uncle Horace, "but this time, Herbert, I am urging you to be especially brave. Get away from the open window, by all means, but do not leave the room. I have hoped and prayed for this thunderstorm, for I am now ready to conduct a small experiment of my own."

Of course, Herbert had to show his uncle that he was especially brave, so he did not leave the room. Over at the chemical cabinet, Uncle Horace was working, setting out a mortar into which he poured all the blue powder he had in an

envelope, and arranging certain wires and gadgets that led from the mortar containing the blue powder to a lightning rod that had just recently been installed directly outside the window. "Now if Nature will cooperate, we shall see what we shall see," said Uncle Horace, joining Herbert, who was standing as far away from the chemical cabinet as he could get without leaving the room.

Even as Uncle Horace spoke, there was a flash and a crash and a strong smell of burning. Brave though he was, Herbert would have left the room if Uncle Horace's strong hand had not held him back. "We're not hurt. It's all over. Praise be, the lightning did strike again," cried Uncle Horace. "Quick," he urged, pulling Herbert over to where the mortar containing the blue powder lay in fragments.

"Why, the blue powder isn't blue any more. It's red!" cried Herbert.

"Taste it, Herbert. Taste it," ordered Uncle Horace in such a severe voice that Herbert immediately obeyed. He touched the red powder with a reluctant forefinger and raised his finger to his lips. "It's still hot and it's bitter," he complained. "What's the big idea?"

Uncle Horace suddenly laughed a booming laugh and hugged Herbert hard. "It worked! It worked!" he shouted, for once forgetting his dignity.

"What worked?" Herbert wanted to know, but even before he rushed to a mirror he had seen his hands suddenly appear at the ends of his coat sleeves. "Well, what do you know?" he cried happily, and made a face at himself in the glass. There he was just as he had been a month before, the same

eyes, the same nose, the same ears that stuck out a little and were slightly dirty, because while they had been invisible, his mother had forgotten to tell him to wash his ears—the same all of him.

"Well," said Herbert, grinning at his reflection, "it certainly does seem good to see myself again."

The next week, there was a meeting of eminent scientists to discuss Herbert's remarkable recovery. "I had a hunch," said Uncle Horace, "that if the powder that had been struck by lightning could be struck again, it might prove to be a cure for the condition of invisibility brought about by tasting it while blue. And with the cooperation of Nature, gentlemen, I am thankful to relate that Herbert has been made visible once more." And he had Herbert come out on the platform and bow in order that the eminent scientists could see how he looked when visible.

A few of the eminent scientists wanted Uncle Horace to go on experimenting to see if he could make Herbert invisible again, but Uncle Horace curtly refused. "I shall conduct no further chemical experiments on Herbert," he said firmly.

Herbert's father had to buy a special file to hold all the articles written by scientists about Herbert's strange case of invisibility and his surprising and successful cure. Herbert did not bother to read any of the articles. They were too full of big words. "It didn't hurt at all to be invisible," he would tell people airily. "If so many people hadn't tried to pinch me, I wouldn't have minded it a bit."

AUTHOR

If you enjoyed "Herbert's Chemistry Set" by Hazel Wilson, you'll undoubtedly enjoy reading *Herbert*, the book from which it is taken. Mrs. Wilson has written four other books about Herbert. They are: *Herbert Again, Herbert's Homework, Herbert's Spacetrip,* and *More Fun with Herbert.* She says that many of her ideas for these books were inspired by her son Jerry when he was a young boy. Jerry is now a reporter for a television station in New York City.

Mrs. Wilson is a native of Portland, Maine, but she has lived for many years in the Washington, D.C. area. A former librarian, she has taught classes in children's literature, and she reviews children's books for a Washington newspaper. Mrs. Wilson is often asked to speak to children in grades four to six. She feels that many of the boys and girls she meets are a little like Herbert.

People often ask Mrs. Wilson why she writes books for children. Her answer is a simple one. She says it's because she loves books and children. In addition to the Herbert books, Hazel Wilson has written several other books for children. They include *His Indian Brother, Jerry's Charge Account,* and *Story of Lafayette.*

YOUR SENSES CAN FOOL YOU

The Deceptive Bobby Pin

Bend open a bobby pin until the two ends are about an inch and a half apart. Have a friend close his eyes while you press the points of the bobby pin against his forearm.

*See if he can tell you when **both** points are touching his arm, and when only **one** end of the pin is touching his skin. You'll be really surprised when you try it. Believe it or not, he'll be unable to tell the difference.*

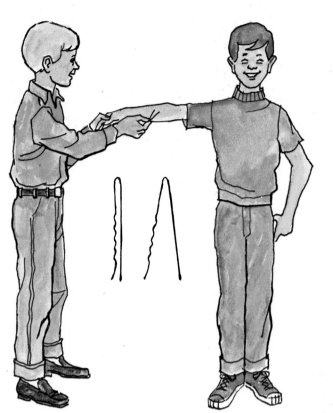

The Floating Hot Dog

*Hold out your two index fingers horizontally, and place the tips of them together. Hold them about six inches in front of your eyes. Instead of looking at the fingers, however, look **past** the fingers, focusing your eyes on the opposite wall of the room.*

Now separate your fingertips about half an inch. A small hot dog will appear, floating in the air midway between your fingertips.

355

THE WOLF AND THE FOX

A foolish fox once made friends with a wolf.
With his silky brush and pointed nose,
he fancied himself a fine smart fellow,
and hardly knew at first which way to look
he was so vain of his new company.
But he soon found out that his new friend
was not in love with him for his own sweet sake only,
and that *being* a wolf, a wolf he *was*. For one thing,
he was a greedy glutton and could never eat enough,
and next, he had no manners.
"And what's for supper tonight?" he would say, his white
teeth glinting in the moon. "Bones! Bones! Again! Lor',
friend Fox, if you can't get me anything really worth eating,
I shall soon have to eat *you*." This was an old joke now, but
even though he grinned as he said it, his sharp fangs and
bloodshot eyes looked none too pleasant.

As for the fox, he smiled on one side of his face, but not
on the other. "Well, friend Wolf," he said, "keep up your
spirits. There's a farmyard over the hill where some plump
young lambs are fattening. Softly now, and away we go!"

So off they went together. When they reached the farmyard,
the fox sneaked in through the gate, snatched up one of the
lambs, leapt over the stone wall, and carried it off to the wolf.

After which, he trotted
round to the henhouse
to get his own supper
in peace. But when the wolf
had finished off his lamb —
leaving not so much as a bone
for his friend to pick —
he felt hungrier than ever,
and determined to slip away
himself and get the other.

But he was so clumsy in scrabbling over the stone wall of
the farmyard that the old mother sheep heard him, and began
bleating aloud in the darkness. At this, the farmer, who was
sitting in his kitchen, ran out with his dog and a cudgel,
and managed to give the wolf such a drubbing as he climbed
back over the wall, that he came creeping back to the fox as
wild with pain as he was with rage.

"A nice thing *you've* done," he said to the fox. "I went to
fetch another lamb, and I'm beaten to a jelly."

"Well," said the fox, "one's one and two's two, but enough
is as good as a feast." And he thought of the tasty young
pullet he had stolen for his own supper.

Next day they decided to be getting off into country where they were less well known. After a pleasant afternoon's journey, they found themselves on the edge of a small green coppice basking in the sun. The wolf stretched himself out and soon fell asleep. He woke up as surly as a bear with a sore head.

"Come, rouse, friend Fox! Supper!" he bawled. "What's for supper? No more lamb tonight. I'd sooner eat *you*!"

The fox trembled with rage, but he answered him civilly and said, "I seem to smell pancakes, rich pancakes. Squat here awhile, friend Wolf, and I'll see what I can do."

He slipped off and away to the other side of the wood, and came to a house from whose brick chimneys a faint smoke was wreathing up into the evening air, laden with so sweet and savory an odor of pancakes that the fox lifted his nose into the air and snuffed and snuffed again. Then first he crept this way, and then he crept that way, and at last he stole in through an open window, and so into the pantry. Leaping up on to a shelf, he carried off at least six of the pancakes.

The wolf swallowed them down without so much as a thank'ee, and champed for more. The glutton then asked the fox which way he had gone. The fox told him.

"You'll know the house by the smoke," he said, "and the window is by the water barrel. But step quiet, my friend, if go you must, for I heard voices." The greedy wolf, thinking that if the fox came with him to the house, he would expect a share of the pancakes that were left, at once scuffled off alone into the night to finish the dish.

But he made such a hullabaloo in the pantry as he went sprawling along the shelf, upsetting a great cooking crock as he did so, that the farmer and his wife, and the friends who had been supping with them, heard the noise and came rushing in, and gave him such a basting that he hardly escaped with his life.

When he had licked his bruises and got some breath into his body again, he came snarling back to the fox, and blamed *him* for his beating. The fox coughed and turned his head aside. He could hardly speak for rage and contempt. However, the duck he himself had supped off was still sweet in memory, so he answered the wolf smoothly, reminding him that he had been given a fair warning. "Besides," said he, "as I've said before, enough is as good as a feast, friend Wolf, and with *some* sauces, much better."

Yet, even now, the wolf had not learned his lesson. For, a very few evenings afterwards, though he could only limp along on three legs, and every bone in his body ached, he turned sullenly on his friend the fox, and said, "Friend Fox, I'm sick and tired of you. You've no more wits than a rabbit. *Sly*, indeed! Now, see here. If before that moon up there has climbed an inch in the sky, you don't get me a meat meal, a tasty meal, and plenty of it—a supper worth a gentleman's eating, I'm saying—then it will surely be the last of you, for I'm *done* with your shilly-shallying."

The fox trembled and said, "Softly, softly, friend Wolf, why lose your temper? I do my best. This very morning I heard that the human who lives by the stream on the other side of the hill yonder has been killing a pig, a fat pig, a very fat pig, a pig *stuffed* with fatness. And the salt pork of that pig is packed in a barrel in the human's cellar. Ah, I see your mouth watering. Come, we will go together."

"Why, yes," said the wolf, "and you shall keep watch while I eat."

So the fox led him off by a green ride through the woods and over the crest of the hill, and by a cart-track, till at last they came down to a mill. It was a clear moonlight night, with a sparkle of frost in the air. And as it chanced, there was a small, round-topped outside little door under the wall of the house that led into the cellar. The fox pushed up its latch, paused, sniffed, listened, and sniffed again.

His green eyes glistened like fireballs, as he turned his sharp muzzle and looked back at the wolf. "Follow," he said, "and do not so much as grin or gruff. The human of this house has a gun."

The wolf, being overfed and overfat, only just managed to scramble through the doorway. But at last he followed the fox into the cellar and was soon guzzling away at the barrel of salted pork.

"Tell me, friend Fox," he said, glancing over his shoulder, his jaws dripping, "why do you keep sniffing and snuffing about like that? Restrain yourself. It vexes me, it annoys me. How can I feed in comfort with you fidgeting and fretting? Keep still, and you shall, perhaps, have a gobbet or two for yourself by and by. All depends on what I leave!"

"Gobble on, gobble on," said the fox meekly. "There's plenty of time for me. But I warn you. Don't make a noise, and don't eat too heartily!"

"Ah," said the wolf, "you thought this fat, luscious feast of pork was for you, did you? And after all my pains in finding it! Have no fear, greedy one, there won't be much left when *I've* finished with it."

At this, with a stroke of his paw and a heave of his shoulder, he turned the great salty tub clean over on the stones of the cellar. A fine clatter it made.

Indeed, the miller, who was at that moment shaving himself in a looking-glass, hearing this noise in his cellar, supposed for a moment there was an earthquake. Then he snatched up his blunderbuss, and with the soapsuds still foaming on his cheek, came clumping down the steep stone steps into the cellar.

At first sound and whiff of him, the fox was out through the hole at a bound, and in a moment or two his friend the wolf, stricken with terror, was struggling hard to follow him. But the greedy guzzler had so puffed and swilled himself out with his feast of pork that, wriggle and wrench as he might, he could not squeeze through the hole. So there he stuck. And the miller, although he had lost a good half of his pickled pork, at least gained a thick, warm wolf's skin in exchange.

Meanwhile, the fox on the crest of the hill, hearing the roar of the blunderbuss, shivered a little, then danced a little dance all to himself in the moonlight. There and then he made up his mind that his next friend should be neither wolf nor glutton, but of his own size and liking, and one with a brush.

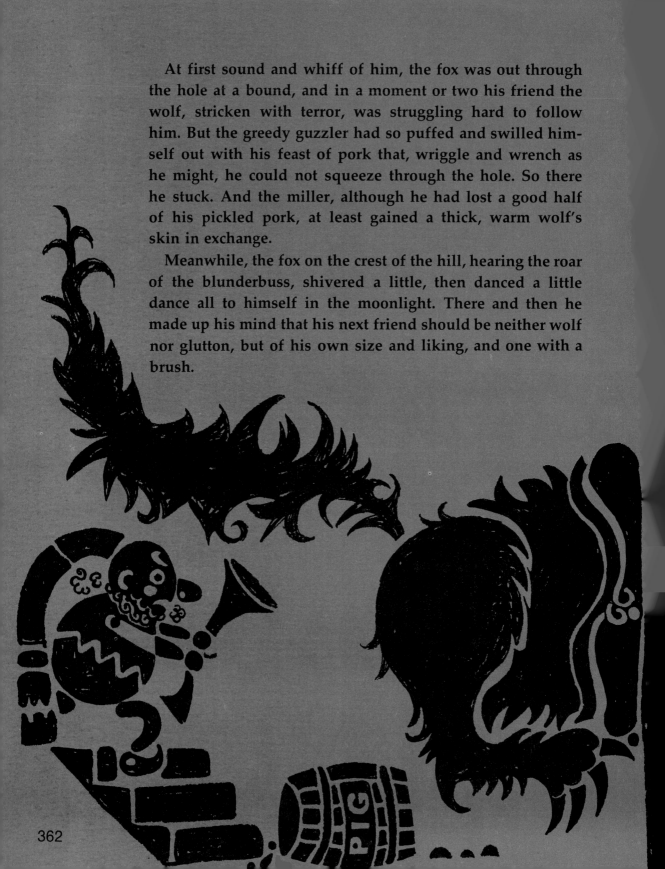

AUTHOR

Walter de la Mare once said, "What we see and hear is only the smallest fraction of what is." He loved to write tales about the part that we don't see and hear—tales about the unknown and about the dreamy, enchanted worlds of fairies, mermaids, elves, and talking animals.

Mr. de la Mare was born in England in the little village of Charlton in Kent. He was a shy, dreamy boy and, as a result, his school days were not very happy. As a young man, he spent eighteen years working for an oil company. Mr. de la Mare found the work so boring that he spent time at his desk composing stories and poems. Then, and for a number of years after, his writings began to appear in magazines under the name Walter Ramal, the pen name he used. At the age of thirty-five, he was able to retire and devote most of his time to writing until his death in 1956.

"The Wolf and the Fox" is from Walter de la Mare's collection of stories entitled *Animal Stories.* Some of his other books are *Tales Told Again, Bell and Grass, The Magic Jacket,* and *Peacock Pie.*

OFF TO HIS DEN 'O

by George Laycock

The red fox is a tricky, medium-sized, doglike animal that doesn't care at all what you think of him. He eats well, wears a beautiful coat, is good to his family, and has a sly sense of humor. And regardless of the fact that men and boys are always trying to take away his fancy coat, the red fox has prospered.

He was living here when the white man came. But the people who study such things believe that many of our red foxes today

descended from those brought over from England a century ago to run before the hounds. The red fox has increased as the country was settled. He is not an animal of the great forest. He lives better near civilization, not in the barnyard, but within reach.

There is an old story that tells how foxes get rid of fleas, and whether true or not, the story does indicate the respect men have for the intelligence of the red fox. Fleas often make life miserable for foxes. But the fox,

so the story goes, learned to outsmart the flea. He comes down to the water's edge carrying in his mouth a piece of bark. He swims out into the millpond and, with the bark still in his mouth, gradually submerges until only his nose sticks out. The fleas avoid drowning by moving out of the fox's fur and onto the piece of bark. The fox, greatly relieved, scrambles out of the water and scampers off through the woods, leaving the fleas to paddle their own canoe. Naturalists insist this never happens. But it sounds like something every fox should know.

Fox hunters agree that the fox is smart. They may deny that he is smarter than their hounds, but he is. There are times when the fox seems to enjoy the chase almost as much as the hounds. Rather than dashing for the nearest hideout, he may pass den after den and keep the chase alive.

He has a top speed of about twenty-six miles an hour, but he is not a strong runner. In a showdown fight with a hound, the fox, which weighs in at about ten pounds, is a goner. His strategy is to keep the contest from coming to blows. He does this with brain, not brawn. He will wade in streams, cross on logs, or run along the top of a stone wall or rail fence. And once the hounds are thoroughly confused, the fox may offer his yapping laugh from over the hill.

But when the fox is not being chased by hounds, he has plenty to keep him busy. Family duties demand a lot of his time. The male and female are usually lifelong partners. The young, five or six to the litter, come in March or April. For the first ten days, with eyes still closed, they look like fuzzy kittens. While they stay in the den for five or six weeks, the vixen keeps her mate outside. But he is still the family hunter, and he brings to the door of the den a variety of treats—fish, mice, snakes, turtles, insects, small birds, poultry—and leaves them for his family. His eating habits are both good and bad from the farmer's point of view. So farmer and fox usually ignore each other, until the pullets begin to disappear.

When her family is five or six weeks old, the female lets them go outdoors and play in the warm sunlight. There they romp and engage in foxy little games until mama barks and herds them back inside. If you happen on a family of foxes at this moment, the old mother may go house-hunting. She moves her whole

family, one at a time, cat-fashion, to a new den. Our fox researcher observed a fox that moved her family a mile. A week later she moved again, this time a half-mile. Maybe she was tired. She made four moves before she finally gave the fox-watcher the slip and settled down unmolested to raise her young.

The fox, wary though he is, may show real courage in defending the family. One observer reports watching from seventy-five yards while a family of kits played before the den. The unsuspecting vixen finally ambled off in his direction and didn't discover him until she was only ten feet away. She dashed to a ridge a hundred yards distant and barked excitedly for the kits to go below. Busy at play, however, they ignored her.

The man moved toward the young foxes to test the mother's reaction. Three of the kits dashed into the den, but the fourth one stayed outdoors. Such disobedience was more than a mother could bear. She dashed right past the observer, cuffed her offspring into the den, and dashed off again.

The fox family stays together until fall. During the last part of the summer, the young go along on hunting trips and study their parents' techniques in searching out food with the aid of their sensitive noses, eyes, and ears.

Well before the cold of winter, usually by mid-October, the young foxes are practically full grown. Their coats are smooth and immaculate, reddish above, white below, black tips on feet and nose, and white tip on the tail—a striking color scheme.

The tail is especially important to the fox. It is his counterbalance when he makes swift turns while pursuing food. It is his

blanket on cold winter nights. When he lies down, he drapes the long, beautiful brush over himself.

You may or may not like the colorful and dashing red fox, depending perhaps on whether you hunt foxes or raise chickens. But the fox, it appears, is here to stay. And surely the countryside would be less interesting without him. So the wisest counsel is to accept the fox for what he is, tie a watchdog on the turkey range, and keep the shotgun available as a final solution.

Outsmart the red fox if you can and live with him if you can't. He'll do as much for you. And he'll keep you alert, for the fox is nimble and the fox is quick, and the old English folk tune tells it well with "John, John, the gray goose is gone and the fox is off to his den 'o."

George Laycock was born in Zanesville, Ohio, and now lives in Cincinnati, Ohio, with his wife and children. As a boy, he hoed corn, pitched hay, and milked cows on his father's farm. Later he worked in a grocery store and for a railroad in order to earn money to go to college.

In college, Mr. Laycock studied wildlife management. After three years, his college studies were interrupted by World War II. He served with the U.S. Army in Europe, but returned to school after the war to complete his college education.

Following college, Mr. Laycock worked for a farm magazine publisher in Cincinnati. But after five years, he gave up that job in order to spend all of his time writing his own stories. Since then he has written hundreds of stories and articles, most of them about nature, camping, fishing, or conservation. Four of his books about animals are: *Never Trust a Cowbird; Big Nick*, a story about a black bear; *Whitetail*, a story about a whitetail buck; and *Never Pet a Porcupine*, from which the article you have just read was taken.

ASK A SILLY QUESTION...

Tracy: What has eighteen legs and catches flies?
Casey: A baseball team.

Milly: Why did Humpty Dumpty have a great fall?
Tilly: To make up for a miserable summer.

Lamb: Where do sheep get their hair cut?
Sam: In a baa-baa shop.

Fido: If a puppy loses his tail, where can he go for another?
Felix: To a retail store.

READING MAPS

A map is a drawing that shows all or part of the earth's surface. Almost everyone uses a map at one time or another. Travelers use maps to find out where they are and where they want to go. Pupils often use maps in their study of history and geography to locate such things as cities, states, countries, and continents.

But maps may be used to show many things besides the location of a place. For example, a map can answer such questions about a state as: How does it compare in size with other states? Does it lie on the coast or inland? Does it have any major rivers flowing through it? What is its capital city? A map provides a great deal of information about its subject, but the amount of information that you can learn from any map depends on your ability to read that map.

Obviously it would be impossible to draw a map of a country, state, or even a city the same size as that place really is; therefore, the area shown on a map must be drawn in a much smaller size. In order to be accurate, a map must be drawn to **scale.** Scale means the relation between the actual size of something and its size in a picture or model. Look at the map of the state of Iowa on the next page. Notice that the scale of that map is shown at the lower left-hand corner. The scale is shown by means of a bar on which distances have been marked off. You can see that the scale is labeled *Scale of Miles,* so the distances marked 50, 100, and 150 on the scale represent distances of 50 miles, 100 miles, and 150 miles on the earth's surface.

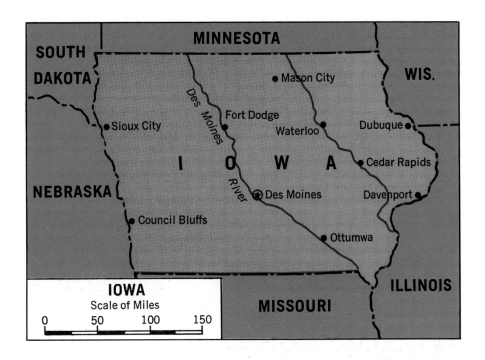

A map's scale makes it possible for you to determine the real distance on the earth's surface between any two points shown on that map. Suppose, for example, you want to use the map of Iowa to find what the distance is between the cities of Waterloo and Cedar Rapids. One good way to do this is to lay a piece of paper flat on the map with one edge of the paper touching the two points that represent Waterloo and Cedar Rapids. Then mark the paper at each of those points like this:

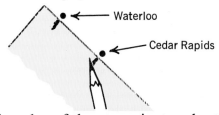

Then place the edge of the paper just under the scale of miles like this:

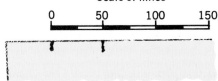

Notice that the first mark, at the left, is placed directly under the **0** mark on the scale. By looking directly above the second mark, you can determine from the scale the distance between Waterloo and Cedar Rapids. You can see the scale shows that the distance between those two cities is about 50 miles. Use that method now to find the approximate distance between Des Moines and Davenport on the same map.

Some maps have a different kind of scale. Look at the scale shown on the map of Kansas on the next page. That scale shows that 1 inch on the map equals 88 miles on the earth's surface. If you want to find the distance between any two points on the map, simply use a ruler to measure the number of inches between the two points and multiply that number by 88. For example, the distance on the map between Hutchinson and Topeka is 1½ inches. By multiplying 1½ by 88, you will find that the approximate distance between those two cities is 132 miles. Use that method now to find the approximate distance between the cities of Liberal and Kansas City.

It is easy to find direction on a map. On most maps, north is toward the top of the map, south is toward the bottom, east is toward the right side of the map, and west is toward the left side. On some maps there is a picture of a compass, called a compass rose, or an arrow which tells you where north is located on the map.

Through the use of **map symbols,** many kinds of information can be shown on a single map. Map symbols are used to stand for natural features of the land such as rivers and mountains. Symbols are also used to stand for man-made features such as cities and railroads. Most maps have a **key** or **legend** that explains what each of the symbols shown on the map represent.

Look at the legend shown on the map of Kansas. You can see that it shows three different symbols for cities. One symbol stands for the state capital, another for cities having a population over 100,000, and the third for other important cities and towns. Can you decide what city is the capital of Kansas?

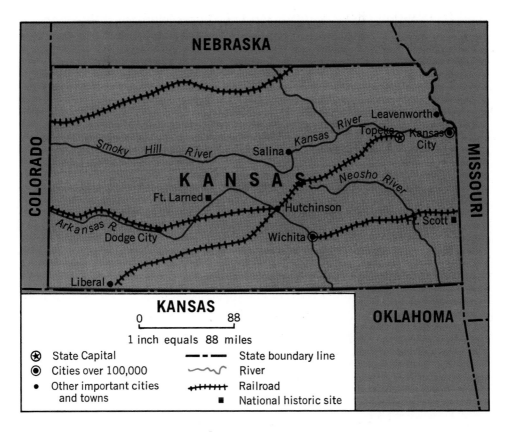

What is one city that has a population over 100,000? What is one other important city that does not have a population over 100,000?

Find the symbol in the legend that represents state boundary lines. Can you find the boundary line between Kansas and Nebraska? What are the names of the other states that border Kansas?

The maps of Iowa and Kansas used in this lesson are **political maps.** Political maps show political divisions of the earth's surface, such as countries and states.

Maps that show landforms such as mountains, hills, and plains are called **physical maps.** The map of the United States shown on the next page is a physical map. Notice that different colors are used to show what the surface of the land is like. The map legend shows what kind of landform is represented by each color. What kind of land is represented by the green areas on the map? By the dark brown areas?

Political maps and physical maps are only two of the many different kinds of maps which give special or general information about the parts of the earth's surface that they show. Whenever you use any map, first read its title to determine what the map is showing. Then see if the map has a legend. If it does, study it carefully to learn what each of the symbols used on the map represents. The map's scale is usually shown in the legend. Even if a map does not have a legend, its scale is usually shown somewhere on the map. When you know what the map is showing, what its scale is, and what all the map symbols mean, you should be able to read that map easily.

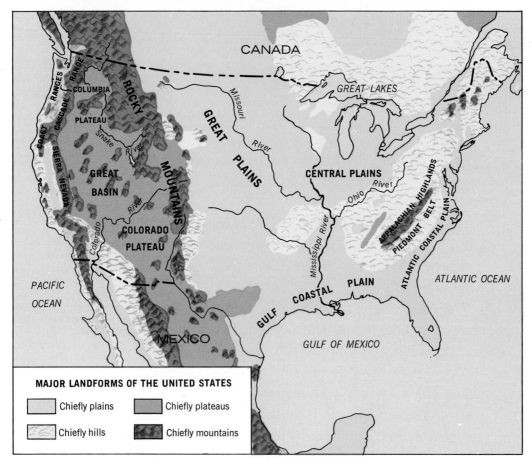

MAJOR LANDFORMS OF THE UNITED STATES

Chiefly plains | Chiefly plateaus
Chiefly hills | Chiefly mountains

Discussion

Help your class answer these questions:

1. What does a map's scale tell you?
2. What is the approximate distance in miles between Liberal, Kansas and Kansas City, Kansas?
3. How can you tell direction on a map?
4. How does a map's legend, or key, help you to read that map?
5. What are the names of the states that border Kansas? What are the names of two rivers that flow through Kansas?
6. What is a political map? What is a physical map?

On your own

Use the three maps shown in this lesson to help you answer the questions that follow. Copy the number of each question on a sheet of paper, and then write your answer to it.

1. What is the approximate distance in miles between Council Bluffs, Iowa and Des Moines, Iowa?
2. What is the approximate distance in miles between Hutchinson, Kansas and Leavenworth, Kansas?
3. What are the names of two cities shown on the map of Kansas that have a population over 100,000?
4. What cities are connected to Hutchinson, Kansas by railroad?
5. Near what cities shown on the map of Iowa does the Des Moines River flow?
6. Are most of the mountains and plateaus in the United States located in the eastern, central, or western part of the country?
7. Is the land in the central part of the United States mostly hills, plains, or mountains?

Checking your work

If you are asked to do so, read aloud some of your answers. Check your paper as others read their answers. If you made a mistake in any, be sure to find out why it was a mistake.

THE EARNED NAME

by Shannon Garst

Before an Indian boy was given a man's name by his tribe, he first had to prove that he was a man. Until he earned his man's name, he was called by his childhood name. In this story, Shannon Garst tells how a very famous Indian earned his proud name.

As the hunters rode into the Oglala (ahg′lah-luh) village, laughing and jabbering, the Indian women came out to meet them and ran beside their horses. Has-ka's sister, Laughing-One, and his stepmother, Gathers-Her-Berries, ran beside his horse and chattered like magpies over his kill.

Reaching camp, the women seized the meat and threw the hunks onto beds of leaves. Then they deftly sliced it into strips that they threw over pole racks to dry, out of reach of the dogs.

That night, the campfires sputtered and blazed as the buffalo fat dripped onto them. The air was savory with fine smells of roasting hump and ribs. The Oglalas ate until they were stuffed. Never had food tasted so good to Has-ka. The fact that he had helped provide meat for the camp made him feel pleasantly important.

He purposely walked through the camp to see if he would be noticed. He was. Men pointed to him and said, "There goes Has-ka. His arrow brought down a buffalo. He was the youngest one on the hunt." It was very agreeable to be pointed out and noticed this way.

When the Oglalas had eaten so much that they could not cram down another mouthful, they danced to the throbbing drums until the food was jounced down enough so that they could eat some more. Has-ka ate and danced with them. He was aware of No-Water's glowering, envious glances upon him, but this only increased his feeling of triumph. The older boy, who was Has-ka's rival, had gone along on the hunt, but only as one of the boys who led a pack horse on which to bring back the meat. He had had no part in the kill, and no one after the hunt had pointed him out as he walked through the village.

Has-ka gorged himself and danced until he grew so sleepy that he crawled off to his sleeping robes. However, he was up at dawn the next morning, eager for more excitement.

Mock buffalo hunts were always a favorite pastime of Sioux (soo) youngsters. After one of the real hunts, there were often buffalo calves which had been unable to keep up with the herd after it had been stampeded, and so were left behind on the plains. It was the delight of the boys to chase these calves, shooting at them with the blunt arrows they used in their games.

Has-ka, filled with elation over his first buffalo hunt, joined in the noisy horseback chase of one of these young calves. His pony, Strongheart, was the first to catch up with it. With a yell of triumph, the boy shouted, "I, Has-ka the buffalo hunter, will ride this calf!"

Leaning over, he grabbed a handful of the woolly hair of the hump and threw himself onto the calf's back. More frightened than ever by this new terror, the young buffalo increased his speed so that the Indian boys' ponies could scarcely keep up. But what they lacked in speed, they made up for in yelling as they gave chase.

The calf suddenly stopped running and tried by bucking to rid itself of the strange and frightening thing clinging to its back. Has-ka found this change of pace not at all to his liking. His head was rammed down between his shoulders. With each jump that jounced him first to one side, then to the other, he thought he could not stick on, but he righted himself and managed. His companions were not going to

be given a chance to laugh at him. He must not lose the importance he had gained. Most of all, he dreaded giving No-Water an opportunity to ridicule him. Once he was tipped clear over to the side of the calf. It was only the realization of how his comrades would whoop with glee if he were thrown that gave him the determination to right himself and hang grimly on.

Gradually the bucking eased off, then ceased, when the calf became tired.

"I, Has-ka, did ride the buffalo calf!" he cried, raising his hand in triumph.

"Has-ka did ride the buffalo calf!" his companions chanted.

"I, Has-ka, will ride the buffalo calf into the village!" he shouted.

"*Hoka hey! Hoka hey!*" his friends cried, crowding their ponies close to the buffalo calf and driving it toward the Oglala camp. The riderless Strongheart trotted at the rear of the yelling horde.

Drawn by the shouts of the boys, the people came from their tepees to see the procession led by young Has-ka riding the buffalo calf.

"Has-ka did ride the buffalo calf!" his friends shouted.

The warrior Hump stood in front of his lodge laughing at the sight. "The buffalo calf seems too tame a mount for you, my friend," he said.

"He was wild enough out there on the hills," young Hump said. "You should have seen Has-ka ride. I thought the calf's bucking would snap his head off as we snap off the head of a grouse."

"It was easy," Has-ka said modestly. A new hope, however, was born within him that his people would now give him a man-like earned name such as Rides-the-Buffalo-Calf instead of the one he so detested.

But the next day he was still called Has-ka.

A few days later, No-Water raced through the village shouting, "*Che-hoo-hoo! Che-hoo-hoo!* All who are brave and strong, line up for che-hoo-hoo."

This was a wrestling game in which the Sioux boys chose sides, each boy picking his own opponent. When a wrestler's shoulders were forced to the ground, he was "dead."

Young Hump was one of the leaders, and No-Water, as usual, was the other. Hump chose Has-ka to be on his side. Has-ka looked over the "enemy" line to pick out someone about his own size and weight to challenge.

He was startled when he heard No-Water shout his own name.

"I, No-Water," the enemy leader yelled, "do challenge the One-Who-Cries-When-the-Wasps-Sting-Him."

The older boy could not have chosen a surer way of arousing Has-ka to anger than with this almost-forgotten taunt. Sudden fury boiled through his veins. Yet he was no fool. No-Water, who was larger and heavier, had every chance of winning. But, of course, he had to accept the challenge or be disgraced in the eyes of his comrades.

Soon enemy was upon enemy, and the ground was covered with writhing, struggling pairs. Has-ka braced himself as No-Water seized him. He fought with every ounce of strength that was in him. When his breath rasped in his throat and he was so exhausted that every muscle felt limp, he gritted his teeth and kept on struggling and straining, until unknown reserves of strength came to his help. But grit and determination were not sufficient against superior strength and weight.

At last, when many shoulders were pinned to the ground, the victors pretended to take the scalps of those whom they had defeated. It was not until most of the pairs had ended their struggles that No-Water managed to throw Has-ka and leap upon him to pin his shoulders to the ground. According to the rules of the game, that was supposed to be the end of it except for the pretended scalping, but No-Water knelt on Has-ka's shoulders while his thumbs pressed the beaten boy's windpipe.

Has-ka's breath came out with a gurgling groan—almost a cry. His good friend, He-Dog, pulled No-Water off.

The che-hoo-hoo winners danced the victory dance about the defeated enemy who hunched sullenly in the center of the ring. No-Water pointed triumphantly to Has-ka and shouted, "*Hopo!* I, No-Water, did beat my enemy, He-Who-Cries-When-the-Wasps-Sting. And I did make him cry out again. Has-ka has not the brave heart! Has-ka is a girl!"

The beaten boy's spirits sank to his moccasins. He had thought he was making headway in gaining the respect of his comrades. Now, even though he had done his best, he had disgraced himself again. He had given his rival another chance to gloat over him. Why did the older boy hate him so? Why did he always try to belittle him before his companions?

Disgraced and unhappy, Has-ka shunned his comrades until an exciting event made him forget his personal troubles.

An unknown disease had swept through the pony herd the previous winter, and there was talk of the need of new horses. Has-ka listened eagerly. He hoped that a pony-stealing expedition was afoot.

The easiest method of acquiring new horses, and the one the Sioux liked best because of the excitement it afforded, was to creep at night into some camp of their enemy, the Crows, and drive their tamed horses away. But now the Crows were far beyond the Big Horns, so the Oglalas must round up wild horses to replenish their herds. This method was harder work, for the horses so caught must be broken,

and the Sioux would be denied the sly pleasure of besting the enemy Crows.

An excited longing swept through Has-ka as he listened to the plans for the wild horse hunt. He made up his mind to go along.

Nearly all of the men, and some of the boys who were old enough, joined the wild horse hunt. Scouts rode out ahead toward the sand hills to see if they could locate a herd of wild horses. After riding for nearly half a sun, they gave the blanket signal from a hilltop that they had discovered a herd in the valley below. The Indians scattered, circling the valley, but staying out of sight of the horses. Has-ka was riding Strongheart. He quivered with excitement as his group waited beneath the brow of the hill for the signal to advance.

When the surround was complete, several of the hunters on the south side rode over the hill yelling. The wild horses stampeded in the opposite direction, where Has-ka and his companions were waiting. Some of the hunters strung out across their path. The horses galloped in another direction only to have more hunters block their way. Finding every direction of escape closed to them, the frightened, bewildered animals started circling. When they were milling in a compact bunch, the hunters closed in on them and started thrusting their long sticks with hair-rope loops over the heads of the horses they wanted to capture.

Has-ka caught sight of a pony the color of a red autumn leaf. It carried its small, well-shaped head high, nostrils distended. Its eyes were wide open, but there was more a look of fight in them than of fear. The instant he saw the red stallion, Has-ka knew that it was a spirited and intelligent animal, and he wanted it with all of his heart. So also did Lone-Bear and he thrust out his loop trying to get it over the animal's head, but missed. Has-ka thrust out his loop, but he missed, too, for even though the red horse was frightened, he was wise and wary.

Finally, Lone-Bear gave up with a grunt of disgust and concentrated his efforts on a less crafty animal, but no other would satisfy Has-ka. Already some of his comrades were riding toward home trailing their mustangs, which they called crazy horses, tied to the tails of their tame ponies.

At last Has-ka's loop settled over the neck of the red horse. With a yell of triumph he jerked on the willow pole, drawing the loop tight. The animal reared and snorted, but it could not rid itself of the thing around its neck that was fast choking its breath from it.

Has-ka edged Strongheart close to the wild pony, and then he did a daring thing. He threw himself onto the red pony's back, with nothing in the world with which to control it but the hair loop around its neck.

With a shrill whinny of rebellion, the red horse broke loose from the herd and galloped into the open, bucking, rearing, turning, twisting, omitting none of the tricks a wild horse knows, in an effort to dislodge its rider. But Has-ka clung to its mane, tightening the noose around its neck when necessary, but giving the magnificent animal its head as much as possible. A wild sense of elation swept through the boy. He yelled and his heels pounded the sides of the wild horse. He would ride this horse and finally conquer him.

The hunters stopped trying to capture mustangs to watch the performance that went on all over the hillside between Has-ka and the wild horse. Soon the horse was flecked with foam, and finally it stood with drooping head and heaving sides, too spent to struggle longer. It recognized a master.

Has-ka was spent, too. Yet a thrill of triumph swept through him. He had conquered this splendid beast. Loosening his noose, he reached forward and, grasping an ear, he

turned the pony's head, his heels pounding its sides. Slowly the red pony obeyed his master's will and stumbled in the direction Has-ka wanted to go.

When Has-ka, astride the horse he had conquered, rode up to his companions, they shouted, "He has ridden a crazy horse! *Tashunka-Witko!* Crazy Horse! Crazy Horse! His name shall be *Tashunka-Witko!* Crazy Horse!"

The boy's heart beat faster. At last he had an earned name —and a splendid one. It was the name of his father, but one that he himself had earned. To the Indians, the name meant an untamed, splendid horse of great spirit and courage. He could not have earned a finer name, even if he had chosen it.

Young Crazy Horse grew up to become one of the greatest of Indian leaders. You can learn more about the life of this great Sioux Indian chief by reading Shannon Garst's book CRAZY HORSE, *from which this story was taken.*

AUTHOR

Shannon Garst says that she has written over forty books, but that she considers her greatest achievements to be her three children and now a crop of lively grandchildren who keep her viewpoint young. When her daughter had a light case of scarlet fever, Mrs. Garst also had to be quarantined. It was then that she got her first book written.

Mrs. Garst was born in Ironwood, Michigan, and has lived in Denver, Colorado, and Hood River, Oregon. Most of her life, however, has been spent in Douglas, Wyoming. There Mrs. Garst felt that she was living in an area of the country that was rich in history. She wanted to share her knowledge of some of the famous people who lived in that area. Most of her books have been biographies of men whose names have earned a place in our history. Other books written by Shannon Garst have been fictional stories based on her own childhood.

MUSTANGS—THE WILD HORSES

by Liva Baker

In the Nevada mountains long ago, there lived a blue-black stallion and his herd of mares. He was so swift that the Indians named him Blue Streak, and many a brave tried to capture him. Several times he was driven into blind canyons, but the great horse always managed to leap up rocks and over crevices and escape.

Finally he and his herd were cornered by a band of Indians on the edge of a high cliff. As the Indians closed in, the stallion hurled himself off the cliff. His loyal mares followed and died with him.

This is only one of the many tales told about the millions of wild, spirited horses called mustangs that galloped freely over the Western plains a hundred years ago.

They could be seen running in immense herds over the open ranges. Sometimes stallions tore the hide from each other as they fought over mares. They outraced the wind as they fled from men or panthers.

Prehistoric horses roamed the Western plains for a million years, but they were wiped out by some unknown cause, possibly 15,000 years ago. Horses were not seen again until 1493, when Columbus brought twenty-four stallions and ten mares for his ranch in Santo Domingo. Other ranchers followed, stocking ranches in Jamaica, Puerto Rico, and Cuba.

In 1518, Hernando Cortes landed in Mexico, bringing fifteen horses to the North American mainland from Cuba. A thousand

more horses were brought the following year.

They often stampeded to freedom. Left on the open range, they thrived on the lush grasslands of the New World, and bred swiftly. Many wandered north to what is now western United States. By the mid 1800's, the horses had increased in number to millions. They roamed the plains in bands which the Spanish called *manadas*. A band consisted of the "master" stallion and his fifteen to twenty mares.

The stallion ruled his herd like a true monarch. He would often punish idlers, and would even force a mare to leave her colt behind if the young one could not keep up with the rest. He drove his band hard, biting, kicking, and raking his mares.

But he also gave them his fatherly protection. When the animals approached a water hole, he found high ground where he could be on the lookout for danger. He never relaxed.

Stallions controlled their herds as long as their strength held out. There were always lone stallions that followed the band to challenge the master stallion whenever he showed weakness. He had to fight constantly to keep his mares.

When the Indians first saw these huge animals, they were afraid of them. But, while working on the Spanish ranches, they soon discovered that what they at first had thought were gigantic god-dogs were only beasts of burden. They were bigger and wilder, perhaps, but similar to the dogs they had long used to pull their own sled-like vehicles. Soon the Indians were buying, stealing, and picking up stray wild horses. Therefore, most of the Plains Indians were riding horses long before the Pilgrims landed in America.

The Indian and the mustang were natural allies. There was still much untamed savage in the man and there was some intelligence in the wild horse. The two creatures reached an understanding seldom achieved between man and animal. A cowboy might jump on the back of a captured mustang and ride it until either the horse was broken in or the rider was thrown. But an Indian could break a wild horse just by stroking it and talking to it in the quiet "hoh, hoh, hoh" and the hissing "shuh, shuh, shuh"

of horse talk. In a very short time, the wild beast was calmed.

The Indian was superb at riding. He rode bareback, with nothing but thin hide leggings between him and the horse. He took advantage of the best qualities of the horse—its speed, courage, eagerness, alertness, and pride.

War horses, the Indians' most prized possessions, were trained to take riders on the run and keep going without breaking pace. Meanwhile, the riders clung to the horses' sides and shot their arrows, and later on their guns, from under the horses' necks. The horses learned to respond to the touch of a rider's leg or foot so that the rider's hands stayed free to shoot.

The Indians were not the only people who wanted to own the wild horses. As settlers pushed across our country, every cowboy, lawyer, miner, and storekeeper wanted to possess at least one. Men called "mustangers" ran prize horses out of the herds and into pens and then sold them. Sometimes they captured the animals by "walking them down." This meant that a man on horseback would follow the band of mustangs for many days. At first, he kept his distance as the horses fled, but gradually as they got used to him, he rode closer. In time he could "take up" with them. Finally the mustanger slowly drove them into a pen.

More and more settlers moved west. They built farms and planted the prairies where the horses' water holes had been. They brought herds of cattle and sheep, which ate the grasses. They laid railroad tracks and cut up the open plains with roads. There was no more use for the mustangs.

Legends like the one about Blue Streak and a few western places such as *Mustang* Bayou, *Pinto* Canyon, *Horsehead* Crossing, and *Wild Horse* Draw are almost all that is left today to remind us of the wild horses.

However, there are still a few places where the sons of wild horses, like Blue Streak, can run free and guard their mares. In 1962, the Bureau of Land Management, United States Department of the Interior, set aside a 435,000-acre wild-horse refuge in Nevada.

In 1965 a wild-horse protection and management area was established in the Cedar Mountain area of Utah.

Not long ago the Director of the Bureau of Land Management announced that more efforts would be made to protect wild horses and burros on the 170 million acres of public land in the West.

This is good news to people who value the mustangs as a colorful part of the Old West and as a brave and beautiful species of wildlife.

THE PANTHER by Ogden Nash

The panther is like a leopard,
Except it hasn't been peppered,
Should you behold a panther crouch,
Prepare to say Ouch.
Better yet, if called by a panther,
Don't anther.

A PLAY: RIP VAN WINKLE

by Adele Thane

Cast

RIP VAN WINKLE

DAME VAN WINKLE, *his wife*

JUDY, *his daughter*

LUKE GARDENIER ⎤

KATCHEN, *a girl* ⎟ *Judy's*

MEENIE, *a girl* ⎬ *playmates*

JACOB ⎦

DERRICK VAN BUMMEL ⎤ *men*

PETER VANDERDONK ⎬ *of the*

BROM DUTCHER ⎦ *village*

NICHOLAS VEDDER,
landlord of the King George Inn

HENDRIK HUDSON

SAILORS, *Hudson's crew*

ORATOR

JONATHAN DOOLITTLE,
owner of the Union Hotel

JUDITH GARDENIER,
Judy grown up

LITTLE RIP, *Judy's son*

TOWNSPEOPLE *and* CHILDREN

Scene 1

Time: Early autumn, a few years before the Revolutionary War.

Place: A village in the Catskill Mountains in the colony of New York. At the right there is an inn with a sign, KING GEORGE INN, and a picture of King George III. A British flag hangs on the flagpole.

(Nicholas Vedder, Derrick Van Bummel, Brom Dutcher, and Peter Vanderdonk are seated outside the tavern. Dutcher and Vanderdonk are at the table playing a game of checkers. Van Bummel is reading aloud from a newspaper. From time to time, a rumble of thunder can be heard in the distance.)

Reprinted from *Plays from Famous Stories and Fairy Tales* by Adele Thane. Copyright © 1966 by Plays, Inc., Publishers, Boston, Mass. 02116.

VAN BUMMEL (*Reading*): ". . . and it has been learned that Massachusetts favors a Stamp Act Congress to be held in New York to protest English taxation in the colonies."

DUTCHER (*Looking up from his game*): Good! It's high time we did something about this English taxation.

VANDERDONK: Taxes and more taxes! The English are a pack of rascals with their hands in our pockets.

VAN BUMMEL: There's even a revenue stamp on our newspapers. One of these days the people here in the American Colonies will revolt, you mark my words.

VEDDER (*Pointing off right as a merry whistle is heard*): Well, here comes one man who is not troubled by these problems — Rip Van Winkle.

(*Rip Van Winkle enters, a wooden bucket in one hand, his gun in the other.*)

RIP: Good Afternoon Nick Vedder, Brom, Peter, Derrick. (*They return his greeting. Again there is a loud rumble of thunder.*) Just listen to that, will you!

DUTCHER: We're probably in for a thunder storm after this heat all day.

VEDDER: Sit down, Rip, Derrick is reading us the news.

VANDERDONK: How about a game of checkers, Rip?

RIP (*Hesitating*): I don't know. Dame Van Winkle sent me for a bucket of water, but — maybe one game. (*He sets down the bucket and draws a stool up to the table.*)

DUTCHER: Your move, Rip.

DAME VAN WINKLE (*Calling from off right*): Rip! R-i-p! Rip Van Winkle!

RIP: Oh my galligaskins! It's my wife!

(*Before he can get to his feet, Dame Van Winkle enters with a broom.*)

DAME VAN WINKLE: So this is how you draw water from the well! Sitting around with a lot of lazy good-for-nothing loafers. (*She tries to hit Rip with the broom.*) Pick up that bucket, you dawdling Dutchman, and fill it with water!

RIP (*Snatching up the bucket and dodging out of the way*): Hey there, Dame, I'm not an old rug to be beaten with a broomstick.

DAME VAN WINKLE: Well, you might better be. An old rug is more use than you. At least it would keep our feet warm in winter, which is more than you can do. Little you care that your family is starving and the cow is gone.

RIP: The cow gone?

DAME VAN WINKLE: Aye, the cow is gone and the cabbage trampled down. When are you going to mend the fence?

RIP: It rained yesterday—

DAME VAN WINKLE: If excuses were money, we'd be rich!

RIP: I'll mend the fence tomorrow.

DAME VAN WINKLE: Tomorrow, tomorrow! All your work is going to be done tomorrow! You show enough energy when there's a husking bee or an errand to run for the neighbors, but here at home. . . . (*She exits. Rip lowers his bucket into the well.*)

VEDDER: Poor Rip! His wife has the scoldingest tongue in the Hudson Valley.

VAN BUMMEL: A sharp tongue is the only tool that grows keener with use.

DUTCHER: What would you do, Derrick, if you had a wife like Van Winkle's?

VAN BUMMEL: War could be no worse. I would enlist.

(They all laugh and exit through the door of the inn. Rip turns to leave, then stops, and smiles as children's voices are heard. Judy, Luke, Katchen, Meenie—holding a kite—and Jacob—carrying a bow—run in.)

CHILDREN: There he is! There's Rip Van Winkle! *(They surround him, chattering excitedly.)*

JUDY: Hello, Father. I've brought some of my friends.

RIP: Glad to see you, children.

JACOB: Oh, Rip, there's something wrong with my bow. Every time I go to shoot, the cord slips.

(Rip takes the bow, draws his knife from his pocket, and cuts the notch deeper for the cord.)

RIP: There, Jacob, try that, and see if it doesn't work.

JACOB *(Pretending to shoot)*: Yes, it's all right now.

MEENIE: My kite won't stay up, Rip.

RIP *(Taking off part of the tail)*: Now it will, Meenie. This breeze is just right for it. *(He hands the kite to Meenie.)*

KATCHEN: My mother wants you to plug up her rain barrel, so she'll be able to wash next week.

RIP: Tell her I'll fix it tonight, Katchen.

LUKE: Rip, will you see what's the matter with my whistle? I made it just the way you showed me, but it isn't any good.

RIP *(Examining the whistle)*: You haven't whittled it right there, Luke. Here, I'll fix it for you. *(He sits on the bench under the tree and begins to whittle.)*

JUDY: Tell us a story, Father.

LUKE: Yes, you tell better stories than anybody in the Catskills.

RIP: What shall it be about?

JACOB: Indians!

KATCHEN: I like witches and goblins best.

(A long roll of thunder is heard.)

JUDY: Oh, Father, hear that thunder!

RIP: Why, don't you know what that is, Judy? That's Hendrik Hudson and his famous crew, playing ninepins up in the mountains.

(*More thunder is heard.*)

MEENIE: Oh, what a noise they make!

RIP: Yes, they are jolly fellows. They sail the wide sea over in their ship, the Half-Moon. Then every twenty years they come back to the Catskills.

JACOB: What do they do that for?

RIP: Oh, old Hendrik Hudson likes to revisit the country he discovered and keep a watchful eye over his river, the Hudson.

JACOB: I wish I could see Hendrik Hudson and his crew.

RIP: Peter Vanderdonk says his father saw them once in their funny breeches, playing at ninepins up in the hills. (*A loud peal of thunder is heard.*) Listen to those bowling balls! That must be Hendrik Hudson himself, the Flying Dutchman!

(*Dame Van Winkle enters with broom as Rip is speaking.*)

DAME VAN WINKLE: So! Here you are, telling stories without a word of truth in 'em! Oh, I could tell a story or two myself about a shiftless husband who does nothing but whittle and whistle. Whittle and whistle! What a job for a grown man! (*She snatches the whistle from Rip.*)

LUKE (*Pleadingly*): It's my whistle! Please don't break it, Dame Van Winkle.

DAME VAN WINKLE: Take it and begone! (*She gives Luke the whistle and he runs off.*) Judy, you go and ask Dame Vedder for an armful of wood. Your father is too busy spinning yarns to split wood for our fire. (*Judy goes off behind the inn.*) As for the rest of you, go home if you have any homes, and don't keep hanging around here like stray dogs looking for bones. (*She sweeps the children off the stage with her broom.*) Get along! Begone, all of you! (*With arms at her waist, she faces Rip.*) Well, what do you have to say for yourself? (*Rip shrugs, shakes his head, and says nothing.*) Nothing as usual. (*Rip goes to the tree for his gun.*) What are you getting your gun for? Going off to the mountains, no doubt. Anything to keep you out of the house.

RIP (*Good-naturedly*): Well, wife, you have often told me that *my* side of the house is the *out*side. Where's my dog? Where's Wolf?

DAME VAN WINKLE: Wolf is tied up in the cellar.

RIP: You didn't tie up Wolf?

DAME VAN WINKLE: I certainly did. That dog tracked up my kitchen floor right after I'd finished scrubbing it. Well, if you're going hunting, go, and don't come back until you bring us something for supper. And if you can't bring any supper, don't bring yourself.

JUDY (*Re-entering, with her arms full of logs*): But, Mother, it's going to rain.

DAME VAN WINKLE (*Taking the wood*): Pooh! Your father won't get as wet as we will in the house, with the roof leaking and the windows broken. You hurry home now. And bring that bucket of water your father managed to get this far. (*Dame Van Winkle starts to exit, but Judy stays behind with Rip.*)

RIP (*Calling after his wife*): Wife, turn Wolf loose when you get home.

(*Dame Van Winkle looks back at him angrily, tosses her head, and exits.*)

JUDY: Oh, Father, I hope you have wonderful luck. Then Mother won't be so cross.

RIP: I don't blame her for being cross with me sometimes. I guess I don't do much work around here. But I'm going to do better, Judy. I'm going to do all the jobs your mother has been after me about.

DAME VAN WINKLE (*Calling from offstage*): Ju-dee! Ju-dee!

RIP: There's your mother. I'd better be off. Good-bye, Judy. Come, Wolf! Come, boy!

JUDY: Good-by, Father. (*Luke enters and joins Judy as loud crash of thunder is heard.*) Oh, Luke, listen to that thunder!

LUKE: It's only Hendrik Hudson's men playing ninepins. Don't be scared, Judy.

JUDY: I'm not—that is, not very.

DAME VAN WINKLE (*Calling from offstage*): Judy! Ju-dee!

LUKE: You'd better go in or you'll catch it. Your mother is getting awfully free with her broomstick lately. Here, I'll carry your bucket for you.

Scene 2

Time: Later the same afternoon.

Place: An open space among the trees, high in the Catskill Mountains. There is a tree stump at the center and a large bush to one side.

(*Rip, carrying his gun, enters from the left, dragging his feet wearily. He sinks down on the stump.*)

RIP: Whew! That was a climb! All the way up the mountain. How peaceful it is up here. No one to scold me, no one to wave a broomstick. Ah, me! I wonder where Wolf is. Wolf! Here, boy! That's it, Wolf, sick 'em! I hope we get something this time. We can't go home until we do. (*A loud crash of thunder is heard.*) That thunder sounds much louder up here in the mountains than down in the valley. Maybe it's going to rain after all.

VOICE (*Calling from offstage*): Rip Van Winkle! (*Rip looks around wonderingly.*) Rip Van Winkle!

RIP (*Rising*): That's my name. Somebody is calling me.

VOICE (*Offstage*): Rip Van Winkle!

RIP: Is it Dame Van Winkle? No. she would never follow me up here. (*Sound of a ship's bell is heard from off right.*) What was that? (*Bell rings again.*) A ship's bell! But how can that be? A ship? Up here in the mountains? (*He gazes off to the right, in astonishment.*) It *is* a ship! Look at it! Sails all set and a Dutch flag at the masthead. (*Ship's bell is heard again, but fainter.*) There, it's gone. I must have imagined it. (*First sailor with a keg on his back enters, as Rip watches him in amazement.*) By my galligaskins, what a funny little man! And how strangely he's dressed. Such old-fashioned clothes! *(Rip goes to meet the sailor.)* Hello, old Dutchman. That keg looks heavy. Let me carry it for you. *(He picks up the keg.)* By golly, it is heavy! Why did you bring this keg all the way up here to the top of the mountain? And who are you, anyhow?

FIRST SAILOR *(Gruffly)*: Don't ask questions. Set it down over there. *(He points to a spot beside the bush.)*

RIP *(Obeying cheerfully)*: Anything to oblige. *(There is a commotion off to one side, and Hendrik Hudson and his crew enter, capering and shouting. They carry bowling balls and ninepins and a drum. Second sailor has a burlap bag containing drinking mugs thrown over his shoulder. Rip turns to the first sailor.)* Why, bless my soul! Here are a lot of little fellows just like yourself. *(To all the sailors)* Who are you?

SAILORS *(Shouting)*: Hendrik Hudson and his merry crew!

HUDSON (*Stepping forward*): Set up the ninepins, men, and we'll have a game. (*Two or three sailors set up the ninepins at one side. Hudson speaks to the first sailor.*) You there, fill up the mugs! (*Second sailor opens the sack and passes out the mugs. Hudson turns to Rip.*) Now then, Rip Van Winkle, will you drink with us?

RIP: Why, yes, thank you, Captain Hudson. I'm quite thirsty after my long climb up the mountain.

(*The mugs are filled from the keg.*)

SECOND SAILOR (*Raising his mug to toast*): To Hendrik Hudson, the Half-Moon, and its merry crew!

ALL (*As they raise their mugs*): To Hendrik Hudson, the Half-Moon, and its merry crew!

RIP (*Lifting his mug*): Well, gentlemen, here's to your good health. May you live long and prosper. (*Rip drinks and smacks his lips.*) Ah! This is the best drink I have ever tasted, but it makes me feel very sleepy. (*Hudson and his men begin to bowl. As they roll the balls, the thunder increases. Rip yawns.*) Ho, hum. I can't keep my eyes open. I guess I'll lie down. (*Carrying his gun, he goes behind the bush and lies down out of sight.*)

HUDSON (*To sailors*): Now, men, let's stop our game of ninepins and be off, to return again in twenty years.

(*First sailor points to bush where Rip is sleeping.*)

FIRST SAILOR: Look! Rip Van Winkle is asleep.

HUDSON: Peace be with the poor fellow. He needs to take a good long rest from his nagging wife. Sh-h-h-h!

(*Hudson places his finger to his lips, and they all go about quietly gathering up the ninepins, balls, mugs, and keg. Then they tiptoe off the stage, their voices dying away to a whisper. The lights may dim briefly to indicate the passage of twenty years. When the lights come up, Rip is heard yawning behind the bush. Then he stands up with great difficulty. He limps to center, carrying a rusty gun. His clothes are shabby, and he has a long white beard.*)

RIP *(Groaning)*: Ouch, my back! It's so stiff. And my legs—just like pokers. My, my, but I'm shaky. I feel as if I've grown to be an old man overnight. It must be rheumatism. Well, I'd better get along home to Dame Van Winkle. *(He looks at the gun he is carrying.)* Why, this rusty old thing is not my gun! Somebody has played a trick on me. *(Suddenly remembering)* It's that Hendrik Hudson and his men! They've stolen my gun, and left this rusty one for me! Another scolding in store from the Dame. Wolf! Here, Wolf! Have those scamps stolen my dog, too? He'd never leave me. Come on, old boy! Maybe he found it too cold and went home to be warmed by his mistress's broomstick. Well, I will follow after and get my hot welcome, too. *(He carries the rusty gun and totters off.)*

Scene 3

Time: Twenty years after Scene 1.

Place: Same as Scene 1, except that the sign above the inn reads: UNION HOTEL—OWNER, JONATHAN DOOLITTLE. A picture of George Washington has replaced that of King George III. Washington's name is printed below the picture, and an American flag flutters on a pole above it. *(An orator is standing on a bench, speaking to a crowd of townspeople.)*

ORATOR: Remember the Boston Tea Party! Remember Bunker Hill! Who saved this country? Who is the father of this country?

TOWNSPEOPLE: George Washington! Washington for President! *(Rip enters with a troop of children, who laugh and jeer at him.)*

CHILDREN: Look at him! He looks like a scarecrow! Where did you come from, Daddy Longlegs? Where did you get that gun? *(First child stands in front of Rip and crouches down, pulling on an imaginary beard.)*

FIRST CHILD: Billy goat, billy goat! *(Children begin stroking imaginary beards until Rip does the same. He is amazed to find that he has a beard.)*

RIP: By my galligaskins, what's this?

SECOND CHILD: It's a beard, old Father Time. Didn't you know you had a beard?

RIP: But I didn't have one last night.
(Children laugh and mock him.)

ORATOR *(To Rip)*: What do you mean by coming here at election time with a gun on your shoulder and a mob at your heels? Do you want to cause a riot?

RIP: Oh, no sir! I am a quiet man and a loyal subject of King George!

CHILDREN and TOWNSPEOPLE: A spy! Away with him! Lock him up

JONATHAN DOOLITTLE *(Stepping forward from the crowd)*: Hold on a minute! We must get to the bottom of this. *(To Rip)* Aren't you a supporter of Washington for President?

RIP *(Puzzled)*: Eh? Supporter of Washington? *(Shaking his head, wholly bewildered)* I don't understand. I mean no harm. I only want to find my friends. They were here at the inn yesterday.

DOOLITTLE: Who are these friends of yours? Name them.

RIP *(Hesitantly)*: Well, one is the landlord—

DOOLITTLE: I am the landlord of this hotel—Jonathan Doolittle.

RIP: Why, what happened to Nicholas Vedder?

FIRST WOMAN: Nicholas Vedder? Why, he's dead and gone these eighteen years.

RIP: No, no, that's impossible! Where's Brom Dutcher? And the schoolmaster, Van Bummel?

FIRST MAN: Brom Dutcher was killed in the war at Stony Point.

SECOND MAN: And Van Bummel went off to the war, too. He became a great general, and now he's in Congress.

RIP: War? What war?

SECOND MAN: Why, the war we fought against England, and won, of course.

RIP: I don't understand. Am I dreaming? Congress? Generals? What's happened to me?

DOOLITTLE *(Impatiently)*: Now, we've had enough of this nonsense. Who are you, anyway? What is your name?

RIP *(Completely confused)*: I don't know. I mean, I was Rip Van Winkle yesterday, but today—

DOOLITTLE: Don't try to make sport of us, my man!

RIP: Oh, indeed, I'm not, sir. I was myself last night, but I fell asleep on the mountain, and Hendrik Hudson and his crew changed my gun, and everything's changed, and I'm changed, and I can't tell what my name is, or who I am!

(Townspeople exchange glances, nod knowingly, and tap their foreheads.)

SECOND MAN *(Shaking his head)*: Hendrik Hudson, he says! Poor chap. He's mad. Let's leave him alone.

RIP (*In great distress*): Isn't there anybody here who knows who I am?

SECOND WOMAN (*Soothingly*): Why, you're just yourself, old man. Who else do you think you could be?

(*Judith Gardenier enters, leading Little Rip by the hand. He hangs back, afraid of Rip.*)

JUDITH: Hush, Rip! The old man won't hurt you.

RIP (*Turning in surprise*): Rip? Who said Rip?

JUDITH: Why, I did. I was just telling my little boy not to be frightened.

RIP (*Scanning her face*): And what is your name, my good woman?

JUDITH: My name is Judith, sir.

RIP: Judith? Did you say Judith? (*In great excitement*) And your father—what was his name?

JUDITH: Ah, poor man, his name was Rip Van Winkle. It's twenty years since he went away from home. We never heard of him again.

RIP (*Staggered*): Twenty years!

JUDITH: Yes, it must be all of that. His dog came back without him. I was a little girl then.

RIP: And your mother—where is she?

JUDITH: My mother is dead, sir.

RIP: Ah, but that woman had a tongue! Well, peace be with her soul. Did you love your father, Judith?

JUDITH: With all my heart. All the children in the village loved him, too.

RIP: Then look at me. Look closely, my dear Judy. I am your father.

JUDITH: You? My father?

RIP: Do you remember, Judy, that I told you the story of how Hendrik Hudson and his crew played ninepins in the mountains just before I went off hunting with Wolf?

JUDITH (*Excitedly*): Yes! And Wolf was our dog's name! Oh, Father, it's really you!

RIP: Yes, my little Judy. Young Rip Van Winkle once, old Rip Van Winkle now.

(Townspeople talk excitedly among themselves as they watch Rip and Judith.)

JUDITH: Dearest Father, come home with me. Luke and I will take good care of you.

RIP: Luke?

JUDITH: Luke Gardenier, my old playmate. You used to make whistles for him and take him fishing. We were married when he came back from the war.

RIP: Ah, the war. There is so much I have to catch up with.

JUDITH: You will have plenty of time to do that. And you must tell us what happened to you.

RIP: Maybe you won't believe what happened to me, Judy. It was all so strange. *(Rip reaches out a hand to Little Rip, who shyly takes it, and they start off, Judith following. A loud clap of thunder stops them. Rip turns and shakes his fist toward the mountains.)* Oh, no you don't, Hendrik Hudson! You don't get me back up there again. *(There is an answering roll of thunder.)*

What Is Orange?

Orange is a tiger lily,
A carrot,
A feather from
A parrot,
A flame,
The wildest color
You can name.
Orange is a happy day
Saying good-by
In a sunset that
Shocks the sky.
Orange is brave
Orange is bold
It's bittersweet
And marigold.
Orange is zip
Orange is dash
The brightest stripe
In a Roman sash.
Orange is an orange
Also a mango.
Orange is music
Of the tango.
Orange is the fur
Of the fiery fox,
The brightest crayon
In the box.
And in the fall
When the leaves are turning
Orange is the smell
Of a bonfire burning. . . .

Mary O'Neill

FROM THE WIND IN THE WILLOWS

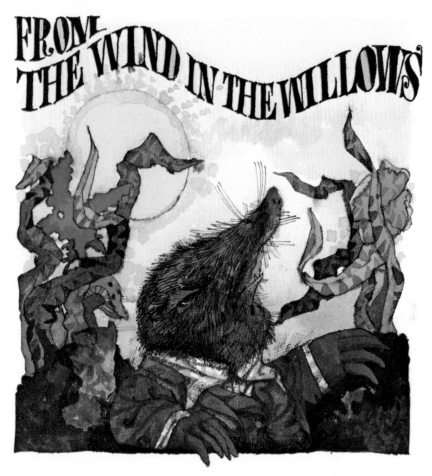

by KENNETH GRAHAME

The mole was very busy cleaning his dark little home which, of course, was deep underground. But something kept calling him from above. It was spring! The Mole could not resist the call so he said, "Hang the spring cleaning!" and dug himself a tunnel up, up, and up until his little snout finally broke through the surface of the ground and into the sunlight. The Mole strolled across the meadows enjoying the sunshine, the birds, the flowers, and all of the other delights of spring. It all seemed too good to be true. Suddenly, he found himself standing on the bank of a river. The Mole who had never seen a river before was quite fascinated by it. As he stood on the bank marveling at the river, he spied a small brown face with whiskers looking at him from a hole in the opposite bank of the river. The face belonged to Water Rat.

THE RIVER BANK

"Hullo, Mole!" said the Water Rat.

"Hullo, Rat!" said the Mole.

"Would you like to come over?" inquired the Rat presently.

"Oh, it's all very well to *talk*," said the Mole, rather pettishly, he being new to a river and riverside life and its ways.

The Rat said nothing, but stooped and unfastened a rope, hauled on it, and then lightly stepped into a little boat which the Mole had not observed. It was painted blue outside and white within, and was just the size for two animals. The Mole's whole heart went out to it at once, even though he did not yet fully understand its uses.

The Rat sculled smartly across and made fast. Then he held up his forepaw as the Mole stepped gingerly down. "Lean on that!" he said. "Now then, step lively!" and the Mole to his surprise and rapture found himself actually seated in the stern of a real boat.

"This has been a wonderful day!" said he, as the Rat shoved off and took to the sculls again. "Do you know, I've never been in a boat before in all my life."

"What?" cried the Rat, open-mouthed. "Never been in a—you never—well, I—what have you been doing, then?"

"Is it so nice as all that?" asked the Mole shyly, though he was quite prepared to believe it as he leaned back in his seat and surveyed the cushions, the oars, the rowlocks, and all the fascinating fittings, and felt the boat sway lightly under him.

"Nice? It's the *only* thing," said the Water Rat solemnly, as he leaned forward for his stroke. "Believe me, my young friend, there is *nothing*— absolutely nothing—half so much worth doing as simply messing about in boats. Simply messing," he went on dreamily, "messing — about — in — boats; messing——"

"Look ahead, Rat!" cried the Mole suddenly.

It was too late. The boat struck the bank full tilt. The dreamer, the joyous oarsman, lay on his back at the bottom of the boat, his heels in the air.

"—about in boats—or *with* boats," the Rat went on composedly, picking himself up with a pleasant laugh. "In or out of 'em, it doesn't matter. Nothing seems really to matter, that's the charm of it. Whether you get away, or whether you don't; whether you arrive at your destination or whether you reach somewhere else, or whether you never get anywhere at all, you're always busy, and you never do anything in particular; and when you've done it, there's always something else to do, and you can do it if you like, but you'd much better not. Look here! If you've really nothing else on hand this morning, supposing we drop down the river together and have a long day of it?"

The Mole waggled his toes from sheer happiness, spread his chest with a sigh of full contentment, and leaned back blissfully into the soft cushions. *"What* a day I'm having!" he said. "Let us start at once!"

"Hold hard a minute, then!" said the Rat. He looped the painter through a ring in his landing-stage, climbed up into his hole above, and after a short interval reappeared staggering under a fat, wicker luncheon basket.

"Shove that under your feet," he observed to the Mole, as he passed it down into the boat. Then he untied the painter and took the sculls again.

"What's inside it?" asked the Mole, wriggling with curiosity.

"There's cold chicken inside it," replied the Rat briefly; "cold-tonguecoldhamcoldbeefpickled-gherkinssaladfrenchrollscresssand-widgespottedmeatgingerbeerlemon-adesodawater——"

"O stop, stop," cried the Mole in ecstasies. "This is too much!"

"Do you really think so?" inquired the Rat seriously. "It's only what I always take on these little excursions, and the other animals are always telling me that I'm a mean beast and cut it *very* fine!"

The Mole never heard a word he was saying. Absorbed in the new life he was entering upon, intoxicated with the sparkle, the ripple, the scents, the sounds, and the sunlight, he trailed a paw in the water and dreamed long waking dreams. The Water Rat, like the good fellow he was, sculled steadily on and forebore to disturb him.

"I like your clothes awfully, old chap," he remarked after some half an hour or so had passed. "I'm going to get a black velvet smoking suit myself someday, as soon as I can afford it."

"I beg your pardon," said the Mole, pulling himself together with an effort. "You must think me very rude; but all of this is so very new

to me. So—this—is—a—River!"

"*The* River," corrected the Rat.

"And you really live by the river? What a jolly life!"

"By it and with it and on it and in it," said the Rat. "It's brother and sister to me, and aunts, and company, and food and drink, and (naturally) washing. It's my world, and I don't want any other. What it hasn't got is not worth having, and what it doesn't know is not worth knowing. Lord! the times we've had together! Whether in winter or summer, spring or autumn, it's always got its fun and its excitements. When the floods are on in February, and my cellars and basement are brimming with drink that's no good to me, and the brown water runs by my best bedroom window; or again when it all drops away and shows patches of mud that smells like plum cake, and the rushes and weeds clog the channels, and I can potter about dry-shod over most of the bed of it and find fresh food to eat, and things careless people have dropped out of boats!"

"But isn't it a bit dull at times?" the Mole ventured to ask. "Just you and the river, and no one else to pass a word with?"

"No one else to—well, I mustn't be hard on you," said the Rat with forbearance. "You're new to it, and of course you don't know. The bank is so crowded nowadays that many people are moving away altogether. O no, it isn't what it used to be, at all. Otters, kingfishers, dabchicks, moorhens, all of them about all day long and always wanting you to *do* something—as if a fellow had no business of his own to attend to!"

"What lies over *there?*" asked the Mole, waving a paw towards a background of woodland that darkly framed the water meadows on one side of the river.

"That? O, that's just the Wild Wood," said the Rat shortly. "We don't go there very much, we river-bankers."

"Aren't they—aren't they very *nice* people in there?" said the Mole a trifle nervously.

"W-e-ll," replied the Rat, "let me see. The squirrels are all right. *And* the rabbits—some of 'em, but rabbits are a mixed lot. And then there's Badger, of course. He lives right there in the heart of it; wouldn't live anywhere else, either, if you paid him to do it. Dear old Badger! Nobody interferes with *him.* They'd better not," he added significantly.

"Why, who *should* interfere with him?" asked the Mole.

"Well, of course—there—are others," explained the Rat in a hesitating sort of way. "Weasels—and stoats—and foxes—and so on. They're all right in a way—I'm very good friends with them—pass the time of day when we meet, and all that—but they break out sometimes, there's no denying it, and then—well, you can't really trust them, and that's the fact."

The Mole knew well that it is quite against animal-etiquette to dwell on possible trouble ahead, or even to allude to it; so he dropped the subject.

"And beyond the Wild Wood again?" he asked. "Where it's all blue and dim, and one sees what may be hills or perhaps they mayn't, and something like the smoke of towns, or is it only cloud drift?"

"Beyond the Wild Wood comes the Wide World," said the Rat. "And that's something that doesn't matter, either to you or me. I've never been there, and I'm never going, nor you either, if you've got any sense at all. Don't ever refer to it again, please. Now then! Here's our backwater at last, where we're going to lunch."

Leaving the main stream, they now passed into what seemed at

first sight like a little landlocked lake. Green turf sloped down to either edge, and brown snaky tree roots gleamed below the surface of the quiet water. Ahead of them the silvery shoulder and foamy tumble of a weir, arm-in-arm with a restless dripping mill wheel that held up in its turn a grey-gabled mill house, filled the air with a soothing murmur of sound, dull and smothery, yet with little clear voices speaking up cheerfully out of it at intervals. It was so very beautiful that the Mole could only hold up both forepaws and gasp, "O my! O my! O my!"

The Rat brought the boat alongside the bank, made her fast, helped the still-awkward Mole safely ashore, and swung out the luncheon basket. The Mole begged as a favor to be allowed to unpack it all by himself. The Rat was very pleased to indulge him, and to sprawl at full length on the grass and rest, while his excited friend shook out the tablecloth and spread it, took out all the mysterious packets one by one, and arranged their contents in due order, still gasping, "O my! O my!" at each fresh revelation. When all was ready, the Rat said, "Now, pitch in, old fellow!" and the Mole was indeed very glad to obey, for he had started his spring-cleaning at a very early hour that morning, as people *will* do, and had not paused for bite or sup; and he had been through a very great deal since that distant time which now seemed so many days ago.

"What are you looking at?" said the Rat presently, when the edge of their hunger was somewhat dulled, and the Mole's eyes were able to wander off the tablecloth a little.

"I am looking," said the Mole, "at a streak of bubbles that I see traveling along the surface of the water. That is a thing that strikes me as funny."

"Bubbles? Oho!" said the Rat, and chirruped cheerily in an inviting sort of way.

A broad glistening muzzle showed itself above the edge of the bank, and the Otter hauled himself out and shook the water from his coat.

"Greedy beggars!" he observed, making for the provender. "Why didn't you invite me, Ratty?"

"This was an impromptu affair," explained the Rat. "By the way— my friend Mr. Mole."

"Proud, I'm sure," said the Otter, and the two animals were friends.

"Such a rumpus everywhere!" continued the Otter. "All the world seems out on the river today. I came up this backwater to try and get a moment's peace, and then stumbled upon you fellows! At least—I beg pardon—I don't exactly mean that, you know."

There was a rustle behind them, proceeding from a hedge wherein last year's leaves still clung thick, and a stripy head, with high shoulders behind it, peered forth on them.

"Come on, old Badger!" shouted the Rat.

The Badger trotted forward a pace or two, then grunted, "H'm! Company," and turned his back and disappeared from view.

"That's *just* the sort of fellow he is!" observed the disappointed Rat. "Simply hates Society! Now we shan't see any more of him today. Well, tell us *who's* out on the river?"

"Toad's out, for one," replied the Otter, "in his brand-new wager-boat, new togs, new everything!"

The two animals looked at each other and laughed.

"Once, it was nothing but sailing," said the Rat. "Then he tired of that and took to punting. Nothing would please him but to punt all day and every day, and a nice mess he made of it. Last year it was house-boating, and we all had to go and stay with him in his houseboat, and pretend we liked it. He was going to spend the rest of his life in a houseboat. It's all the same, whatever he takes up, he gets tired of it, and starts on something fresh."

"Such a good fellow, too," remarked the Otter reflectively, "but no stability—especially in a boat!"

From where they sat they could get a glimpse of the main stream

across the island that separated them. Just then a wager-boat flashed into view, the rower—a short, stout figure—splashing badly and rolling a good deal, but working his hardest. The Rat stood up and hailed him, but Toad—for it was he—shook his head and settled sternly to his work.

"He'll be out of the boat in a minute if he rolls like that," said the Rat, sitting down again.

"Of course he will," chuckled the Otter. "Did I ever tell you that good story about Toad and the lock-keeper? It happened this way. Toad . . ."

An errant Mayfly swerved unsteadily across the current in the excited fashion affected by young bloods of Mayflies seeing life. A swirl of water and a "cloop!" and the Mayfly was visible no more.

Neither was the Otter.

The Mole looked down. The voice was still in his ears, but the turf whereon he had sprawled was clearly vacant. Not an Otter to be seen, as far as the distant horizon.

But again there was a streak of bubbles on the surface of the river.

The Rat hummed a tune, and the Mole recollected that animal-etiquette forbade any sort of comment on the sudden disappearance of one's friends at any moment, for any reason or no reason whatever.

"Well, well," said the Rat, "I suppose we ought to be moving. I wonder which of us had better pack the luncheon basket." He did not speak as if he was frightfully eager for the treat.

"O, please let me," said the Mole. So, of course, the Rat let him.

Packing the basket was not quite such pleasant work as unpacking the basket. It never is. But the Mole was bent on enjoying everything, and although just when he had got the basket packed and strapped up tightly, he saw a plate staring up at him from the grass, and when the job had been done again, the Rat pointed out a fork which anybody ought to have seen, and last of all, behold! the mustard pot, which he had been sitting on without knowing it—still, somehow, the thing got finished at last, without much loss of temper.

The afternoon sun was getting low as the Rat sculled gently homewards in a dreamy mood, murmuring poetry-things over to himself, and not paying much attention to Mole. But the Mole was very full of lunch, and self-satisfaction, and pride, and already quite at home in a boat (so he thought), and was getting a bit restless besides. Presently he said, "Ratty! Please, *I* want to row, now!"

The Rat shook his head with a smile. "Not yet, my young friend," he said. "Wait till you've had a few lessons. It's not so easy as it looks."

The Mole was quiet for a minute or two. But he began to feel more and more jealous of Rat, sculling so strongly and so easily along, and his pride began to whisper that he could do it every bit as well. He jumped up and seized the sculls, so suddenly, that the Rat, who was gazing out over the water and saying more poetry-things to himself, was taken by surprise and fell backwards off his seat with his legs

in the air for the second time, while the triumphant Mole took his place and grabbed the sculls with entire confidence.

"Stop it, you *silly* fool!" cried the Rat, from the bottom of the boat. "You can't do it! You'll have us over!"

The Mole flung his sculls back with a flourish, and made a great dig at the water. He missed the surface altogether, his legs flew up above his head, and he found himself lying on the top of the prostrate Rat. Greatly alarmed, he made

a grab at the side of the boat, and the next moment—Sploosh!

Over went the boat, and he found himself struggling in the river.

O my, how cold the water was, and O, how *very* wet it felt. How it sang in his ears as he went down, down, down! How bright and welcome the sun looked as he rose to the surface coughing and spluttering! How black was his despair when he felt himself sinking again! Then a firm paw gripped him by the back of his neck. It was the Rat, and he was evidently laughing—the Mole could *feel* him laughing, right down his arm and through his paw, and so into his—the Mole's—neck.

The Rat got hold of a scull and shoved it under the Mole's arm. Then he did the same by the other side of him and, swimming behind, propelled the helpless animal to shore, hauled him out, and set him down on the bank, a squashy, pulpy lump of misery.

When the Rat had rubbed him down a bit and wrung some of the wet out of him, he said, "Now, then, old fellow! Trot up and down the towing-path as hard as you can till you're warm and dry again, while I dive for the luncheon basket."

So the dismal Mole, wet without and ashamed within, trotted about till he was fairly dry, while the Rat plunged into the water again, recovered the boat, righted her and made her fast, fetched his floating property to shore by degrees, and finally dived successfully for the luncheon basket and struggled to land with it.

When all was ready for a start once more, the Mole, limp and dejected, took his seat in the stern of the boat. As they set off, he said in a low voice, broken with emotion, "Ratty, my generous friend! I am very sorry indeed for my foolish and ungrateful conduct. My heart quite fails me when I think how I might have lost that beautiful luncheon basket. Indeed, I have been a complete fool and I know it. Will you overlook it this once and forgive me, and let things go on as before?"

"That's all right, bless you!" responded the Rat cheerily. "What's a little wet to a Water Rat? I'm more in the water than out of it most days. Don't you think any more about it. Look here! I really think you had better come and stop with me for a little time. It's very plain and rough, you know—not like Toad's house at all—but you haven't seen that yet; still, I can make you comfortable. I'll teach you to row and to swim, and you'll soon be as handy on the water as any of us."

The Mole was so touched by his kind manner of speaking that he could find no voice to answer him, and he had to brush away a tear or two with the back of his paw. But the Rat kindly looked in another direction, and presently the Mole's spirits revived again. He was even able to give some straight back talk to a couple of moorhens who were sniggering to each other about his bedraggled appearance.

When they got home, the Rat made a bright fire in the parlor, and planted the Mole in an armchair in front of it, having fetched down a dressing gown and slippers for him, and told him river stories till suppertime. Very thrilling stories they were, too, to an earth-dwelling animal like Mole. Stories about weirs, and sudden floods, and leaping pike, and steamers that flung hard bottles—at least bottles were certainly flung, and *from* steamers, so presumably *by* them; and about herons, and how particular they were whom they spoke to; and about adventures

down drains, and night fishings with Otter, or excursions far afield with Badger. Supper was a most cheerful meal. But very shortly afterwards, a terribly sleepy Mole had to be escorted upstairs by his considerate host, to the best bedroom, where he soon laid his head on his pillow in great peace and contentment, knowing that his new-found friend the River was lapping the sill of his window.

The Mole and the Water Rat became great friends and shared many adventures together with Toad, Badger, and Otter. You can share these adventures with them by reading the rest of Kenneth Grahame's THE WIND IN THE WILLOWS.

ABOUT THE AUTHOR

Kenneth Grahame was born in Edinburgh, Scotland, in 1859. He was brought up in England by his grandmother after losing his parents as a boy. He was a good student and yearned to go to college but, for lack of money, had to go to work instead. From his first position as a clerk, he eventually rose to a high post in London's Bank of England.

Long days at work, plus many hours spent enjoying the outdoors, left Kenneth Grahame little time for writing. However, one of the few books he did write—*The Wind in the Willows*—is considered a masterpiece and made him famous. You have just read part of its opening chapter, "The River Bank." The book grew out of bedtime stories that Mr. Grahame made up for his young son, Alastair, affectionately nicknamed "Mouse." Although it was intended for children, it has delighted readers of all ages ever since its publication in 1908.

In that same year, poor health forced the author to give up his bank work and most of his writing. After his only son died tragically at the age of twenty, Mr. Grahame retired to a village beside the River Thames in southern England and lived quietly there until his death in 1932.

MORE BOOKS TO ENJOY

THE MATCHLOCK GUN, *by Walter D. Edmonds*

This adventure story of colonial New York State tells of a brave boy who must fire an old Spanish gun to save his mother and little sister from a band of Indians.

THE RELUCTANT DRAGON, *by Kenneth Grahame*

This is a humorous story about a boy who makes friends with a timid, peace-loving dragon.

SKID, *by Florence S. Hayes*

Skid has just been made captain of his baseball team in Georgia when he moves to Connecticut. It is lonely and hard for him, the only Negro boy in his new school, but quick thinking makes him a hero.

MISTY OF CHINCOTEAGUE, *by Marguerite Henry*

Paul and Maureen want to purchase Misty, a wild Chincoteague pony who loves his freedom.

OLD TANGLE EYE, *by Ralph E. Johnston*

A boy moves to Colorado in the early pioneering days. He finds a life of action and danger among cowboys, Indians, and claim-jumpers

MISS BIANCA, *by Margery Sharp*

Miss Bianca, a clever white mouse, and her friend Bernard, of the Mouse Prisoner's Aid Society, have exciting adventures.

PAGEANT

Contents

PAGEANT

THE COMPUTER TRIUMPHS AGAIN

by Clem Philbrook

The problem with the Red Sox was not that they had the only lady coach in the whole Tom Thumb League, for Miss Carmody was a very fine coach. The problem was that every boy on the team thought he should be a pitcher. Instead of paying attention to the position he was playing during a game, each boy was thinking about what he would do if he were pitching. Then Ollie had his brainstorm. His father was a computer programmer, and one of the things a computer could do was to process aptitude tests and select the best person for a particular job. So Ollie had his father make up a baseball aptitude test for the team to take. Perhaps the computer could figure out the best position for each player on the team.

The computer put Ollie exactly where he was—behind home plate. Barney was best suited to first base, Mike to second, Herbie to shortstop, and Billy to third base—the same positions they were already playing. There was a change in the outfield. Tony Girard went from center to left field, Art Finnegan from left to right and Larry Donovan from right to center. But that was it. Everything else stayed the same. Dusty was still the first-line pitcher, with Tony second, and Art to back them up.

Ollie's father read the computer results before practice on Friday afternoon. The questionnaires had contained multiple choice items, such as: *(1) Infielders are more important than outfielders, (2) Pitchers are more important than catchers, (3) The coach is the most important member of a team.* The boys circled *Agree, Neutral,* or *Disagree.* Then there were items like: *A. Usually calm and passive, B. Usually active and energetic.*

"The questionnaires gave us profiles of you as individuals," Mr. Scruggs explained. "We learned your interests and personality characteristics. The computer then selected your position for you according to the data you gave."

When he had finished, Miss Carmody faced them, hands on slim hips. "Well, you asked for it, gang. The Red Sox have been data-processed by the latest in computer equipment. Let's hope you will now quit crabbing and settle down to business."

Ollie's father grinned. "Anybody want to question my computer?"

"How can you argue with a computer?" Barney wailed. "If it says I'm a first baseman, then I must be a first baseman."

"Yeah, I'll buy that," Mike agreed, "and I've got a lot to learn about my position too."

Herbie drove his right fist into his glove with a loud smack. "Hey, Coach," he said grimly, "how about giving us a few pointers?"

Miss Carmody was quick to take advantage of the situation. "Don't think I won't," she assured him. "You all have a lot to learn about baseball. Fundamental things, like making the right play in the blink of an eye. If you hesitate, you are lost. This is a game of split-second timing."

She paused to let this sink in. "There is one thing you want to watch out for—chatter from the other team. They are trying to rattle you, so you will hesitate that all-important fraction of a second, or will make the wrong play. You will have to close your ears to all this and learn to make the right play instinctively, guided by the teammate nearest you."

She smiled. "There is only one way to learn how to do that—practice. We are going to drill and drill and drill, and then drill some more, until making the right move will be automatic. There's no time like the present, so take your positions."

She picked up a bat and walked to home plate. "I want a lot of chatter out there. Try your best to confuse the man who gets the ball. Dusty, you throw them in. Let's go!"

She squared off at the plate. "Man on first, one out," she called. On the first pitch, she hit a slow bounder back at Dusty.

"Go to second with it, go to second!" Billy Young hollered.

"Hold it, hold it," Herbie Snell advised. "Too late all around!"

"Play the batter!" Barney Sawyer counseled.

Dusty fielded the ball and threw to second. Miss Carmody shook her head. "Wrong move, Dusty. On a hard hit ball, you have a chance for the force play. On a slow hit ball, you don't stand a chance of nailing the runner at second. Always go to first with it."

On the next pitch, Miss Carmody lined one to left field. "Tying run on second, one away!" she sang out.

Coming in fast, Tony Girard took the ball on the first bounce and threw to home. Dusty was in line with the throw. "Cut it off, Dusty!" Mike Turner called. "Let it go!" Ollie shouted. Dusty cut it off.

"That ties up the old ballgame," Miss Carmody told him. "It was a perfect strike to home plate. If you're not in a position to use your own judgment, then listen to your catcher."

She gave Dusty a rest on the next one and hit a high fly to short right field. Mike Turner and Art Finnegan both scrambled for it. "I got it, I got it!" Art yelled.

"It's all yours, Art," Barney Sawyer advised from first.

At the last moment, Mike peeled off and let Art take it. "That's the spirit out there," Miss Carmody said. "Now you're making sense. You infielders, always let the outfielder take it when possible. He's charging the ball, while you're going away from it. And always—I repeat, always—call it loud and clear. The infielder nearest the catch directs the play. Don't listen to anyone else."

That was the beginning of better things. On the next few plays, they started to click. What followed was the liveliest practice session of the year. Oh, they were not suddenly transformed from Willowdale's worst team into the best, Ollie realized. But there was a real change in their attitudes.

Even Sir Winston, Ollie's dog, seemed to sense their mood. For the first time he stayed awake and watched the action, barking his approval.

"I begin to see a glimmer of hope," Miss Carmody said, as practice drew to a close. "At least you are trying."

"You certainly are," Mr. Scruggs agreed heartily. "You are probably the most trying baseball team in the state."

Miss Carmody smiled as the team gathered in a circle around her. "Seriously, I'm proud of you, boys, and I have a strong hunch you will give a good account of yourselves in tomorrow's game against the Yankees."

"We'll be right here to help you," Deedee said. "We have some new baseball cheers, haven't we, Elmira?"

"Har de har har," Dusty said. "What do girls know about baseball?"

"Oh, we know a lot about baseball," Deedee tittered.

"Yes, we read up on it," Elmira chimed in. "Tell me, Deedee, why does it take longer to go from second base to third than it does from first base to second?"

Deedee's brown eyes sparkled. "Because there's a *short stop* in between."

They covered their mouths and burst into giggles. Ollie cringed. Dusty held his nose.

When they subsided, Deedee winked at Elmira. "Tell the boys what baseball stockings are, Elmira."

Elmira beamed. "Why certainly, Deedee. Baseball stockings are stockings with runs in them!"

Ollie glanced disgustedly at Dusty as the girls covered their mouths again and burst into fresh gales of giggles. "Tell me, Miller," he said. "What is square and has bats in the belfry?"

Dusty grinned. "That's easy, Scruggs—girls!"

Not a man on the field was grinning Saturday afternoon, though. They were determined to make good when Mr. Scruggs called, "Play ball!" They even looked as though they meant business. Uniforms had been altered, cleaned, and pressed. The boys wore them with pride.

No one was more determined to make good than Ollie. He had spent two hours the night before and all that morning studying *How to Play Baseball*. He had read the chapters on pitching many times before, but this was the first time he had really concentrated on the chapters on catching. They had been an eye-opener, too. Gosh, the catcher was just about the most important man on the whole team! He had never realized it until then, even though Miss Carmody had told him so many times. Now, at long last, he knew it was true.

To begin with, the catcher really ran the team. He was in a position to see everything that went on. It was up to him to direct many plays. He should tip off the pitcher when a runner was threatening to steal. The other players, too, depended on him for advice, such as the number of outs and the proper play to make. To coin a phrase, a catcher must be right on the ball, Ollie decided.

"Ho, ho, what do you know," he sang out, as he started the ball on a final trip around the horn, "the Red Sox are ready to go-go-go!"

Yankee lead-off man Ed Smith smirked as he strolled up to the plate. "Hey, hey, what do you say," he answered, "the Yankees will beat you guys today!"

Sir Winston growled at him.

Ed's smirk disappeared as Dusty whistled a couple of smokers past him. The third pitch he lined between first and second base. Barney and Mike both went for the ball, and Mike came up with it. Dusty showed he had been doing his homework too. He remembered that a pitcher should cover first on hits to his left. A scowling Ed Smith was out by a stride.

"The way to go in there, gang," Ollie chirped. "Nobody gets to first."

"Two up, two down," Barney chattered as Rex Noyes moved in, a mean look on his face. Rex tapped the plate with the tip of his bat and squared off.

Five pitches later he had worked Dusty up to a full count. On the next one, Rex hit a screamer to Herbie at short. It was too hot to handle and Herbie juggled it. When he finally got a grip on it, his peg to Barney was wide.

But suddenly Ollie popped out of nowhere to take the wild throw. He had remembered that when there was no runner in scoring position, a catcher should back up throws to first base. Rex was held to a single, when two bases seemed assured. Sir Winston noted Ollie's pleased grin and yipped his approval.

"Heads up baseball, Ollie!" Miss Carmody cried.

Ollie felt a warm glow of pride. Hey, this was good. It was kind of nice to do something right, for a change. He signaled Dusty for a low curve ball as Bob Wilson stepped into the box. According to the book, that could make Bob hit a grounder to the infield.

Sure enough, he did. After taking a called strike, he golfed a low one to Barney at first base. Yankee base runner Rex Noyes could not tell whether Barney would take it on the fly or on a pickup, so he hesitated with a short lead. Barney fielded the ball on the first bounce, stepped on the bag, then tagged Rex for a double play before he could break for second.

An organized cheer went up from the Red Sox side of the field: "Big dog, little dog, floppy-eared pup. Come on, Red Sox, let's chew 'em up!" Deedee and Elmira were doing their stuff. Deedee executed a sprightly cartwheel, and Elmira tried to follow suit. She fell on her back with a thud.

"That was a real smart move, Barney," Miss Carmody said as they came in to the bench. "If you had thrown to second instead of tagging Rex, he could have returned to first and been safe, since the force was removed."

"Yeah, I know," Barney said with a grin. "I read the rule book all morning. As I said, if that computer calls me a first baseman, then a first baseman I'm going to be."

Ollie clapped his hands together. "And a winning ball club this is going to be," he said. "Let's go out there and pile up a few runs."

Herbie Snell swept off his cap and made a low bow. "Your wish is my command, O Sire."

As lead-off man, Herbie was not normally a heavy hitter. He was so charged up, however, that he proceeded to pick up a bat and belt one over the right-field fence.

"Not so fast, not so fast," Ollie reprimanded him as he came trotting in from the round tripper. "You're supposed to save those home runs until we load the bases."

"Sorry, Sire," Herbie apologized with a long face. "I'll try to do better the next time."

It was a long inning for the hapless Yankees. Visibly shaken by the Red Sox's unexpected display of smart baseball, they could not seem to put a good play together. Miss Carmody was experimenting with the batting order. Billy Young followed Herbie to the plate and rapped out a single. Then Larry Donovan hit a slow bounder at Yankee pitcher, Bob Wilson, who went for the double play. His throw to second was not

434

in time, and both men were safe. Mike worked Bob for a base on balls, and Ollie stepped up to the plate.

"Swing, bat man," Deedee and Elmira chanted.

"Over the fence, chum," Herbie chided him. "As you said, we need the home runs when the bases are loaded."

Ollie did not waste much time. On the second pitch, he stepped into the ball with a clean, level swing, met it solidly with the fat of the bat and kept on going in a full follow through. He straightened up in time to see the ball drop from sight behind the center-field fence. Caught up in all the excitement, Sir Winston was barking himself hoarse.

That was the second of five home runs. Bob Wilson was shelled from the mound. The Yankees finally rallied in the last two innings, but they were too late with too little. Final score: Red Sox, 13; Yankees, 11.

Coach Carmody called her team together after the customary three cheers had been given. "That was more like it," she said. "If you keep playing that brand of ball, we may stand a chance." She smiled at Ollie's father, who had just joined them. "I think we all owe a vote of thanks to Mr. Scruggs. It was not easy to make out that questionnaire and process the data."

A rousing "yeaaa" was heard for Mr. Scruggs, which he acknowledged with a broad grin. "Believe me, it was well worth it," he told them. "Never have I seen such a change in a team. I predict that you will win the Willowdale Tom Thumb League Championship, because you have been scientifically selected by a computer. Data-processing will triumph again."

"What's this all about?" demanded Nosy Newman, elbowing his way through the group. If anyone ever could smell out news, Nosy could. He covered sports for the weekly *Courier*. He also covered births, deaths, social, business, crime, and all other news. He was tall and hawklike, with dark eyes behind horn-rimmed glasses.

He peered at Mr. Scruggs. "What were you saying about data-processing?"

Mr. Scruggs and Miss Carmody exchanged glances. Finally Miss Carmody shrugged and spread her hands. "Oh well, I guess you might as well know. Some of my players felt they were placed in the wrong positions. Mr. Scruggs offered to devise a questionnaire—an aptitude test, of sorts—which the boys filled out. The data was then fed into one of Mr. Scruggs's computers, which analyzed each player and suggested what position he was best suited for."

Nosy whipped out his notebook and pencil. "And it really worked!" he squeaked. "What a story! What a miracle! What an idea!" He frowned at Miss Carmody. "And whose idea was it, by the way—yours or Big Ollie's?"

Miss Carmody shook her head. "Neither one. The idea was young Oliver's."

Chief Aldrich had been scouting the game. He nodded knowingly. "You sure have a good head on your shoulders, Little Ollie. I could use you on my Braves. You never choke up. You always manage to hit your way out of trouble."

Ollie had to confess that he was proud of the idea also. He was now the center of an admiring throng. Deedee, Elmira, Wilfred, and some of the other girls and boys had gathered around. Nosy Newman was pumping Ollie with questions. He was going to run a feature story in the *Courier*.

Yes, Ollie decided, he was proud of his idea. It had turned out to be a blockbuster. Best of all, it had enabled the Red Sox to break out of their slump.

AUTHOR

Clem Philbrook is interested in all sports, especially skiing, fly fishing, and baseball. The selection you have just read is from his book *Ollie's Team and the Baseball Computer*. While Mr. Philbrook was working on the book, he once wrote, "I decided I needed to bring myself up to date on junior baseball. Consequently, I have been attending Little League games like mad—and enjoying them. In fact, I got so carried away the other night that I instinctively fielded a ball thrown my way, thereby disrupting the game!"

Mr. Philbrook was born in Old Town, Maine. After attending schools in Maine, he worked at various jobs. He is presently working for a book publishing company in New Hampshire.

BRAIN TEASERS

Here are three puzzles for you to try to answer. If you can't figure out the answer to a puzzle after you've thought about it a while, turn the book upside down and read the answer.

A big Indian and a little Indian stood on a hill. The little Indian was the big Indian's son, but the big Indian wasn't the little Indian's father. How was this possible?

A group of people are picking oranges and putting them into a large basket. They work at such a speed that the number of oranges in the basket doubles every minute. At the end of an hour, the basket is finally filled with oranges. When do you think it was half full?

In the Robinson family, each daughter has the same number of brothers as she has sisters, and each son has twice as many sisters as he has brothers. How many sons and daughters are there in the family?

The big Indian was the little Indian's mother.
The basket was half full at the end of 59 minutes.
There are four daughters and three sons.

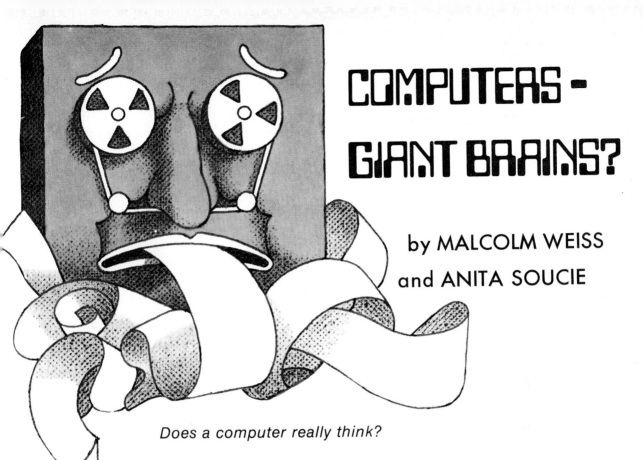

COMPUTERS — GIANT BRAINS?

by MALCOLM WEISS
and ANITA SOUCIE

Does a computer really think?

News item: Recently, two computers battled it out over the chessboard. Things were nip and tuck for a while. Then finally one computer won. The men who arranged the game said their computer could win a second round — with a little work.

Are computers "brainy"? The above news item might lead you to believe so. But men who work with computers say: "GIGO!"

GIGO stands for *Garbage In, Garbage Out.* In other words, if you put wrong information into the computer, you will automatically get wrong results out of it. This does not necessarily happen with the human brain.

For example, take the 17th-century Italian scientist Galileo (gal-uh-lee′oh). He was taught that the heavier an object is the faster it falls. Books said so. But Galileo thought the books and the men were wrong. Through careful experiments, he proved them wrong.

Computers do not think up new ideas in this way. On the other hand, modern computers can do routine jobs much faster than people can. They can make millions of calculations in one second. A man would take years to do this much work!

What's the difference between human thinking and computer "thinking"? Let's take another look at the chess-playing computers mentioned earlier. Suppose these machines could "think" ahead for five moves at a time. If that were true, said a scientist, one move would take years. Here's why:

Chess is an extremely complicated game. There are 400 possible ways of playing the first two moves. After that, the number of possible moves grows rapidly into thousands and millions of choices.

A human player does not consider all these choices. He does not have time to. More important: in order to play a good game, he does not *have* to.

The human player only looks at a few of the possible choices—those that he judges to be best. If he is a good player, his judgments will often turn out to be correct. But the computer would have to try all the possibilities.

How does the human brain make judgments? Scientists are not sure. We do not as yet know much about how the brain thinks.

But scientists do know how computers "think."

The working parts of a computer are much like tiny electric switches. Like the switches in your home, they can turn either on or off. But a computer's switches, called relays, can turn on or off hundreds of millions of times each second.

The computer can "think" only in such on-or-off patterns. The patterns are a kind of simple code. Information and instructions are translated into this code and then fed into the computer on cards or tape.

It may seem strange that such a code can hold so much information. But think of the Morse code. This code also uses only two symbols, a dot and a dash. You can think of them as representing either "on" or "off." It takes 26 simple patterns of dots and dashes to stand for all the letters of our alphabet.

A computer can try out hundreds of millions of such patterns in one second. It can also store them in its "memory."

In order for the chess-playing computers to find the best moves, they had to search through all the moves stored in their "memory." As we have seen, this search goes on at incredible speed. Yet the computers in the chess match sometimes took several hours to make a move. Human chess players may be slow, but not that slow.

The computer's "memory" is huge, but it cannot cover all the possible moves in chess. When its "memory" runs out, the computer's instructions "tell" it to pick out any move that does not break the rules of the game. That is where the judgment of the human player has the edge on the machine.

The instructions fed into a computer are called a *program.* The men who prepare the instructions are called *programmers.* A program must tell the computer what to do at each step. It must tell the computer how to use the information stored in its "memory," the information fed into it beforehand. Nothing can be left to the imagination because the computer doesn't have any imagination.

"Stupid" as the computer may be, its fast "thinking" makes it a valuable tool in modern life.

EVALUATING STATEMENTS
OF FACT AND OPINION

If you were reading an encyclopedia article about shells, you'd be surprised, wouldn't you, to come across the sentence below?

"Collecting shells is a much less interesting hobby than saving stamps."

Material in encyclopedias and certain other kinds of reference books is usually strictly factual, and when you are reading for information, you expect that most of what you read will be statements of fact. In such books, instead of the sentence quoted, you would be more likely to find a statement like this:

"Many people collect shells as a hobby."

You know that a statement of fact can be tested to determine whether or not it is true. And you've learned that, if you actually want to test a statement of fact, you can do so by using your own knowledge and experience. For example, "A football game has four quarters" is a statement of fact. You may be able to test that statement from your own knowledge, as one who plays football or watches football games. Or to test the statement "Water expands when it freezes," you yourself could conduct an experiment by putting a full pan of water in the freezing compartment of your refrigerator.

If you tried to check most statements of fact, however, you would have to use reference books and other sources. For instance, you couldn't test by your own experience the statements "Columbus sailed to America in 1492" and "The first man to land on the moon was Neil Armstrong." You couldn't transport yourself in time and space to be with Columbus during his voyage and to be on the moon when Armstrong landed. The statements could be tested, nevertheless, by checking such sources as a history book, an encyclopedia, an almanac, newspapers, and magazines.

A statement of opinion is based, not on fact, but on what one individual or group thinks, feels, or believes to be true. For example, "Summer is the nicest time of the year" is a statement of opinion because it tells how one person feels and what he believes. Other people may like fall, spring, or winter better. There is no way to prove which season is nicest; it is a matter of personal opinion.

Sometimes what you are looking for are statements of fact. For a school report, you may want to know just how long it takes to travel from earth to the moon. You're not interested in knowing how long someone *thinks* the trip takes; you want to know the exact number of hours. You're looking for a statement of fact.

But sometimes you're looking for a statement of opinion. If you're trying to learn to swim and are reading a book written by a champion swimmer, you may want to get his opinion about which swimming stroke he thinks a beginner should practice first.

There are some subjects about which only statements of opinion can be made. You may wonder, for instance, if there has ever been any kind of plant or animal life on Mars, but you can't at present find statements of fact to answer that question. No one can give a first-hand report from having been on Mars, and no one can say for certain whether there is evidence of life on the planet or not. However, scientists who have spent years studying Mars have formed opinions, and you would undoubtedly be interested to read their statements of opinion.

Statements of opinion can be just as valuable to you as statements of fact. What is important is for you to be able to distinguish one from the other, and this is especially important when you are reading material which contains both kinds of statements. Suppose you and your family are planning a trip to Washington, D.C., and you are reading a travel book about the city to find out what you might see while you're there. If you can't tell the difference between fact and opinion, how might this sentence from the book affect your sightseeing plans?

"Near the Washington Monument stands the most interesting building in the city to visit, the Bureau of Engraving and Printing where our paper money and postage stamps are printed."

If you took the entire sentence as a statement of fact, wouldn't you think that the Bureau of Engraving and Printing was the first building you should go to see? But if you recognized that one part of the sentence — "The most interesting building in the city to visit" — is merely a statement of the author's opinion, you might decide that there are several other buildings which you personally would rather visit first.

When weighing a statement of opinion that you read, keep in mind that the author is acquainted with the subject you are reading about. When an author refers to a building as "most interesting," you can be fairly sure that it is an exceptionally interesting building, although you may not consider it "most" interesting. Even when you yourself are well informed on the subject about which you are reading, don't just ignore any statement of opinion made by the author which disagrees with what you think. If you can find out on what the author's opinion is based, you may well decide to change your own opinion.

Keep in mind, too, that an author sometimes wants to persuade you to share his opinion on a subject. You may have noticed this in newspaper columns about politics, for example, or in sports articles in magazines. In order to convince you to think as he does, the author may emphasize points that support his opinion, but he may only touch on or perhaps not even mention points that oppose it.

And don't forget that everyone makes mistakes. It is not unusual for people to be wrong in their opinions or in their facts, but statements of fact remain statements of fact even though they are incorrect or untrue. If you read "The Mississippi is the world's longest river," you would recognize it as a statement of fact, but you might doubt that it is true. When you found in other references that the Mississippi is not the world's longest river, you would conclude that the author was mistaken. Although he made a statement of fact, the statement was untrue.

Similarly, in a statement of opinion an author might say, "Probably the number of space flights to the moon will increase rapidly." If that number does not increase rapidly, the author's opinion will turn out to be incorrect, but the statement he made will still be a statement of opinion.

Discussion

Help your class answer the following questions:
1. How does a statement of fact differ from a statement of opinion?
2. What example can you think up of a statement of fact that is true? Of a statement of fact that is not true?
3. What example can you give of a statement of opinion that you believe is correct? Of a statement of opinion that you believe is incorrect?
4. When might you be interested to read statements of opinion? For what different purposes would you want to read statements of fact?

On your own

Some of the following sentences are statements of fact, some are statements of opinion, and some contain both statements of fact and statements of opinion. After the numbers 1 to 10 on your paper, write *F* if the sentence is a statement of fact only, *O* if it is a statement of opinion only, and *B* if sentence contains both a statement of fact and a statement of opinion.

1. I think they are going to the park after school.
2. Jack weighs more than ninety pounds.
3. The forests in the northern part of that country may eventually be a valuable resource.
4. California was the fiftieth state to become part of the United States.
5. The Alps, which cover most of Switzerland, are the most beautiful mountains in the world.
6. Babe Ruth, the greatest player in baseball, hit sixty home runs in 1927.
7. There are twenty-five players on a major-league baseball team.
8. People from the earth can never live on Mars.
9. Today's automobiles are not built to fly, but someday all automobiles will be able to travel in the air as well as on the ground.
10. Tom, who was elected president of the student council, seemed very happy.

Checking your work

If you are asked to do so, read your answer for one or more of the sentences above and tell why you answered as you did.

ALBERT SCHWEITZER: *Jungle Doctor*

by ANITA DANIEL

Albert Schweitzer has rightfully been called one of the greatest men of our time. He was born in Germany in 1875, and before he was thirty years old, he had accomplished far more than most men accomplish in a lifetime. While still in his twenties, Schweitzer had earned a wide reputation as an organist, as an authority on the music and life of Johann Sebastian Bach—the great German composer, and as a writer on theology—the study of religion. Then at the age of thirty, Schweitzer gave up his successful, comfortable life and set out to become a medical missionary so that he might devote the remainder of his life to serving his fellow men. After finishing his medical training, Schweitzer left for French Equatorial Africa, where, he felt, there was the greatest need for a doctor.

In this story from the book THE STORY OF ALBERT SCHWEITZER, *Anita Daniel tells about the beginning of Schweitzer's long service to humanity in Africa.*

On a glorious spring day of the year 1913, Albert Schweitzer, accompanied by his wife, left Europe and all he knew behind him and soon sailed for the Africa he knew only from books and from hearsay.

With seventy boxes of medicines and surgical instruments, equipped with unshakable faith and tremendous goodwill, he began his long voyage into the unknown.

The crossing lasted several weeks and the weather was very stormy. Most of the passengers were seasick. But not Schweitzer. Having met a specialist in tropical medicine aboard, he spent hours every day in discussion with him.

It was from this doctor that he accidentally received his first warning, "Never, never take one step in Africa without a tropical helmet on your head." For if a white man exposed his bare head to the sun for even a few minutes he might become delirious. Only the natives were safe, with their heads protected by thick black hair, and their bodies shielded by the dark pigment of their skin.

While almost everyone on board was worn out by the long and uncomfortable trip, Albert Schweitzer was full of joy and excitement when the ship finally weighed anchor at the coastal city of Libreville (lee′bruh-vil).

As the small white steamer, which they had boarded at Cape Lopez (loh′pez), slowly wound its way up the broad Ogowe (oh′goh-way′) River, the Schweitzers had their first taste of the almost unbearable tropical heat and felt the fierce bites of the African mosquitoes. The first impressions were overwhelming. Here and there the dark foliage of the jungle was aflame with the bright flowers of lianas, green and red parrots, crested cranes, weaverbirds, kingfishers, flashy gold and green pippios, and round-eyed owls. Birds

of every color and shape were flying, singing, and fishing under the eyes of the excited voyagers. Gorgeously colored butterflies fluttered in the still air. And there were the first monkeys! They stared at the Schweitzers from the palm trees, while from the muddy banks, crocodiles sleepily blinked at the familiar sight of the paddlewheeler.

At sundown the steamer anchored in a small bay, leaving again at dawn on the last leg of the journey. As the river narrowed, the current became stronger, and it took another day before the Schweitzers finally had the first glimpse of their destination, Lambaréné (lahm/buh-ray/nay).

Lambaréné was an ideal spot for a hospital. The Ogowe River, with its hundreds of miles of waterways reaching far into the jungle, was most convenient for the natives traveling in their canoes. Besides, there was not a single physician within a hundred miles.

But this ideal spot in 1913 had no decent landing place. So the Schweitzers were forced to abandon their steamer and transfer once more, this time to native canoes made of hollow tree trunks. These were long, very narrow, and very delicately balanced boats

that required in their handling a great deal of skill and, on the part of the Schweitzers, a great deal of confidence. But courageously they let themselves down, and— holding fast to the sides of the canoe—they completed the last lap of their long, long journey.

It was a gay trip. The young paddlers sang merry native songs all along the way, while they paddled standing up, keeping their canoes in balance with their bodies.

White mission people, black people, and swarms of black children, all wanting to help unload the luggage, greeted the Schweitzers upon landing.

They were home at last!

But it soon appeared that it was not much of a home. Inspecting the small house with the aid of a kerosene lamp, the Schweitzers saw to their horror a room full of flying cockroaches and an enormous spider, so disgusting that impulsively Schweitzer killed it. It was the first and probably the last time he ever killed a spider. This repulsive insect, he soon learned, was very useful since it fed on the malaria-bearing mosquito.

The house stood high above the

ground on iron pillars. It was surrounded by a porch. Through the window, the view was wonderful. But inside, there was nothing to look at—just two small, bare rooms.

Schweitzer cared little how he was housed, at least in the beginning. But where, where was there even a crude structure that he could use to start the hospital?

The lumbering season was in full swing, explained the missionaries who had welcomed him. All hands were busy cutting mahogany, rosewood, and other fine wood for export. It was impossible to build without help.

Where, then, would he store his seventy precious cases of medical supplies, the arrival of which he expected within a week or two?

Above all, what was he to do with all these people? Surrounding Schweitzer was a crowd of men, women, and children. Their eyes were fixed upon him, silently but ardently pleading.

The word had spread far and wide that a doctor was coming, and nothing would stop the natives from journeying to Lambaréné. Canoes loaded with the sick and their families continued to arrive. The sick painfully climbed up from the river, or were carried by their relatives up to Schweitzer's little house on the hill. He must look after them—but how, and where . . . ?

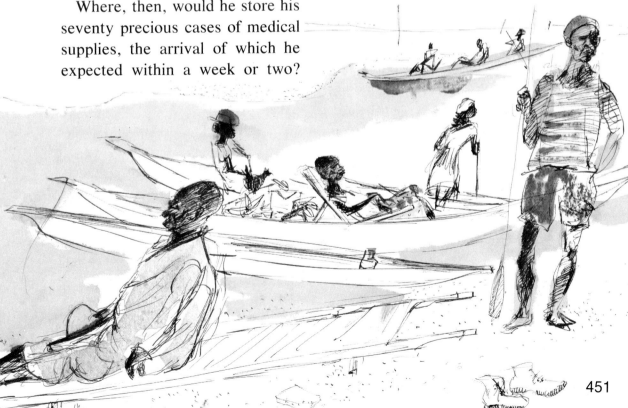

Right from the start, from the moment he set foot in Lambaréné, Albert Schweitzer faced the simple, yet overwhelming and ever present fact that whatever it was he wanted, he had to do it himself.

Some natives had contagious diseases. Fearing others might catch them, he would not allow the sick into the two little rooms of his house. As a result, he started practicing in the open air. Drenched with sweat, he worked under the torrid African sun. Regularly every evening thunderstorms came. Rain poured down in sheets. All the supplies had to be rushed under the porch.

He would have to find some other way of providing a roof over his head when he was operating. Searching the hospital grounds, he discovered an empty chicken house, long in disuse. Why not use it?

The necessary repairs were soon made. The Schweitzers patched the holes in the roof as best they could. With brooms and brushes they scrubbed and whitewashed the walls. A cot borrowed from the mission house was placed in the center of the floor and served as an operating table.

In this tiny, windowless room, the heat was atrocious. To make matters worse, the thatched roof let the dangerous sun rays come through. Neither the Doctor nor the nurse, who was his wife, dared take off their heavy helmets.

No sooner had Albert Schweitzer found this temporary and uncomfortable solution than he was faced with the next problem. Every tribe spoke a different language. How was he to understand them all and how could he be understood?

A lucky discovery brought the answer. Among a batch of new patients there arrived one day a bright-looking native, by the name of Joseph Azvavanu (ahz′vah-vah′noo), who spoke French fluently. He had been working as a cook for European settlers but had lost his job because of ill health. Schweitzer easily persuaded Joseph to remain at Lambaréné as assistant and interpreter.

Joseph was both bright and very able. He had an incredible memory. In no time, he had learned to recognize the various medicines by the shape of the characters on their labels, though he continued to be unable to read them! To his new job, the medical assistant brought a colorful touch.

His anatomic descriptions were expressed in the language of his former culinary job. He would say, "This man has pains in his right leg of mutton." Or, "This woman has pains in her upper left cutlet and in her filet."

Medical consultations started at eight-thirty in the morning.

The patients sat waiting for the Doctor on shaded benches in front of the chicken house. Every morning, Joseph recited the Doctor's orders:

1. The Doctor forbids you to spit on the hospital grounds.
2. The Doctor forbids you to talk in a loud voice.
3. The Doctor cannot take care of everybody during the morning. So the sick and those who accompany them must bring food for one day.

Joseph ended by requesting that the words of the Doctor be spread to all the neighboring villages. After each sentence, the natives shook their heads in acknowledgment. When Joseph had

finished, they commented endlessly upon the meaning of every word.

Some sort of hospital organization slowly started to emerge. The Doctor's invaluable aide, Mrs. Schweitzer, took care of the instruments and assisted with all the surgical cases. She distributed the food, and she supervised the washing of the linen and the bandages. Nothing in Lamberéné was ever thrown away. Bandages were washed, disinfected, and used over and over again.

Before leaving the hospital, every patient was carefully labeled. Hung around his neck was a piece of cardboard on which were inscribed his name and the number corresponding to the case history in the Doctor's book. In this book, against the patient's name, the thrifty Doctor listed not only his diagnosis and prescriptions, but also every little glass bottle or tin box in which the medicine was supplied. How precious these things were thousands of miles away from civilization, no one can imagine unless he himself has lived in the middle of the jungle. It was of the utmost importance that every one of these receptacles be returned to the hospital. Only glass or tin protected the medicine —pill, powder, liquid, or cream— against the tropical humidity.

But it was a hopeless task to try to recover those precious vials. The natives found them much to their taste and wore them as ornaments, so much so, that in every one of his letters, Schweitzer implored his friends in Europe to send him empty bottles, corks, tubes, and tin containers.

At each and every step there were difficulties that no one in Europe could have understood. Even Dr. Schweitzer himself, with all his foresight, could never have imagined such difficulties. Take, for instance, the matter of the prescriptions—how to use the medicine that was packed in the precious bottle. It took a great deal of time and patience to teach the natives that the box or bottle carried a label that told the exact amount of medicine to be taken. Those who could read were asked to help the others. Before the patient was dismissed, Schweitzer rehearsed the prescription, "Three drops in the morning and three drops in the evening." But more likely than not, once away, the patient would swallow the entire contents of the bottle at one gulp, eat the pomade instead of rub-

bing it into his skin, and spread the powder given him to swallow over his ulcerated wounds. It was hopeless!

"The Doctor kills a man, then he brings him to life again," was the way the natives explained anesthesia. To Dr. Schweitzer's amazement, they all wanted to be operated on and resented it when it was not necessary!

But it was not always so easy. Whenever a patient died because his case was hopeless, rumor had it that the white man had killed him. There was a girl who used to shriek each time she met the Doctor, "I saw with my own eyes how a living man was brought here. The Doctor stayed alone with him the whole night, and the next day the man was dead." Some said that he must be a "white leopardman," the most dreaded kind of man among the natives.

At times Schweitzer fell into deep despair. Would he be able to cope with his self-imposed task, with no cooperation from anywhere? His supplies of medicine and money were soon coming to an end. The heat wore him down, and the lack of facilities sapped his strength. What could one man do in the face of such misery?

"Yet what are all these disagreeable things compared with the joy of being here, working, helping?" he wrote during this same period. "However limited one's means, how much one can do! Just to see the relief and joy of those who have been treated, bandaged, and given rest after they have dragged their poor, bleeding feet through the jungle. That in itself makes work here worthwhile."

Over the years, Dr. Schweitzer built a large hospital and medical center that served thousands of African people yearly. This great man died in 1965, fifty-two years after he began his first hospital in a chicken house. But his great work is being carried on by other dedicated people.

AUTHOR

Anita Daniel was born in Rumania. She attended school in France, and later moved to the United States.

For many years, Mrs. Daniel wrote articles for newspapers and magazines. Her job was an exciting one because it enabled her to meet and talk with artists, kings, and statesmen.

During her extensive travels, Mrs. Daniel often visited Dr. Schweitzer at his hospital in Africa. She decided to write a book about this great man for boys and girls.

456

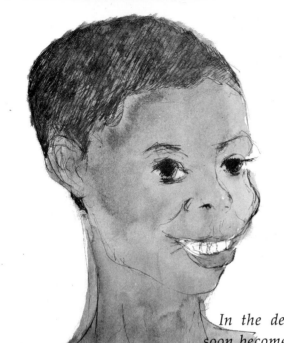

MY FRIEND IN AFRICA

By Frederick Franck

In the dense jungles of Africa, a small wound can soon become a serious problem if it is not given proper medical attention. Bolo, a young African boy, had suffered from an ulcer on his foot for several weeks. Then one day Dr. Franck, a dentist at Dr. Schweitzer's hospital in Lambaréné, came through the village where Bolo lived. He saw the ugly sore on the boy's foot and persuaded Bolo and his parents that Bolo should return with him to the hospital. But once at the hospital, Bolo became a problem because he refused to stay in bed.

The story you are about to read is true, and it is just a small part of the book MY FRIEND IN AFRICA. *The story was written and illustrated by Dr. Frederick Franck, the dentist who brought Bolo to the hospital.*

One morning Dr. Schweitzer came into the ward. With him was a tall boy a little older than Bolo. Dr. Schweitzer looked around as if he were searching for someone. "Where is 'the-boy-who-will-not-stay-put?'" he demanded.

Everyone laughed, but Bolo ducked his head. Then, without waiting for an answer, the Old Doctor and the tall boy went straight to Bolo's bed.

The white-haired doctor looked thoughtfully at Bolo.

"What is your great trouble with that bunk?" he asked solemnly.

Bolo said, "There is so much I want to see outside."

"H'm," said the Doctor. "Well, perhaps that is a good enough reason for driving my orderlies crazy." Then he introduced the tall boy at his side. "This boy is Darri. He has come to visit you."

Darri and Bolo smiled at each other. The Old Doctor smiled at them both and went away.

"He has so much to do," Darri said. "All day long someone wants him: doctors and nurses and patients, and visitors, too. People come from over the sea to talk to him and look at the Hospital."

Bolo said, "I like him, and I like the Hospital, but I do not like being a patient. I thought it would be fun, but it isn't. I want to get up and see things."

The older boy sat on the foot of the bed, cross-legged. Bolo sat at the head, hugging his knees.

"I was in bed here a long, long time," Darri said. "I was so sick I didn't mind being in bed. Sometimes I think I was so sick I didn't know *where* I was."

Bolo was startled. He had never seen anyone so sick as that. Then he noticed Darri's arms for the first time. They were so thin they looked like sticks, Bolo thought.

"Was what happened to your arms your sickness?" he asked.

"Yes," said Darri. "But the English doctor here stopped the sickness and saved my life. They said he had to work very hard to make me well."

"Do you feel bad about your arms?" Bolo thought he would feel terrible if they were *his* arms.

The older boy said, "Yes, at first I couldn't do anything with my arms. I couldn't even hold anything in my hands, but now I can. See?" And he picked up a wooden stool and lifted it from one side of the bunk to the other.

Suddenly he scowled so fiercely that Bolo wondered what was the matter. "You must do what the doctors tell you, Bolo!" Darri exclaimed. "Don't you want to have a good leg instead of a bad one?"

"Of course I do!"

"Don't you want to get outside? I could take you all around the Hospital and show you all the animals. Wouldn't you like that?"

"Yes, of course," said Bolo. "That is just what I want to do!"

"Then you must stay on your bunk. I heard the doctors say your foot will heal if you give it a chance. But when you get up and move around, you keep it from healing. You are a silly boy if you keep yourself in here when you could be getting outside soon!"

It really wasn't long after that when Bolo heard a cheerful voice saying, "Bolo, you can get up today." What an exciting

announcement! Bolo bounced out of his bunk. Then he bounced back again, fearfully. "Are you sure?"

He was worried because it was his friend the dentist who brought him the good news. "You are not a foot doctor, you are a tooth doctor. Are you sure it is all right for me to get up now?"

Dr. Frederick was certain. "I have checked with all kinds of doctors," he said. "You have been so good that your foot is healing nicely. I will show you how to use a stick to help you walk, and then you may go out. Darri will be here soon to go with you."

"Outdoors, outdoors!" sang Bolo. Never had he wanted anything so much, and never had the world seemed so pleasant. The Hospital was the finest place, and the doctors were the greatest people — in all Africa!

After that happy day, Bolo said two important things to himself every night before he fell asleep. "I love the Hospital. Some day I will be a doctor here." Sometimes he added, "I hope a boy like me could become a doctor. . . ."

He had always taken animals for granted, but here in the Hospital he began to see them in a new way.

Any animal that happened to come to the Hospital, from the jungle or with people, was welcome, and it could stay forever if it wanted to. So there were nearly as many animals about as there were people. The Old Doctor did not take them for granted. He seemed to love the animals just as much as he did people, people of his own family. It made Bolo think.

All the doctors and nurses at the Hospital soon discovered that Bolo had learned to love animals and that animals loved him. Before long, the doctors were calling on Bolo whenever any creature, wild or tame, needed looking after.

"Bolo, watch over that dog Bumble today. I think he is not very well."

"Bolo, don't let Petite, the cat, run around today or she

will hurt her bad foot again. And see that she doesn't tear off the bandage."

"That white-faced monkey has to be fed carefully for a while. Tell Bolo. He'll take good care of the little creature."

Bolo was delighted. He looked after the lively animals, as well as the sick ones. He checked up every morning on the ducks and the chickens, the goats and the sheep, and the pelicans and parrots. He visited the wild boars in their fenced-in yard, and the graceful, soft-eyed antelopes in theirs.

He talked to the tame stork and the sleepy-looking owl that had once been patients and were now pets. He had more than a dozen dogs and cats of all kinds, a young chimpanzee, and a monkey to play with.

He called all of them by name — Mombambra, the stork; Fritzli, the chimp; Tecla, the wild boar; Jackie, the toucan; and all the dogs and cats. Sometimes a little parade went up or down one of the Hospital streets, Bolo with a white-nosed monkey on his shoulder and Fritzli at his heels, grabbing at his ankle with every step. Then a dog or two followed, and perhaps a goat.

When the dogs were not around, a shy young antelope followed Bolo wherever he went. The antelope limped from a broken leg, and Bolo limped because of his healing foot. Bolo would hold out his hand, and the antelope would stop to be petted and stroked by the boy.

The patients and their families and the doctors and nurses were amazed at the sight. People in Africa usually are not so friendly with animals.

Early one morning, Bolo was going to call on the wild boars when he heard a big voice booming his name.

"Bolo! Bolo!"

That was Dr. Schweitzer's voice! Bolo was so surprised he didn't answer. He just stared up the street toward the sound of the voice. What could it mean, the great Doctor,

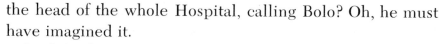

the head of the whole Hospital, calling Bolo? Oh, he must have imagined it.

"Bolo! Where are you?"

Then Bolo believed his ears. He moved faster than he had ever moved before. Half hopping, half hobbling, he hurried up the Hospital street.

There was Dr. Schweitzer outside the Pharmacy, the building where much of the Hospital work was done. With him was the tooth doctor who was already Bolo's great friend, Dr. Frederick from America.

There were a nurse and two men of Bolo's own people. And there was a monkey. No, it was a baby gorilla.

The nurse was holding the little animal, and it was bleeding badly. Dr. Schweitzer and Dr. Frederick were talking angrily about people with guns, and Bolo realized that the little gorilla had been shot.

Bolo's eyes grew wide and his mouth made a big circle. He sucked in his breath when the little gorilla cried out with pain.

Bolo could almost feel what the animal felt. He felt great anger, too, that such a little animal had been hurt.

The gorilla cried again, and Bolo pushed into the group around Dr. Schweitzer.

"There you are, Bolo," said the Doctor. "You are the one who is so good with animals. Come and help me take care of this poor fellow. We must get the bullet out."

Bolo's eyes grew even wider, and for a moment he was frightened.

"I do not . . . I do not know how," he stammered.

"I know how!" said the Old Doctor gruffly. "I will take out the bullet and you will hold the gorilla on the operating table. Then you can care for him afterward. Come now! Be a man! You will see blood more than once in your life. I want you to help me."

With the little gorilla in his arms, the Doctor went off to the operating room in the Pharmacy. Bolo squared his shoulders and followed. "After all, if I want to be a doctor . . ." he mused.

The next day a bandaged gorilla baby sat on Bolo's lap under a palm tree, eating its dinner from a spoon and holding tight to one of Bolo's hands.

People stopped to talk when they saw the pair. "Look. Bolo has a new patient."

Dr. Frederick came by and asked how the patient was doing. "Is he eating well? Let me know if he needs a tooth filled!"

Bolo laughed. "I will. But you can draw a picture of him any time." Dr. Frederick drew pictures when he was not treating people's teeth. Around the Hospital, everyone called him "the-tooth-doctor-who-draws." Bolo thought the drawings were beautiful, especially the drawings of animals.

"I'll give you the first picture I do of your new friend," Dr. Frederick promised. "Have you given him a name, Bolo?"

"I am just giving him one now," said Bolo. "I think I will name him Peter."

"Peter is a funny name for a gorilla!"

"It is a *good* name," Bolo insisted, frowning. "It is just as good as Percival is for a pelican, or Mombambra is for a stork!"

Dr. Frederick laughed. "You are right. It certainly is. Well, Peter seems to like you very much. But what will you do when he grows big? You cannot hold him on your lap then. After he is grown, he could crush your bones with a friendly hug, you know."

Bolo knew that. He had often heard tales of what a huge gorilla could do to a man. Yet Peter could not go back to the jungle if he stayed at the Hospital very long. An animal raised among people does not know how to live in the jungle anymore. It is killed soon by the wilder animals that have always lived there.

"I will think of something to do," Bolo said, "before Peter gets too big to stay here." He stroked the gorilla's head with the back of his hand.

Peter looked very sad and serious, as if he understood the problem.

AUGHOR

AUTHOR

In 1959 Dr. Frederick Franck set up a dental clinic for Dr. Albert Schweitzer at Schweitzer's hospital in Lambaréné, Africa. There Dr. Franck and his wife spent three summers treating people who came hundreds of miles for dental care. During that time, Dr. Franck, who is an excellent artist, made hundreds of drawings of the people and things he saw there. He also wrote three books about his experiences in Africa: *African Sketchbook, My Friend in Africa,* and *My Days with Albert Schweitzer.* Dr. Franck and his wife still continue to write to Bolo, the boy you just read about. Bolo is now a college student in Africa. Dr. Franck was born in Holland, but is now an American citizen. Although he had to devote most of his time to studying dentistry, he still managed to find time to study drawing and painting.

THE GHOST OF BLACK JOHN

by William MacKellar

Chuck Adams finds that a small
Scottish island can provide even
more excitement than
Long Island, New York.

A soft mist drifted down from the mountains, wreathing the trees in drab gray cloaks so that they stood out in the gloomy half-light like sad and abandoned ghosts. Wearily, Chuck Adams withdrew his face from the window.

"Rain and fog and herring! I wonder if the sun ever shines in these Scottish islands? Boy, will I be glad to see Long Island again!"

Mrs. Adams smiled at her son.

"It's really not that bad, Chuck. At least the people in the Hebrides who live here all the year round don't mind it. Besides, we'll only be here for a few more weeks until your father finishes his survey for the government."

"Just the same, Pop can't finish counting these herring soon enough for me. No kidding, did you ever see such a sleepy place?"

"It's quiet, naturally, Chuck. And it's not just counting herring. Your father has been invited by the British Government to suggest methods of processing and canning herring. It will mean more fish for the people in Scotland."

"They can have my share," he said, "any time!" He went over to the window and gazed out at the desolate scene that met his eye. The mist had lifted somewhat. Gray, ominous clouds rushed past, trailing thin serpents of vapor over the bleak mountaintops. What a place!

Suddenly he spied the compact figure of a boy coming towards the cottage from the direction of the glen. Chuck turned to his mother with a smile.

"Here comes Sandy MacLean with the weekly newspaper! Beats me how they ever get enough news to fill it." He opened the door and greeted the dark-haired youth.

"A bonnie day, is it no?" Sandy's voice rose and fell in the gentle Highland tongue. His speech held little of the difficult brogue that the American boy had assumed was natural to all Scotsmen.

"A bonnie day?" repeated Chuck, startled. "Why it's raining!"

The ghost of a smile visited the Scottish boy's lips. "*Och* (ahk), but the sun will be out soon, Chuck. Wind, sun, and rain: it's lucky we are in the islands to see so much of nature."

What's the sense of arguing, thought Chuck. He wouldn't

understand. Besides he's really not a bad fellow. A little serious in his ways but friendly enough. Glancing at him again, Chuck marked the finely developed shoulders under the heavy wool jersey and the strong, thick fingers that cupped the newspapers. Make a good end on a football team back home, he thought.

"Anything new, Sandy?" said Chuck, glancing hopefully at the front page of the paper. "Surely something must happen here once in a while?"

"Well, now, there will be the new minister coming soon," intoned Sandy in his soft voice, "aye something, it seems."

Chuck nodded wearily and tossed the paper over on the bureau. "I can imagine," he muttered absently. He was instantly aware that the Scottish boy was eyeing him quietly. "No offense, Sandy. It's just that, well, a tiny island off the Scottish coast. I mean, what should I expect to happen here?" He hoped he hadn't offended Sandy.

A tiny glint of light glimmered in the brooding eyes of the Scottish youth. "There will be things happening this day on the island," he said softly, "that in

all America, there will not be the like."

"What things?" said Chuck.

"Oh, things," repeated Sandy slyly. "Like ghosts for instance."

"Ghosts?" echoed Chuck in surprise. Had he heard right?

Sandy nodded, and his mysterious manner gave way to an expression of quiet, Gaelic pride.

"Aye, for there's few places indeed can boast of a ghost the like of Black John."

"You're not telling me that you believe in ghosts?" Chuck could hardly control his amazement.

"It was three hundred years

ago that Black John saw his son leave for the sea. He never returned. But the old man would not believe he was dead. Aye, every penny he had he spent in the search for him. And when he died, poor and lonely, he was no less faithful. For the ghost of him continued to wait by the water, wrapped in the shrouds of his burial and with a lantern to guide his son home."

He stopped and a look of stubborn pride burned deep in his eyes. "I myself have seen him."

Chuck felt his jaw drop in astonishment as Sandy recited the story.

"You believe in ghosts?" was all he could say.

"In the ghost of Black John, aye," answered Sandy.

It's too crazy to continue talking about, thought Chuck. He stuck his hands deep in his pockets, whistled lightly, and sauntered over to the window.

"You will be thinking Black John does not exist, Chuck?" The soft rhythm of the Highland boy's tongue held no note of resentment or annoyance. Only his dark eyes glowed.

Chuck shrugged with good-humored indifference. Before he could answer, the door opened and his father's friendly voice rang out in the kitchen.

"Boy, am I tired! Really cold out in the water this morning." As he drew off his sea boots, his eyes fell on the Scottish boy. "Hello, Sandy! Stay for lunch?"

"Thank you, Mr. Adams, but it's myself should be getting along with my papers, I'm thinking." He paused at the door. "There will be those anxious for the news. Good day!"

As the door closed softly behind Sandy, Chuck scratched his head in bewilderment. "Imagine anyone believing in ghosts today? I didn't mean to offend Sandy, but this business of Black John!" He shook his head, baffled.

"Black John?" repeated Chuck's father with a frown. "I've been hearing about him. Something of a local celebrity, I guess. Talking about celebrities, we had a few government inspectors from Glasgow today. Seems there's quite a bit of smuggling lately."

"Sure wish somebody would smuggle some of those herring out of here," muttered Chuck gloomily, as he eyed his mother's preparations for lunch. "If I eat any more, they'll be putting a label on me and shipping me back to America in a can," he said with mock horror.

Some time later that day he again met Sandy. The latter was apparently headed for the *clachan* (klak′uhn), or small village, where he lived, but he paused when he saw Chuck.

"Perhaps, Chuck, you would be liking to see Black John for yourself?"

Chuck stared at him. It was about time he settled this business once and for all. "Listen, Sandy," he said bluntly. "I don't want to hurt your feelings, but frankly I wish you'd stop all this talk about ghosts."

"But it's myself has seen him walking from the ruined castle on the mountain of Ben-y-Gloe to the sea." Sandy paused, and the quiet seriousness left him to be replaced by an expression of amused challenge. "Perhaps, being a stranger, you would be a wee bit scared to see for yourself."

Chuck felt a hot flush of anger charge through him.

"Afraid of an old wives' tale?" he scoffed. "Any time you plan a visit to your pet ghost, Sandy, let me know."

Sandy nodded. "Tonight then?" and the same mocking smile was on his lips as he softly said good-bye.

"Tonight," said Chuck grimly. He watched the Scottish lad as he made his way with long, easy strides to his cottage. It would give him a lot of pleasure to convince Sandy that there were no more ghosts in the Hebrides than there were in Babylon, Long Island.

The heavy mists from the sea had rolled away. The night was clear and cool as the boys made their way silently across the field of heather and ferns towards the grim bulk of Ben-y-Gloe, the Mountain of the Mist. A yellow moon, knee-deep in little pools of feathery clouds, sifted a soft light over the stark scene and illuminated the sheer precipice that swept down to the sea. Far off, Chuck could hear the low boom of the Atlantic breakers as they dashed against the rocks. He shivered.

"You're sure old John will be home tonight, Sandy?" He tried to make his voice sound casual, but deep inside he could feel his heart press against his ribs in throbs of excitement.

"Perhaps. We shall see."

The Scottish boy said no more. For the next half hour, Chuck followed him in silence as they clambered up the narrow trail that ran dangerously along the black cliff. Once, Chuck's eyes strayed to the great abyss that yawned up just a foot from the path. A clammy shiver of fear gripped him, and his head swam before he desperately swept his eyes back to the trail. Quite suddenly he felt the ground beneath him level off. They were at the top of Ben-y-Gloe.

Soundlessly, Sandy pulled him down and pointed. Chuck stared in unbelief at the sight that met his eyes.

Silhouetted in stark relief against the moon, a huge black mass of rock soared up from the earth a mere hundred yards away. What must once have been among the noblest Hebridean castles was now a forlorn heap of weather-beaten, ivy-strewed boulders. Three of its enormous walls still stood, and one of its four original turrets continued to face the sea. Something about the melancholy ruin, something menacing and evil, caused tiny beads of perspiration to gather on Chuck's forehead despite the sharp chill in the air.

"The house of Black John," came Sandy's voice, brittle with tenseness. Again Chuck struggled to fight off the nameless feeling of dread that sifted out from the gloomy castle. Again he shivered.

Silently they inched their way on their stomachs across the sparsely vegetated ground towards the grim pile of crumbling stone from which, three hundred years ago, Black John had seen his son depart for the sea. Suddenly from the turret of the castle came a quick stab of light. It was gone as quickly as it had come.

"Did you see that?" The words

seemed to pry themselves out from between Chuck's clenched teeth.

Sandy nodded. "It is Black John lighting his lantern," he whispered, and Chuck felt his skin crawl in a horror he had never known in all his life.

Again there was a flash of light, only now the light came not from the tower but from an opening in the wall facing the sea.

"He is coming down to look for his son," said Sandy, gripping Chuck's arm.

Chuck nodded, afraid that the excitement in his voice might betray him.

"Here he comes!" Sandy's voice was a low hiss beside him. Again Chuck nodded and crouched lower behind a tussock of heather as the flickering light moved slowly away from the castle towards where they lay concealed. Slowly, as the seconds passed, it became possible to see the outlines of a gaunt, shapeless figure. A figure wrapped in a long, black, funeral shroud. The ghost of Black John.

Chuck's breath froze in his throat as the long-dead Highland chieftain made his way slowly towards the sea that had taken his son three centuries ago. He passed only a few feet from where the boys lay, the lantern held rigidly in a bony hand.

"Let us go," whispered Sandy after the ghost had passed. "It is bad luck to watch a man's sorrow." He paused. "Listen."

Slowly at first and then in ever-rising sounds of despair a bloodless wail floated from the lips of the gaunt figure on the edge of the cliff.

"It is Black John calling to his dead son," said Sandy in a low voice. "It is bad luck. Let us go."

"One minute, Sandy." Despite his fear and dread, Chuck lingered. There had been something a moment ago that only now made him pause. Something just as the ghost of Black John passed them. A tiny glint of clear blue light on one of the scrawny fingers that clutched the lantern.

"If Black John spent all his wealth looking for his son, why is he wearing a diamond on his finger?"

"A diamond?" repeated Sandy. He stopped as the American youth dug his fingers sharply into his arm and pointed.

"Look, Sandy, he's signaling to someone out in the water!" Still struck with wonder, the boys watched as the light blinked in spaced intervals of lights and dark. Then, holding their breaths, driven by a need to discover more, they pulled themselves carefully along on their stomachs towards the cliff edge. A scant ten yards away, the hooded figure of Black John continued the systematic flashings of his lantern.

Slowly the minutes passed as the boys gazed, fascinated, at the weird spectacle being enacted before them. At regular intervals, an eerie wail would break from Black John's lips, and each time Chuck could feel his blood run cold within him. And then, quite suddenly, there was a scrape of a shoe, and a voice called cautiously up from below.

"Charlie?"

"Who else?" barked the lantern waver, and Chuck jumped as he heard the shrouded figure speak. "You've got the stuff, Dave?"

The other grunted and pulled himself up over the edge of the cliff. "I'll be right glad when this business is finished," he panted. "Secret trail or not, it's no fun climbing up that cliff at night."

"Shut up, will you?" snapped Charlie, alias Black John. "I'm taking the real risk. What if those local half-wits found out who I am?"

Chuck stared in horror at Sandy. It was easy to see now who was at the bottom of this smuggling business!

"It's the last haul," the man called Charlie was speaking. "We're pulling out tonight. What was that?"

Chuck froze. In seeking to ease his cramped position, his foot had dislodged a small stone. He listened, numb with dread, as it clattered down the precipice.

"I don't know but I'll find out," growled the other, advancing on the boys. A slender blade flashed in his hand.

There was just one thing to do, and the boys did it. Before the astonished Dave was aware of their presence, Chuck lunged desperately and grabbed him tightly around the ankles. At the same moment, Sandy, running low, hurled himself viciously

at the smuggler's midsection. With a grunt of pain and surprise, the man toppled over on the heather, as the boys dashed wildly past Charlie wrapped in his long shroud.

"Make for the castle," cried Chuck, knowing full well that they could never hope to surprise the smugglers a second time in any free-for-all. Sandy nodded and, tucking his head down low, fairly skimmed over the ground towards the castle, with the two men thundering behind.

The boys reached the castle and immediately darted into the shadows. "In here," whispered Chuck, as he pulled himself up to an opening in the thick wall. With a quick effort, Sandy gripped the ledge firmly and scrambled up with the American youth.

Carefully, they let themselves down into the darkness on the other side. Chuck sensed a damp, musty smell, and gingerly extended his hand before him. Something cold brushed against his fingers. He drew himself back sharply before he realized what he had touched. Iron chains! They were in the dungeon of the castle!

"I saw them! This way!" a voice cried out from above them, and with a single action Chuck and Sandy stumbled across the room, hoping to find nearby an exit to the outside.

Suddenly Chuck's fingers, urgently groping along the moist rock wall of the dungeon, came in contact with a beam of wood. The crossbar of a door! With a quick heave, he raised it and, swinging the ancient door wide, dashed frantically up the spiral stairs with Sandy by his side.

It wasn't until they reached the uppermost portion of the castle that Chuck realized they were trapped. There was no way out except the way they had just come up!

Chuck looked around desperately. He could hear the pounding of the smugglers' shoes on the ancient stairs. Wildly he looked around for something with which to defend themselves, and his heart sank as he saw the barrenness of the small tower into which they had been chased.

"Quick, Chuck, the ivy!" It was Sandy calling as he scrambled over the parapet.

Like an agile monkey, Chuck slithered over the wall after his friend. His fingers wound fiercely around the hardy growth that enveloped that portion of the castle. Releasing one hand after the other, he followed Sandy closely down the wall. Once, a clump of ivy came away in his hand, and only a quick lunge by Sandy held him until he could get a fresh grip.

"The door to the stairs!" panted Chuck frantically as they reached the ground. "Hurry, before they get there!"

There wasn't a moment to spare. Already the smugglers, realizing that the ivy could not bear their greater weight, were clattering furiously down the same long stairway they had just climbed. Racing around the wall, the boys made for the dungeon opening. They scrambled through the narrow opening and hurled themselves into the inky blackness of the dungeon.

"Over there," panted Chuck, directed by the clatter of the approaching men. The ring of their boots on the stone steps echoed in the dungeon with terrifying violence. The smugglers could have been no more than three steps away when Sandy's straining hands brushed against the door. It was the work of a second to slam it tight as Chuck brought down the crossbar. A loud roar came from the other side as the two smugglers pounded on the barred door.

Without lingering any more, Sandy and Chuck scrambled out of the dungeon and ran as swiftly as their remaining strength allowed, away from the castle. Crashing wildly down the trail, they finally reached the glen at the bottom of the fearsome Ben-y-Gloe. From there, it was only a short journey across the bogs to Chuck's house, where they blurted out their story to an anxious Mr. and Mrs. Adams.

"Smugglers!" snapped Chuck's father after he had assured himself that the boys were all right. "We'll take care of that. You two wait here while I get the police and go after them!"

It was some time later that Chuck's father and the local constables returned. In their midst were the two smugglers, handcuffed together and looking decidedly unhappy about the whole thing. The one called Charlie, still in his long black shroud, cast an angry glance at the boys as he passed with the police on his way to the jail.

Chuck couldn't suppress a grin. "Now there's a fellow who is really dressed up for his own funeral," he chuckled.

"Aye," added Sandy dryly, "and with his own ghost, no less, to haunt him." He paused and directed a smile at Chuck. "Talking of ghosts, I've been a wee bit of a fool, I'm thinking."

"No more than I've been, Sandy." Chuck colored slightly. He turned impulsively to the Scottish boy and thrust out his hand. Sandy's firm grip was friendliness itself.

There was little sleep in the village that night. Everyone wanted to hear the boys' story and to congratulate them on breaking up the smuggling ring.

"It was really quite clever," said Chuck's father, after the boys had finished for the tenth time their account of the night's happenings. "These two smugglers knew that the local people here have a real respect for ghosts. What could be simpler than to play the role of old Black John? The flashing lights and the ghostly wailings would be sure to keep folks away while, at the same time, our two friends unloaded their illegal merchandise." Mr. Adams nodded his head in approval. "Yes, very clever, indeed—almost professional."

"But how did they get the stuff off this island to the mainland?" said Chuck curiously. "That's what beats me. They must have been slick."

His father blushed slightly. "Seems they were smuggling it out with my herring," he said, casting a sheepish glance at his wife, while the two boys burst into convulsions of laughter.

"You know, Sandy," said Chuck as he showed the Scottish boy to the door, "I take back everything I said about nothing ever happening in the Hebrides. I've had enough excitement tonight to last me a year."

Sandy smiled, "Then you will be back next year, Chuck? Aye, we could have a bonnie time of it."

"I sure will," said Chuck with a wide grin, "even if I've got to come back as a herring to do it."

AUGTHOR

AUTHOR

William MacKellar was born in Glasgow, Scotland. When he was eleven years old, he came to the United States and later became an American citizen. Today Mr. MacKellar, his wife, and three children live in West Hartford, Connecticut.

Many of William MacKellar's stories take place in Scotland. Two of these stories are *Ghost in the Castle* and *A Dog Like No Other*.

WHY I
DID NOT
REIGN

I longed to win the spelling bee
And remembered the rule
I had learned in school:

"I before E,
Except after C."

Friend, believe me,
No one was going to deceive me.

Fiercely I practiced, the scepter I'd wield,
All others their shields in the field would yield!

Alas, before my very eyes
A weird neighbor in a beige veil
Feigning great height and weighty size
Seized the reins and ran off with the prize.

Now I no longer deign to remember that rule.
Neither
Any other either.

Eve Merriam

478

DOUBLETS

Here is a game called Doublets that you can play either by yourself or with a group of friends. It was invented by Lewis Carroll, the author of *Alice in Wonderland.* To play Doublets, you pick a word, such as **pail,** and write it near the top of a piece of paper. Then pick a different word having the same number of letters, such as **belt,** and write that word farther down the paper. The object of the game is to change the top word into the bottom word by changing just one letter at a time.

Look at the example at the right. Notice how the new word in each step is formed by changing just one letter of the word above it.

PAIL
bail
ball
bell
BELT

Now try to play Doublets on your own. Below are the first and last words of two doublets. Clues are given to help you determine the new word for each step in between. Write the first and last words on a piece of paper and fill in each of the in-between words as you figure them out.

READ
????   a tiny ball with a hole through it
????   the bill of a bird
????   the top of a mountain
????   what a bird does to pick up food
PICK

You can even turn **rock** into **gold** or change **hard** to **easy**.

R O C K

a frame to place things on
a short nail
to speak
the opposite of short
what you sometimes must pay to use a highway
said

G O L D

H A R D

a rabbit
what you pay to go on a bus
the front part of your head
truth
rapid
a direction

E A S Y

If you found these easy to figure out, now do some without any clues. Listed below are the first and last words for two doublets and the number of steps needed to change the top word into the bottom word. You can also do these in more steps than the number given.

G I V E

T A K E

B U M P

T A L L

Your teacher can tell you one possible solution for each doublet.

RECOGNIZING
VAGUE EXPRESSIONS

Suppose you were reading an article about a baseball player and came to the sentence "He hit a lot of home runs last season." How many home runs would you think the player had hit? Would five seem "a lot" to you? Would twenty? Thirty? Forty?

Your idea of "a lot of home runs" might be quite different from that of the author of the article. And since the sentence doesn't even suggest an approximate number, you have no way of knowing just how many home runs the author means by "a lot."

Whenever it is important for readers to know exactly what is meant, an author avoids *vague expressions* like "a lot." A vague expression is one which is general or indefinite, and because it has no precise or exact meaning, it is sometimes interpreted incorrectly and given the wrong meaning.

Suppose, for example, that you were reading a mystery and at the high point of the story desperate jewel thieves were hiding in an old house while the hero was in a boat searching for them along a riverbank. In order to picture the scene correctly in your mind, wouldn't you need to know just how close to the river the old house stood? If the author wrote that the house was "near the river," would that tell you just where it was? Although the author might mean that the house was right at the riverbank, you might have a different idea of "near" and be misled into thinking that the house was as much as a quarter of a mile away.

To help you visualize clearly what is being described, the author would avoid using the vague expression "near the river," and would use instead a more exact expression such as "at the very edge of the river" or "within a few feet of the river."

When it is essential to your understanding of an author's story or the information he is presenting, he tries to make clear to you such things as size, distance, weight, and number. He can't do this by using vague expressions like those italicized in the sentences below:

Behind the house was a *big* yard.

Suddenly the car swerved *close* to the man.

The horse was already carrying a *heavy* load.

Marge put *some* money on the counter.

He can do it, though, with exact expressions like the ones in these sentences:

Behind the house was a yard *the size of a football field.*

Suddenly the car swerved *to within a foot of* the man.

The horse was already carrying a *seventy-pound* load.

Marge put *thirty-five cents* on the counter.

You mustn't assume, however, that all expressions in what you read will be exact. While it often is important for an author to be precise in his writing, there are also times when the author's purpose is better served by the use of a vague expression. He may, for instance, want you to form your own mental picture of people or events in a story, and by using a vague rather than an exact expression he enables you to do so.

Compare these two sentences, for example:

Tom put four pieces of candy in his mouth.

Tom stuffed his mouth full of candy.

In the first sentence, the author has told you the exact number of pieces of candy, but the sentence doesn't help you to picture Tom, does it? In fact, it may cause you to forget about how Tom looked and to start wondering why he was trying to eat so much candy at once or why he had taken four pieces. But on reading the second sentence, although the wording is vague and the amount of candy isn't mentioned, you can easily visualize how Tom must have looked as he ate. Being able to form your own picture of characters and events you are reading about often helps to make them more interesting and enjoyable to you.

In the sentence "Tom stuffed his mouth full of candy," it isn't necessary for you to recognize the vagueness of the wording. The author chose to write vaguely to help you picture Tom. If you read "Eddie gave a big grin," you could visualize Eddie's face without wondering just how big the grin was. However, with sentences like "Let the apples simmer for a little while" and "The store is a long distance from the school," unless you recognize that certain expressions are vague, you may misunderstand what you are reading. If you come across an expression and don't realize that it is vague, the meaning you give it may be quite different from the meaning intended by the author. But if you recognize an expression as a vague one that has several possible meanings, you will know that you cannot simply suppose that the first meaning you think of is a good one.

If you have trouble deciding whether a word or phrase is vague, ask yourself, "Does this expression have an exact, definite meaning?" If the answer is no, be on guard against giving the expression a meaning of your own without stopping to think about what the author might have meant. Even when you can't be certain of the author's meaning, recognizing vague language will keep you from assuming a precise meaning when none was intended.

What vague expressions can you find in the following sentences?
1. Joe is six feet tall and weighs a hundred and ten pounds.
2. Joe is very skinny.
3. Because it was warm, we sat in the shade.
4. Because it was 82 degrees, we sat in the shade.
5. The Christmas tree he bought was a tall one.
6. The Christmas tree he bought was eight feet tall.

Discussion

Help your class answer the following questions:
1. What is a vague expression?
2. Should everything be written in exact, precise terms? How do vague expressions sometimes help the reader?

3. Why do you need to be able to recognize vague expressions?

4. How can you help yourself recognize vague expressions?

5. Which of the six numbered sentences on the opposite page contain vague expressions and what are the expressions?

On your own

Some of the following sentences contain vague expressions and some do not. On your paper, copy the number and write each sentence that has a vague expression in it. Then draw a line under that vague expression.

1. Mary came to school twenty minutes late.
2. Glenn's father promised him a long vacation.
3. George ate a good lunch yesterday.
4. Mount McKinley is 20,320 feet high.
5. Several boys started a baseball game at the picnic.
6. The teacher gave Alice a score of 92 on the test.
7. In a short time, we had climbed to the top of the hill.
8. This has been one of the worst winters we've had.
9. Bill asked for a big bicycle for his birthday.
10. The park is only a mile away.
11. We had some sandwiches and cocoa for lunch.
12. Will you look after the four puppies for a few minutes?
13. The hole in my sock was as large as a nickel.
14. Sally gave me a funny look when I walked in.
15. Mark scored ten points in the basketball game.

Checking your work

If you are asked to do so, read aloud one of the sentences you wrote. Tell what vague expression is used in it and explain why you consider the expression vague.

How to Catch a Thief!

by Sid Fleischman

Strike it rich! That's what Jack Flagg and Praiseworthy, his family's butler, planned to do. So they set off to join the rush of gold seekers to California in 1849. While in line to purchase tickets for passage on the California-bound ship, *Lady Wilma,* they discovered to their dismay that their money had been stolen. Still determined to get to the goldfields, the two adventurers sneaked aboard the *Lady Wilma* and hid among the cargo in potato barrels. But a long voyage as cold, hungry stowaways certainly was not to their liking! Cautiously they climbed out of the barrels. . . .

"I suggest that we see what can be done about improving our accommodations," said Praiseworthy, tapping his bowler hat firmly in place. "Shall we go?"

"Go?" Jack replied. "Go where?" He fully expected to pass the voyage below decks with the cargo. He had read accounts of the harsh treatment handed out to stowaways on ships of the sea.

"Why, to pay our respects to the captain," said Praiseworthy.

"The captain!" The words very nearly caught in his throat. "But he'll put us in chains—*or worse!*"

"Leave that to me," said Praiseworthy, with an airy lift of an eyebrow. "Come along, Master Jack."

Jack gathered courage from Praiseworthy's cool assurance. As far back as Jack could remember, he had never known anything to ruffle Praiseworthy's calm. In his black bowler hat, his black coat, and spotless white gloves, he was easily mistaken for a professional man—a lawyer, perhaps, or a young doctor—but he was nothing of the sort. Praiseworthy was a butler.

He was a butler by breeding, by training, and by choice. More than once Jack had heard his Aunt Arabella say that Praiseworthy was the finest English butler in Boston. He had been with Jack's family since before Jack could remember. It seemed to him there had always been a Praiseworthy.

The ship gave a lurch and the stowaways, gathering up their two carpetbags, picked their way through the darkened passages of the hold. Jack saw barrels of smoked fish bound for San Francisco. There were thousands of feet of lumber and enough bricks to build a hotel. He saw boxes of rifles and two brass cannons, to fight off wild Indians, he supposed. And he could make out wet bundles of grape cuttings, enough to plant a vineyard. There were even some live animals, perhaps to provide fresh meat during the voyage.

With his heart thumping, Jack followed Praiseworthy up a ship's ladder to the creaking deck above. He was sure the captain would put them in chains, at the very least. Now the whistling of the wind came to them, and the thrashing of the great side wheels seemed as loud as thunder. They found themselves in the crew's quarters, where daylight barely penetrated. A sailor with a gold ring dancing in his ear was filling a lamp with whale oil.

"My good fellow," said Praiseworthy, "can you direct me to the captain?"

The sailor looked up with a curious squint and the ring in his ear did a jig. "The wild bull of the seas? Aye, mates." He lifted a wet thumb as a pointer. "Up there."

Up there they went, climbing another ladder to another deck, and now Jack was sure the captain would have them walking the plank, at the very least. Wild bull of the seas! But Praiseworthy was a match for anyone, he told himself, and tried to keep a straight and firm jaw.

They entered the main saloon, where shivering passengers were swarming like bees around two potbellied stoves. Everyone seemed to be talking at once, and saying the same thing.

"You been hoggin' that stove long enough!"

"I got here first!"

"Let me in, pardner!"

Jack saw men of every description and some who defied description. There were lanky farm boys in rough boots, dandies in tight pantaloons, and ex-soldiers fresh from the war with Mexico. There were Yankees in beaver hats and Southerners in planters' hats. There were tradesmen and politicans, Frenchmen and Dutchmen, fat men and thin ones, gentlemen and scoundrels — with not a woman among them. They were bound for the goldfields, which was no place for women and children.

"Gimme a turn at that stove, gents!"

"Stop pushing, sir!"

Praiseworthy tapped the nearest gold-seeker on the shoulder, a frock-coated man with a sword cane, and inquired, "Can you direct me to the captain, sir?"

The man lifted his sword cane and pointed. "Up there, up there," he snapped, and returned to the fray.

In due time, after climbing another ladder, the two stowaways found the captain in his cabin, with the door banging open and shut with the roll of the ship. He had just come in from deck and his wet oilskins lay in a heap. The wild bull of the seas, his legs apart, stood bent over a long table. He was trying to thaw the ice in his curly black whiskers over a lighted candle. "Well, don't just stand there invitin' in the weather!" he said, in a voice like the roar of a cannon. "Come in!"

The butler shut the door, only to have it fly open again. "Praise-worthy at your service, sir," he said. "And this young gentleman is Master Jack Flagg, of Boston, who seeks his fortune in the goldfields."

"Bah!" The ship's master, whose name was Joshua Swain, hardly bothered to look up. It was hard to tell whether he was a good man in a bad temper, or a bad man in a good temper. He had a plump nose and wore a long, blue coat with a row of brass buttons the size of gold pieces.

The *Lady Wilma* pitched and rolled, and the candlestick slid from one end of the long table to the other. Captain Swain caught it just in time. "Blasted weather," he growled. "And me racing the *Sea Raven* around the Horn. Me, with my hold full of bricks and twice as many passengers as I ought to carry. But I'll beat the *Sea Raven,* by grabs, even if I have to throw the extra passengers overboard!"

The door banged shut. Jack, now wide-eyed, stared at the ship's master as if he were a stout devil in brass buttons and frozen whiskers. He would give them the plank, for sure.

Again the ship lurched and the candlestick flew, but this time Praiseworthy caught it in midair. "Allow me, sir," he said, and held the candle firmly under the captain's stiff whiskers. But the wild bull of the seas wouldn't stand still, and Praiseworthy was soon following him as he paced the cabin.

"Do you know what the *Sea Raven* carries in her cargo holds!" Captain Swain bellowed. "Miners' boots and flannel shirts and mosquito netting. Mosquito netting! She's so light in the water her keel is hardly damp!" Then he stopped to thaw his beard over the flame, and the roar went out of his voice. "Ah-h-h," he sighed and in another moment a smile appeared in the weathered creases of his eyes. "That's better. Now then, gentlemen, what can I do for you?"

Jack exchanged a quick glance with Praiseworthy, who remained perfectly at ease. "We wish to report a pair of stowaways, sir," said the butler.

At that announcement the captain's smile vanished and he exploded again. "Stowaways!" he roared. "Stowaways! By grabs, I'll skin them alive! I'll put them in chains! Where are they!"

In his fury the captain almost set his whiskers aflame. Praiseworthy pinched out the candle. "Standing right here, sir."

"Here? *Where!* I'll skin them alive and put them in chains! Stowaways on my ship! Where are they!"

"Here, sir," repeated the butler.

And Jack, swallowing hard, decided to make the best or the worst of it. "Standing before you, sir."

It was as if for the first time Captain Swain noticed Jack at all. *"You!"* he bellowed, and his plump nose was red with anger. "Why—you're a mere jib of a boy. A lad of ten!"

"Twelve, sir," said Jack. "But I can do a man's work, sir!"

"By grabs, I'll make you walk the plank—both of you!"

"If I may make an observation," said Praiseworthy, "you are obviously too civilized for such pirate tricks."

"Bah!"

"Permit me to explain," Praiseworthy went on. "It was not our intention to defraud the shipping company. The moment there was posted notice of the *Lady Wilma's* departure for California, Master Jack and I were in line to buy a ticket. But in the push and clamor, some clever cutpurse helped himself to our passage money, leaving us penniless. No doubt, he bought a ticket for himself and is aboard this very ship, sir."

"A likely story," growled the captain.

"An unlikely story," Praiseworthy said, "but true. Naturally, we had no choice but to become stowaways. And if I may add, it is urgent, sir, that Master Jack reach the goldfields and make his fortune without delay."

"Bah! This California fever is spreading like a plague! New England will be left half empty in another six months, by grabs! Anything with a keel is calling itself a gold ship and putting to sea—scows with rotten bottoms, fishing trawlers, whaling ships! Ships of old, they are, chasing after the Golden Fleece. Every man-Jack thinks he will make his fortune. Bah!"

All this while Jack Flagg stood quietly listening, not only to the captain, but to the icy winds in the shrouds and ratlines. He stood straight and tried not to look afraid. He had made up his mind that he must reach the treasure streams of California one way or another—and this was certainly one way or another.

"Blast!" said the captain, standing at a porthole. "There's the

Sea Raven abeam of us now. Standing there as if to thumb her nose at us!"

Jack got a glimpse of the other ship on a rising swell, a two-masted side-wheeler exactly like the *Lady Wilma*.

"If I may observe," Praiseworthy remarked with his perfect calm, "it is a fifteen-thousand-mile voyage around Cape Horn to San Francisco, I believe. It is not the beginning of a race that counts, sir, but the end."

"If I win the race, I'll get command of a new clipper ship building in the yards. She'll be the pride of the seas, and I want her, sir!" Captain Swain unhooked the brass voice tube and bellowed to the engine room below. "More steam, sir! It's all we can do to keep up. More steam!" And then he turned to the stowaways. "You'll work off your passage on this ship, by grabs! You there, boy!"

Jack, who was already standing straight, stood even straighter. "Yes, sir?"

"You'll work as ship's boy. I'll run your legs off—and that's letting you off easy. And you, sir—"

"Praiseworthy, at your service."

"What in tarnation *are* you in that getup?"

"I am a butler, sir."

"A butler!" the captain roared. "A butler! What in the name of Old Scratch can a *butler* do?"

"It's the other way around, sir," said Praiseworthy, who took pride in his calling. "There's nothing a butler *cannot* do. I open doors. I close doors. I announce that dinner is served. I supervise the staff and captain the household—much as you do on this ship, sir. A most exacting job, if I may say so."

"Bah!"

And Jack ventured, "Aunt Arabella says he's the best there is. She says there's no problem too big for Praiseworthy."

"Silence, boy! A butler, are you! By grabs, I know where there's a door you can open. The furnace door—and you can shovel in fuel! To the coal bunkers with you, butler! Now out of my sight before I change my mind and put you both in chains!"

"Sir," said Jack, trembling inwardly. "I don't care to be ship's boy."

"What!"

"If Praiseworthy is going to the coal bunkers, I'll shovel coal too." Jack met Praiseworthy's glance, but only for a moment. "We're partners, sir. Either send me to the coal bunkers or—," he gulped, "or put me in chains."

The wild bull of the seas was struck absolutely speechless.

"Don't pay any attention to Master Jack," said Praiseworthy quickly. "The boy is light-headed from sheer hunger. He hasn't eaten since yesterday and he doesn't know what he's saying."

"Yes, I do," said Jack. "You told me yourself we'd stick together through thick and thin."

By this time the captain had recovered his voice, and a smile lurked in his eye. "By grabs," he said. "By grabs, here's a lad with stuffings. He doesn't want an easy berth. Wants a man's job. All right, to the coal bunkers, *both* of you."

"Thank you, sir," said Jack, picking up his carpetbag.

The captain cocked a shaggy eyebrow. "It wouldn't hurt none if you stopped off first at the galley and told the cook I said to give you something to eat. A man can't shovel coal on an empty stomach—or a lad, either. Now, be out of my sight!"

The door flew open and the stowaways withdrew. They descended one ladder and then another, got their breakfast, and reported to the engineer. He pointed out the boiler furnace, the coal bins, and the shovels. Praiseworthy removed his bowler hat, his white gloves, and the umbrella from the crook of his arm. They made a neat pile of their coats and rolled up their sleeves.

"Unless I miss my guess," said Praiseworthy, "the wild bull of the seas is a gentleman at heart."

"I hope he wins the race," said Jack.

The stowaways set to work shoveling coal into the yellow flames of the furnace—flames that made the steam that turned the great side-wheels. Jack was eager to work beside Praiseworthy, as if it brought them even closer together. Sometimes he wished Praiseworthy were anything but a butler. It imposed a slight distance between them that Praiseworthy was careful to maintain. Jack would be happy to be called Jack, just Jack, and not Master Jack. But Praiseworthy wouldn't hear of it, even though they were now partners.

"Praiseworthy," said Jack, wiping back the hair from his forehead. He had to raise his voice above the howl of the fire and the clank of machinery. "Praiseworthy, do you really believe the cut-purse is aboard the *Lady Wilma?*"

"I do indeed," said the butler, digging into the bunker of coal. "And we shall unmask the scoundrel."

"But how?"

"How? Why, I haven't the faintest idea, Master Jack. But between us, we'll think of something, by grabs."

While the captain went back on deck and froze his whiskers again, and while the passengers huddled around the two potbellied stoves, Praiseworthy whistled and Jack hummed. They alone of the gold-seekers aboard the *Lady Wilma* had a roaring fire to warm them as the side-wheeler went splashing through the sleet and the wind and the sea.

After many days, like a dog after a rain, the *Lady Wilma* shook winter from her masts and riggings. She entered the southern latitudes. The sun came out bright and fresh as if newly forged, and the nights were speckled over with stars. The fires went out in the potbellied stoves and the passengers began to shed their

greatcoats and heavy woolens. In another week they were down to their shirt-sleeves.

In the lower regions of the ship, Praiseworthy and Jack were still at their shovels. They were powdered over with coal dust, but Jack did not mind the work. It would toughen him for digging in the goldfields, he thought. Still, the roaring flames had lost their friendliness. The boiler room was becoming distinctly overheated.

"Master Jack," said Praiseworthy, thinking of the tropic zones that lay ahead, "another week at our post and we shall be roasted alive."

But the heat did not bother Jack, for every turn of the paddle-wheels brought the far country a bit closer. Even though the sea route was the long way around, it was faster than the overland trail across the plains. The ox-drawn wagon trains were sometimes a year in reaching California, and Jack was in a hurry.

Every day counted. It was fine with him that Captain Swain was making a race around the Horn. The captain was in a hurry, too. Still, it would be months before the *Lady Wilma* dropped anchor in San Francisco Bay.

"This infernal firebox!" Praiseworthy said, wiping the sweat from his face. "We must think of a plan. We must expose the rogue who light-fingered our passage money."

The truth of the matter was that neither Jack nor the butler had the slightest idea how to go about catching a thief. But Praiseworthy was undaunted. They would surely think of something.

The following day, toward dusk, Jack was washing up in a bucket of sea water. He had a pig, which he had named Good Luck, with him in the boiler room, and now even the pig was covered with coal dust. Suddenly Praiseworthy was struck as if by lightning. "Master Jack!" he exclaimed. "You have it!"

"Have what?" answered Jack, looking up.

"Why, the answer!"

"The answer? The answer to what?"

Praiseworthy's eyebrows shot up with delight. "We'll catch the thieving scoundrel at last! You've hit it, Master Jack. You have, indeed."

Jack couldn't think what he'd hit, but the next thing he knew he was following Praiseworthy like a squirrel up one ladder and then another to the pilothouse. Captain Swain turned and gave the two intruders a weather-beaten squint. His temper, if not the growl of his voice, had improved with the weather. "How is the blasted voyage agreeing with you, my hearties?"

"No complaints, sir," said Praiseworthy.

"What brings you above decks?"

And Praiseworthy answered, "You may recall that Master Jack and I suffered a slight misfortune at the very outset of this voyage. Some blasted—er, that is to say—some despicable thief made off with our funds. Master Jack here has hit upon a scheme to expose the rascal."

"Me?" said Jack.

"Bah!" the captain erupted. "I don't believe there's any such scamp aboard my ship. I asked the first mate to make a close examination of our passenger list. Gentlemen they are, most of them, and the others are too crude for the clever art of the cut-purse."

"Nevertheless," said Praiseworthy, "I believe he's among your passengers like a fox among sheep. Allow us to prove it."

Captain Swain scratched through his dark whiskers. "How do you figure on exposing him?"

"We won't expose him, sir. He'll expose himself. If you will have all the passengers assembled in the main saloon after dark, we'll know very soon whether or not you have a clever thief aboard."

"By grabs," said the captain thoughtfully. "It's worth a try."

When the sea turned black, the whale-oil lamps were lit in the main saloon and the passengers began to gather. They joked and joshed, glad for something to do, for they were not used to the idleness of life at sea. Jack waited on deck with the black pig from the animal pens. He saw the horse doctor enter on his peg leg, followed by the judge. The ex-soldiers were singing:

I'm going to California
With my washbowl on my knee.

When all the passengers were assembled, the captain made a grand entrance, with his long coat flapping almost to his knees.

"Gentlemen," he said. "I'll get to the point. I am told there may be a thief among us — a cut-purse. We can't have that now, can we?"

"No!" roared out the gold-seekers, giving their purses and money belts a reassuring touch.

"We'll string him up!" yelled a big fellow known as Mountain Jim. He had full red eyebrows and wore a bobcat cap.

The captain held up a hand to stop the voices. "This cut-purse has already struck, gentlemen. He lifted the savings of Mr. Praiseworthy and his young partner. You've seen them working off their passage at the coal bunkers. The thief may strike again. Any one of you may be his next victim. He may be standing at your elbow. I'll now turn the meeting over to the aforementioned persons, who have a plan to capture the scoundrel."

Praiseworthy, tall and calm, stepped forward. "Thank you,

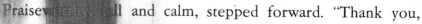

Captain Swain," he said. "Our plan is very simple, gentlemen. Master Jack, the sow, if you please."

At that signal, Jack led the big black hog to the center of the saloon and tied her to a post. The men began to exchange baffled glances. What had a large sow to do with catching a thief? But if there was a thief among them, they wanted him caught. Their own purses weren't safe with a light-fingered fellow aboard.

"A pig is a smart animal," Praiseworthy explained.

"None smarter," yelled out Mountain Jim.

"Take this old sow," Praiseworthy went on. "She's very wise. We've discovered that she can tell a dishonest man by the mere feel of him. She squeals. Gentlemen, you can't even tell a simple lie in her presence. She'll squeal every time. A most remarkable hog, I must say."

Jack looked about at the many faces shining under the flickering whale-oil lamps. There were the horse doctor and the Mexico-fighters and the judge with his sword cane. Not even Mountain Jim, with his fur cap, was above suspicion. Jack fed the black sow a limp carrot to keep her quiet, but he began to feel anxious. What if Praiseworthy was wrong and the thief wasn't aboard the *Lady Wilma* at all?

"I assure you," Praiseworthy was saying, "that if the cut-purse so much as touches this hog, she will squeal. If you will line up, gentlemen, we'll get on with it. After the lamps are blown out and the saloon is dark, come up to the sow one by one. Touch her with your right index finger. When she squeals, we'll have our thief!"

"I'm for it," one of the ex-soldiers said.

"Me, too."

"A good plan," said the judge.

"Suits me," agreed the horse doctor, turning on his peg leg. "Some of you boys get the lamps. Let's see how smart this hog is. If you're an honest man, you've got nothing to fear."

A moment later the saloon was in pitch darkness, and Jack held himself very still, feeding carrots to the animal so she wouldn't squeal. One by one the gold-seekers approached and ran a finger along the sow's back. A minute passed. Two. Not a sound from the hog. The passengers scuffed across the deck in their boots, touched the hog, and retired. The men were silent, listening for the squeal that would trap the guilty man. Ten minutes passed, and still they came. Even Praiseworthy felt a bit tense now.

When finally the whale-oil lamps were relit, the black sow hadn't uttered a sound. She stood in the center of the saloon wondering what all the fuss was about.

Captain Swain stepped forward, scratching his beard as he looked about at his passengers, and then turned to Praiseworthy.

"Looks like you made a mistake. That cutpurse isn't aboard this ship. By grabs, I'm sorry about you and the lad there, but it looks like you'll be shoveling coal all the way around the Horn to California."

"One moment," said Praiseworthy, as unconcerned as you please. "It's true, the sow didn't squeal, but the guilty party stands in this room, sir. Gentlemen, Master Jack and I took the liberty of powdering this black sow with coal dust. If each of you will now examine your right index finger, where you touched her hide, you will find a smudge."

Every man in the saloon instantly turned up his hand where, indeed, was the smudge of black dust.

Praiseworthy didn't waste a moment. "But one of you, fearing that the sow's squeal would give you away—one of you approached but *didn't touch a finger to her back.* Look around you, gentlemen. If there is a man among you without coal dust on his finger, he has exposed himself as the thief!"

Almost at once there was an outcry from one corner of the saloon. "We got him!"

Passengers, suddenly angry, crowded around and Jack couldn't see whom they had pounced upon.

"We'll string him up!"

"Look there! His finger's clean as a whistle!"

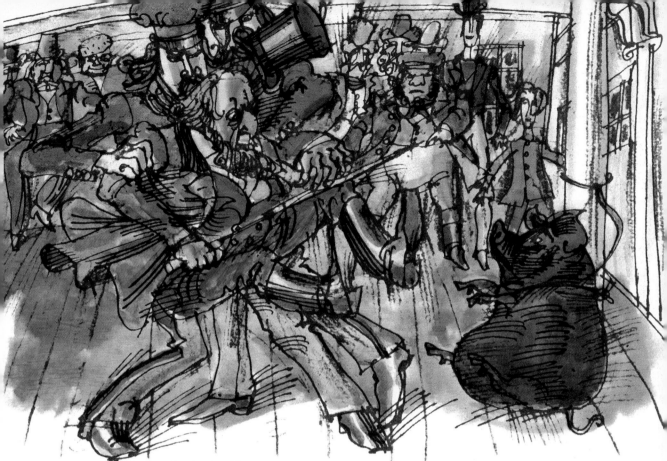

"It's the judge!"

"Judge, my eye! He's an impostor!"

Jack burrowed through the crowd in time to see the "judge" attempt to draw his sword cane. But the Mexico-fighters jumped in and pinned his arms back. By the time the ship's officers got hold of the frock-coated impostor, his hat was caved in. Now the crowd opened up, and Jack had never seen Praiseworthy with such a fierce look in his eye.

"I suppose we'll find the balance of our money in your cabin, sir!"

"Try to find it," spat the thief, peering from Jack to Praiseworthy and back again. "Clever you are. But we'll meet again, I warn you, or my name's not Cut-Eye Higgins."

"Humbug," said Praiseworthy just as sharply.

The miners had their own ideas of justice, and the suggestions went flying around the saloon.

"Pitch him overboard and let him swim to California!"

"String him up!"

"Put him in irons!"

But Captain Swain already had his mind made up. "Take him to the coal bunkers. By the time we cross the equator, by grabs, he'll think he's in Hades!"

Jack and Praiseworthy did find the money, and they did meet Cut-Eye Higgins again, and more than once! How they outsmarted him each time is just part of the story told in Sid Fleischman's exciting book, *By the Great Horn Spoon!*

AUTHOR

Sid Fleischman lives in Santa Monica, California, with his wife and three children. Another member of his household is a rooster named Calamity. For the past fifteen years, Mr. Fleischman has lived there in a large two-story frame house where he does all his writing. He divides his time between writing books for young boys and girls and writing for the movies.

Mr. Fleischman, who was born in Brooklyn, New York, and grew up in San Diego, California, said about himself, "I am an ex-magician and an ex-newspaperman. I started teaching myself sleight-of-hand tricks (from books) in the fifth grade. After graduating from high school, I traveled throughout the United States with a magic show. During four years of active duty in the United States Naval Reserve—the World War II years—I served aboard a destroyer escort in the South Pacific. With the end of the war, I decided to become a writer rather than a magician because the great days of magic were past." Mr. Fleischman spent several years as a newspaperman before he turned to writing books and stories for young people and for motion pictures.

The story you have just read was taken from Mr. Fleischman's book *By the Great Horn Spoon!* Walt Disney made a movie called *Bullwhip Griffin* from this book. Other books written by Mr. Fleischman are *Chancy and the Grand Rascal, Mr. Mysterious and Company,* and *The Ghost in the Noonday Sun.*

HAIKU

Make up your mind, snail!
You are half inside your house
And halfway out!

Richard Wright

In the falling snow
A laughing boy holds out his palms
Until they are white.

Richard Wright

FROM

CALL IT COURAGE

BY ARMSTRONG SPERRY

It happened many years ago, before the traders and missionaries first came into the South Seas, while the Polynesians were still great in numbers and fierce of heart. But even today, the people of Hikueru sing this story in their chants and tell it over the evening fires. It is the story of Mafatu, the Boy Who Was Afraid.

They worshiped courage, those early Polynesians. The spirit which had urged them across the Pacific in their sailing canoes, before the dawn of recorded history, not knowing where they were going nor caring what their fate might be, still sang its song of danger in their blood. There was only courage. A man who was afraid — what place had he in their midst? And the boy Mafatu — son of Tavana Nui, the Great Chief of Hikueru — always had been afraid. So the people drove him forth, not by violence, but by indifference.

Mafatu went out alone to face the thing he feared the most. And the people of Hikueru still sing his story in their chants and tell it over the evening fires.

It was the sea that Mafatu feared. He had been surrounded by it ever since he was born. The thunder of it filled his ears; the crash of it upon the reef, the mutter of it at sunset, the threat and fury of its storms — on every hand, wherever he turned — the sea.

He could not remember when the fear of it first had taken hold of him. Perhaps it was during the great hurricane which swept Hikueru when he was a child of three. Even now, twelve years later, Mafatu could remember that terrible morning. His mother had taken him out to the barrier reef to search for sea urchins in the reef pools. There were other canoes scattered at wide intervals along the reef. With late afternoon, the other fishermen began to turn back. They shouted warnings to Mafatu's mother. It was the season of hurricane, and the people of Hikueru were nervous and ill at ease, charged, it seemed, with an almost animal awareness of impending storm.

But when at last Mafatu's mother turned back toward shore, a swift current had set in around the shoulder of the reef passage — a meeting of tides that swept like a millrace out into the open sea. It seized the frail craft in its swift race. Despite all the woman's skill, the canoe was carried on the crest of the churning tide, through the reef passage, into the outer ocean.

Mafatu would never forget the sound of his mother's despairing cry. He didn't know then what it meant, but he felt that something was terribly wrong, and he set up a loud wailing. Night closed down upon them, swift as a frigate's wing, darkening the known world. The wind of the open ocean rushed in at them, screaming. Waves lifted and struck at one another, their crests hissing with spray. The poles of the outrigger were torn from their thwarts. The woman sprang forward to seize her child

as the canoe capsized. The little boy gasped when the cold water struck him. He clung to his mother's neck. Moana, the Sea God, was reaching up for them, seeking to draw them down to his dark heart. . . .

Off the tip of Hikueru, the uninhabited islet of Tekoto lay shrouded in darkness. It was scarcely more than a ledge of coral, almost awash. The swift current bore directly down upon the islet.

Dawn found the woman still clinging to the *purau* pole and the little boy with his arms locked about his mother's neck. The grim light revealed sharks circling, circling. . . . Little Mafatu buried his head against his mother's cold neck. He was filled with terror. He even forgot the thirst that burned his throat. But the palms of Tekoto beckoned with their promise of life, and the woman fought on.

When at last they were cast up on the coral, Mafatu's mother crawled ashore with scarcely enough strength left to pull her child beyond reach of the sea's hungry fingers. The little boy was too weak even to cry. At hand lay a cracked coconut. The woman managed to press the cool, sustaining meat to her child's lips before she died.

Sometimes now, in the hush of night, when the moon was full and its light lay in silver bands across the pandanus mats, and all the village was sleeping, Mafatu awoke and sat upright. The sea muttered its eternal threat to the reef. The sea. . . And a terrible trembling seized the boy's limbs, while a cold sweat broke out on his forehead. Mafatu seemed to see again the faces of the fishermen who had found the dead mother and her whimpering child. These pictures still colored his dreams. And so it was that he shuddered when the mighty seas, gathering far out, hurled themselves at the barrier reef of Hikueru, and the whole island quivered under the assault.

Perhaps that was the beginning of it. Mafatu, the boy who had been christened Stout Heart by his proud father, was afraid of the sea. What manner of fisherman would he grow up to be? How would he ever lead the men in battle against warriors of other islands? Mafatu's father heard the whispers, and the man grew silent and grim.

The older people were not unkind to the boy, for they believed that it was all the fault of the *tupapau,* the ghost-spirit which possesses every child at birth. But the girls laughed at him, and the boys failed to include him in their games. And the voice of the reef seemed pitched for his ears alone. It seemed to say, "You cheated me once, Mafatu, but someday, someday I will claim you!"

Mafatu's stepmother knew small sympathy for him, and his stepbrothers treated him with open scorn.

"Listen," they would mock. "Moana, the Sea God, thunders on the reef. He is angry with us all because Mafatu is afraid!"

The boy learned to turn these jibes aside, but his father's silence shamed him. He tried with all his might to overcome his terror of the sea. Sometimes, steeling himself against it, he went with Tavana Nui and his stepbrothers out beyond the reef to fish. Out there, where the glassy swells of the ocean lifted and dropped the small canoe, pictures crowded into the boy's mind, setting his scalp atingle: pictures of himself, a babe, clinging to his mother's back . . . sharks cruising. . . . And so overcome would he be at the remembrance of that time that he would drop his spear overboard, or let the line go slack at the wrong moment and lose the fish.

It was obvious to everyone that Mafatu was useless upon the sea. He would never earn his proper place in the tribe. Stout Heart—how bitter the name must taste upon his father's lips!

So, finally, he was not allowed to fare forth with the fishermen. He brought ill luck. He had to stay at home making spears and nets, twisting coir—the husk of

the coconut—into stout sharkline for other boys to use. He became very skillful at these pursuits, but he hated them. His heart was like a stone in his breast.

A nondescript yellow dog named Uri was Mafatu's inseparable companion—Uri with his thin coat which showed his ribs, and his eyes so puzzled and true. He followed the boy wherever he went. Their only other friend was Kivi, an albatross. The boy had once found the bird on his lonely wanderings. One of Kivi's feet was smaller than the other. Perhaps because it was different from its kind, the older birds were heckling and pestering the fledgling. Something about that small bird trying to fight off its more powerful fellows touched the boy's heart. He picked it up, carried it home, and caught fish for it in the shallows of the lagoon. The bird followed Mafatu and Uri about, limping on its one good leg. At length, when the young albatross learned to fly, it began to find its own food. In the air it achieved perfection, floating serenely against the sky, while Mafatu followed its effortless flight with envious eyes. If only

he, too, could escape to some world far removed from Hikueru!

Now, once more, it was the beginning of the season of storms. Men scanned the skies anxiously, watching for the dreaded signs which might spell the destruction of their world. Soon the great bonitos would be swimming beyond the reef—hundreds, thousands of them—for they came each year at this time with the unfailing regularity of the tides. They were held to be the special property of young boys, since it was by killing them that a youth learned to kill the swordfishes and tiger sharks, progressing from one stage to a higher. Every boy in the village sharpened his spear, tested the shaft, honed his shark knife. Every boy, that is, except Mafatu.

Kana stopped one afternoon to watch Mafatu at work on his nets. Of all the youths of his own age, Kana alone had been friendly. Sometimes he even stayed behind when the others were fishing to help the boy with his work.

"The bonitos have begun to run, Mafatu," Kana said quietly.

"Yes," the other returned, then fell silent. His fingers faltered as they flew among the sennit fibers of the net he was making.

"My father brought back word from the reef today," Kana went on. "Already there are many bonitos out there. Tomorrow we boys will go after them. That's our job. It will be fun, eh?"

Mafatu's knuckles whitened. His ears pounded with the swift fury of the sea. . . .

"That will be fun, won't it?" Kana insisted, watching Mafatu closely. But the boy made no answer. Kana started to speak. He stopped, turned impatiently, and walked away. Mafatu wanted to cry out after him, "Wait, Kana! I'll go! I'll try—" But the words would not come. Kana had gone. Tomorrow he and all the other boys would be taking their canoes out beyond the reef. They would return at sunset, loaded down with bonitos, their faces happy, their shouts filling the dusk. Their fathers would say, "See what a fine fisherman is my son! He will be a Chief one of these days." Only Tavana Nui would be silent. *His* son had not gone.

That night a new moon rose above the edge of the sea, silvering the land with a bloom of magic. Wandering along the outer beach with Uri, Mafatu heard laughing voices and drew hastily into the black shadow of a pandanus. A group of boys were pulling their canoes above high watermark, and laying their plans for the morrow. Their voices were shrill with eagerness.

"Tomorrow at daybreak . . ." one was saying.

"There'll be Timi and Tapu and Viri . . . ."

"*Aué!*" another voice broke in. "It's work for us all. How else will we become fishermen and warriors? How else will we feed our families and keep the tribe alive?"

"True! Hikueru is too poor. There are only the fish from the sea. A man must be fearless to provide food. We will all go— every one of us!"

Mafatu, standing tense in the shadows, heard a scornful laugh. His heart contracted. "Not all of us will go," he heard Kana scoff. "Not Mafatu!"

"Ha! He is afraid."

"He makes good spears," offered Viri generously.

"Ho! That is woman's work. Mafatu is afraid of the sea. *He* will never be a warrior." Kana laughed again, and the scorn of

his voice was like a spear thrust
through Mafatu's heart. "Aiá!"
Kana was saying. "I have tried
to be friendly with him. But he
is good only for making spears.
Mafatu is a coward."

The boys disappeared down the
moonlit beach. Their laughter

floated back on the night air. Mafatu stood quite still. Kana had spoken. He had voiced, once for all, the feeling of the tribe. Mafatu—Stout Heart—was a coward. He was the Boy Who Was Afraid.

His hands were damp and cold. His nails dug into his palms. Suddenly a fierce resentment stormed through him. He knew in that instant what he must do. He must prove his courage to himself, and to the others, or he could no longer live in their midst. He must face Moana, the Sea God—face him and conquer him. He must.

The boy stood there taut as a drawn arrow awaiting its release. Off to the south somewhere there were other islands. . . . He drew a deep breath. If he could win his way to a distant island, he could make a place for himself among strangers. And he would never return to Hikueru until he would have proven himself! He would come back with his head high-held in pride, and he would hear his father say, "Here is my son Stout Heart. A brave name for a brave boy. . . ." Standing there with clenched fists, Mafatu knew a smarting on his eyelids and shut his eyes tight and sank his teeth into his lower lip.

Far off in the himene house the Old Ones were singing. Their voices filled the night with rich sound. They sang of long voyages in open canoes, of hunger and thirst and battle. They sang the deeds of heroes. The hair on the boy's damp forehead stirred. The long-drawn mutter of the reef sounded its note of warning in his ears. At his side, Uri touched the master's hand with a cold nose. Mafatu pulled the dog close.

"We're going away, Uri," he whispered fiercely. "Off to the south, there are other islands. . . ."

The outrigger canoes lay drawn up on the beach like long silver fish. Silent as a shadow, the boy crossed the sand. His heart was hammering in his throat. Into the nearest canoe he flung half a dozen green drinking nuts, and his fish spear. He gave his puppy a brave heart. Then he picked up a paddle and called to Uri. The dog leaped into the bow. There was only Kiwi. Mafatu would miss his albatross. He scanned the dark sky for sight of the bird, then gave it up, and turned away.

The lagoon was as untroubled as a mirror. Upon its black face, the stars lay tracks of fire. The boy shoved off and climbed into the stern. Noiselessly he propelled the canoe forward, sending it half a length ahead with each thrust of his paddle. As he drew nearer to the barrier reef, the thunder of the surf increased. The old, familiar dread of it struck at his stomach's pit, and made him falter in his paddling.

The voices of the Old Ones were fainter and fainter now.

The reef thunder mounted: a long-drawn, hushed, yet mighty, sound that seemed to have its being not in the air above but in the very sea beneath. Out beyond lurked a terrifying world of water and wind. Out there lay everything most to be feared. The boy's hands tightened on his paddle. Behind him lay safety, security from the sea. What

matter if they jeered? For a second he almost turned back. Then he heard Kana's voice once more saying, "Mafatu is a coward."

The canoe entered the race formed by the ebbing tide. It caught up the small craft in its churn, swept it forward like a chip on a millrace. No turning back now. . .

The boy was aware of a sudden whir and fury in the sky above, a beat of mighty wings. Startled, he glanced upward. There was Kivi, his albatross. Mafatu's heart lifted. The bird circled slowly in the moonlight, its wings edged with silver. It hovered for a moment just over the bow of the canoe, then it rose easily, lightly in its effortless flight. Out through the passage in the reef. Out into the open ocean.

Mafatu gripped the steering paddle and followed.

Days passed on the open sea, where Mafatu and Uri faced the heat of the scorching sun and the dangers of a hurricane. Then one day Mafatu sighted a distant island. Using all his remaining strength, he managed to reach the island. For several days, Mafatu and Uri explored the island and found that it was deserted. He did, however, find enough food and water. Soon he built a small lean-to hut for shelter and a crude raft.

The days passed in a multitude of tasks that kept Mafatu busy from dawn till dark. His lean-to grew into a three-sided house with bamboo walls and a thatch of palm leaves. The fourth wall was open to the breezes of the lagoon. It was a trim little house and he was proud of it. A roll of woven mats lay on the floor; there was a shelf in the wall with three bowls cut from coconut shells; bone fishhooks dangled from a peg; there was a coil of tough sennit, many feet long; an extra *pareu* of tapa waterproofed with gum of the *artu* tree, for wet weather. All day long the wind played through the openings in the bamboo walls, and at night lizards scurried through the hatch with soft rustlings.

One morning, wandering far down the beach, Mafatu came upon a sheltered cove. His heart gave a leap of joy, for there, white-gleaming in the sun, was all that remained of the skeleton of a whale. It might not have meant very much to you or to me, but to Mafatu it meant knives and fishhooks galore, splinters of bone for darts and spears, a shoulder blade for an ax. It was a real treasure trove. The boy leaped up and down in his excitement. "Uri!" he shouted. "We're rich! Come! Help me drag these bones home!"

His hands seemed all thumbs in his eagerness. He tied as many bones as he could manage into two bundles. One bundle he shouldered himself. The other Uri dragged behind him. And

thus they returned to the camp site, weary, but filled with elation. Even the dog seemed to have some understanding of what this discovery meant. If not, he was at least infected with his master's high spirits. He leaped about like a sportive puppy, yapping until he was hoarse.

Now began the long process of grinding the knife and the ax. Hour after long hour, squatting before a slab of basalt, Mafatu worked and worked, until his hands were raw and blistered and the sweat ran down into his eyes. The knife emerged first, since that was the most imperative. Its blade was ten inches long, its handle a knob of joint.

It was sharp enough to cut the leaves of coconut trees, to slice off the end of a green nut. Ai, but it was a splendid knife! All Mafatu's skill went into it. It would be a fine weapon as well, the boy thought grimly, as he ground it down to a sharp point. Some sea robber had been breaking into his bamboo trap, and he was going to find out who the culprit was! Probably that old tiger shark who was always cruising around . . . just as if he owned the lagoon!

Fishing with a line took too long when you were working against time. Mafatu could not afford to have his trap robbed. Twice it had been broken into, the stout bamboos crushed, and the contents eaten. It was the work either of a shark or of an octopus. That was certain. No other fish was strong enough to snap the tough bamboo.

Mafatu's mouth was set in a grim line as he worked on his knife. That old tiger shark— undoubtedly *he* was the thief! Mafatu had come to recognize him, for every day when the boy went out with his trap, the shark, larger than all the others, was circling around, wary and watchful. The other sharks seemed to treat the tiger shark with respect.

Hunger alone drove Mafatu out to the reef to set his trap. He knew that if he was to maintain strength to accomplish all that lay ahead, he must have fish to add to his diet of fruit. But often as he set his trap far out by the barrier reef, the tiger shark would approach, roll over slightly in passing, and the cold gleam of its eye filled Mafatu with dread and anger.

"Wait, you!" the boy threatened darkly, shaking his fist at the *ma'o*. "Wait until I have my knife! You will not be so brave then, Ma'o. You will run away when you see it flash."

But the morning that the knife was finished, Mafatu did not feel so brave as he would have liked. He hoped he would never see the tiger shark again. Paddling out to the distant reef, he glanced down from time to time at the long-bladed knife where it hung about his neck by a cord of sennit. It wasn't, after all, such a formidable weapon. It was only a knife made by a boy from a whale's rib.

Uri sat on the edge of the raft, sniffing at the wind. Mafatu always took his dog along, for Uri howled unmercifully if he were left behind. And Mafatu had come to rely upon the companionship of the little yellow

dog. The boy talked with the animal as if he were another person, consulting with him, arguing, playing when there was time for play. They were very close, these two.

This morning as they approached the spot where the fish trap was anchored, Mafatu saw the polished dorsal of the hated tiger shark circling slowly in the water. It was like a triangle of black basalt, making a little furrow in the water as it passed.

"*Aiá,* Ma'o!" the boy shouted roughly, trying to bolster his courage. "I have my knife today, see! Coward, who robs traps, catch your own fish!"

The tiger shark approached the raft in leisurely fashion, it rolled over slightly, and its gaping jaws seemed to curve in a yawning grin. Uri ran to the edge of the raft, barking furiously. The hair on the dog's neck stood up in a bristling ridge. The shark, unconcerned, moved away. Then with a whip of its powerful tail, it rushed at the bamboo fish trap and seized it in its jaws. Mafatu was struck dumb. The tiger shark shook the trap as a terrier might shake a rat. The boy watched fascinated, unable to make a move. He saw the muscles work in the fish's neck as the great tail thrashed the water to fury. The trap splintered into bits, while the fish within escaped only to vanish into the shark's mouth. Mafatu was filled with helpless rage. The hours he had spent making that trap. . . . But all he could do was shout threats at his enemy.

Uri was running from one side of the raft to the other, furious with excitement. A large wave sheeted across the reef. At that second, the dog's shift in weight tipped the raft at a perilous angle. With a helpless yelp, Uri slid off into the water. Mafatu sprang to catch him, but he was too late.

Instantly the shark whipped about. The wave swept the raft away. Uri, swimming frantically, tried to regain it. There was desperation in the brown eyes — the puzzled eyes so faithful and true. Mafatu strained forward. His dog. His companion. . . . The tiger shark was moving in slowly. A mighty rage stormed through the boy. He gripped his knife. Then he was over the side in a clean-curving dive.

Mafatu came up under his enemy. The shark spun about. Its

rough hide scraped the flesh from the boy's shoulder. In that instant Mafatu stabbed deep, deep into the white belly of the shark. There was a terrific impact. Water lashed to foam. Stunned, gasping, the boy fought for life and air.

It seemed that he would never reach the surface. Aué, his lungs would burst! . . . At last his head broke water. Putting his face to the surface, he saw the great shark turn over, fathoms deep. Blood flowed from the wound in its belly. Instantly gray shapes—other big sharks— rushed in, tearing the wounded tiger shark to pieces.

Uri! Where was he? Mafatu saw his dog then. Uri was trying to pull himself up on the raft. Mafatu seized him by the scruff and dragged him up to safety. Then he caught his dog to him and hugged him close, talking to him foolishly. Uri yelped for joy and licked his master's cheek.

It wasn't until Mafatu reached shore that he realized what he had done. He had killed the *ma'o* with his own hand, with naught but a bone knife. He could never have done it for himself. Fear would have robbed his arm of all strength. He had done it for Uri, his dog. And he felt suddenly humble, with gratitude.

Should Mafatu return to his home now? Or should he first find proof to convince his father that he has truly conquered his fear? By reading the rest of Armstrong Sperry's book, CALL IT COURAGE, *you will be able to find out what Mafatu did.*

ABOUT THE AUTHOR

When Armstrong Sperry was a young boy, his great-grandfather, who had followed the sea for many years, liked to fill the ears of the boy with tales of tropic islands, of pearl lagoons, and of sharks and whales.

Many years later, when the boy grew up, he followed his great-grandfather's adventurous trail to some of the remotest parts of the world. He even lived for some months on an island in the South Pacific. That visit gave him much of the background for his book *Call It Courage.* His experiences have found their way into the more than thirty books that Mr. Sperry has written and illustrated for young people.

Some of his books are about places, such as the Arctic, the Antarctic, or the Amazon River. Others are about historical figures, such as John Paul Jones and Christopher Columbus. Some, such as *Storm Canvas,* are stories which combine his interest in the past and distant places with his love of adventure and the sea.

Armstrong Sperry was born in 1897 in New Haven, Connecticut. Before he began his travels around the world, he served in the Navy in World War I. Later, he studied art at the Yale School of Art, the Art Students League in New York, and in France. He felt he could best combine his interests by writing and illustrating children's books.

MORE BOOKS TO ENJOY

CHILDREN OF GREEN KNOWE, *by Lucy M. Boston*
A lonely boy in an old English house has adventures with the ghosts of the children who lived in the house in the past.

THE TERRIBLE CHURNADRYNE, *by Eleanor Cameron*
In an unusual kind of mystery, two children in a present-day California coastal town search for a strange prehistoric sea monster.

MY SIDE OF THE MOUNTAIN, *by Jean George*
A city boy spends a year living alone on a mountain in the Catskills. The story of his survival in the wilderness is an exciting one.

THE FIRST BOOK OF AFRICA, *by Langston Hughes*
This book tells the fascinating history of Africa from its ancient civilizations to the development of its new nations. Many photographs illustrate the text, which describes the great variety in the land, the people, and resources of Africa.

THE SECRET OF THE ONE-EYED MOOSE, *by Milton Lomask*
A boy's curiosity gets him involved in a search for a spy in a secret government project.

MY MOTHER IS THE MOST BEAUTIFUL WOMAN IN THE WORLD, *by Becky Reyher*
A little girl tries to find her mother in this Russian folk tale.

GLOSSARY

Some of the words in this book may have pronunciations or meanings you do not know. This glossary can help you by telling you how to pronounce those words and by telling you the meanings with which those words are used in this book.

You can find out the correct pronunciation of any glossary word by using the special spelling after the word and the pronunciation key at the bottom of each left-hand page. Reading Skill Lesson I in this book will tell you how.

The pronunciation key below is a full one that shows how to pronounce each consonant and vowel in a special spelling. The pronunciation key at the bottom of each left-hand page is a shortened form of the full key.

Full Pronunciation Key

Consonant Sounds

/b/	bib	/k/	kick	/sh/	ship, dish
/ch/	church	/l/	lid, needle	/t/	tight
/d/	deed	/m/	man, am	/th/	thin, path
/f/	fast, off	/n/	no, sudden	/*th*/	this, bathe
/g/	gag	/ng/	thing	/v/	vine, cave
/h/	hat	/p/	pop	/w/	with
/hw/	which	/r/	roar	/y/	yes
/j/	judge	/s/	see, miss	/z/	zebra, size
		/zh/	pleasure		

Vowel Sounds

/ă/	pat	/ĭ/	pit	/ou/	out
/ā/	pay	/ī/	pie	/o͝o/	took
/âr/	care	/îr/	fierce	/o͞o/	boot
/ä/	father	/ŏ/	pot	/ŭ/	cut
/ĕ/	pet	/ō/	toe	/ûr/	turn
/ē/	be	/ô/	paw, for	/yo͞o/	use
		/oi/	noise		

/ə/   about, silent, pencil, lemon, circus

This pronunciation key is adapted from *The American Heritage Dictionary of the English Language,* published by American Heritage Publishing Co., Inc. and Houghton Mifflin Company.

A

ab • do • men (ăb′də-mən, ăb-dō′mən). 1. The part of the body in mammals that contains the stomach and organs of the digestive system. 2. In insects, the major rear section of the body.

a • beam (ə-bēm′). At one side of a ship; running at right angles to the keel of a ship.

ab • sorb (ăb-sôrb′, -zôrb′). 1. To drink in; soak in or up. 2. To hold one's interest completely; occupy the full attention, interest, or time of.

a • bun • dance (ə-bŭn′dəns). 1. A great amount or quantity. 2. Fullness to overflowing.

a • byss (ə-bĭs′). A large, deep opening in the earth's surface; a deep hole; a bottomless pit.

ac • com • mo • da • tion (ə-kŏm′ə-dā′shən). 1. A convenience; anything that supplies or fills a need. 2. Lodgings; room and food.

ac • cu • mu • late (ə-kyōōm′yə-lāt′). To gather; pile up; collect.

ac • cu • ra • cy (ăk′yər-ə-sē). Exactness; correctness.

ac • knowl • edg • ment (ăk-nŏl′ĭj-mənt). 1. An admittance or recognition that something is true or right. 2. An expression of thanks for something that has been received. 3. An answer or response in return for something done.

ad • just (ə-jŭst′). 1. To arrange; set in correct order. 2. To change so as to match or fit. 3. To regulate.

af • fec • tion • ate (ə-fĕk′shən-ĭt). Having or showing a warm, friendly feeling; loving; tender.

af • flic • tion (ə-flĭk′shən). 1. A condition of pain, sorrow, or suffering. 2. A cause of pain or suffering.

af • ford (ə-fôrd′, ə-fōrd′). 1. To be able to meet the expense of. 2. To be able to spare or give up. 3. To provide or supply: *Swimming affords good exercise.*

a • fore • men • tioned (ə-fôr′mĕn′shənd, ə-fōr′-). Mentioned or talked about before; mentioned previously.

aft (ăft, äft). Located toward or near the stern or rear section of a boat.

a • gape (ə-gāp′, ə-găp′). In a state of wonder or amazement, often with the mouth wide open.

ag • ile (ăj′əl, ăj′īl). Quick; active; able to move easily and quickly.

air • i • ly (âr′ə-lē). Gaily; in a light, high-spirited manner.

al • fal • fa (ăl-făl′fə). A plant, similar to clover, used as food for horses or cattle.

a • li • as (ā′lē-əs, āl′yəs). Otherwise known as.

al • ler • gic (ə-lûr′jĭk). Having a sensitiveness to certain substances that can cause itching, sneezing, or illness.

al • lot (ə-lŏt′). To give out or distribute to individuals or groups.

al • lude (ə-lōōd′). To refer indirectly to something.

am • ble (ăm′bəl). To walk at a gentle, easy pace or gait; to walk slowly.

a • mi • a • ble (ā′mē-ə-bəl). Friendly; good-natured; pleasant; agreeable.

ă pat/ ā pay/ âr care/ ä father/ ĕ pet/ ē be/ ĭ pit/ ī pie/ îr fierce/ ŏ pot/ ō toe/ ô paw, for/ oi noise/ ou out/ ŏŏ took/ ōō boot/ th thin/ *th* this/ ŭ cut/ ûr turn/ yōō use/ ə about/ zh pleasure

an•a•tom•ic (ăn′ə-tŏm′ĭk). Having to do with the study of the structure of a plant or animal.

an•es•the•sia (ăn′ĭs-thē′zhə). Loss of sensation or feeling brought about by disease or by a medical drug.

an•i•mat•ed (ăn′ə-mā′tĭd). 1. Lively; spirited. 2. Made so as to seem alive and moving.

an•i•ma•tion (ăn′ə-mā′shən). 1. The act of giving life to. 2. Liveliness; spirit.

an•te•lope (ăn′tə-lōp′). A kind of animal, somewhat like a small deer, found in Africa and Asia.

an•tic•i•pate (ăn-tĭs′ə-pāt′). 1. To expect or look forward to. 2. To foresee and plan ahead of time. 3. To cause to happen in advance.

an•tic•i•pa•tion (ăn-tĭs′ə-pā′shən). Expectation; the act of looking forward to.

an•vil (ăn′vĭl). A heavy block of iron or steel, with a smooth, flat top on which metals are shaped by hammering.

ap•pren•tice (ə-prĕn′tĭs). 1. A person who works under a skilled worker to learn a particular skill or trade. 2. Any beginner; learner.

ar•dent (är′dənt). Very enthusiastic and eager.

as•a•fet•i•da (ăs′ə-fĕt′ə-də). A yellow-brown, bitter material obtained from the roots of certain plants, formerly used in medicine.

as•sault (ə-sôlt′). An attack, usually violent or sudden.

as•sume (ə-soōm′). 1. To take for granted. 2. To take up; receive. 3. To pretend; put on falsely. 4. To undertake.

as•sur•ance (ə-shoōr′əns). 1. Freedom from doubt; self-confidence; certainty. 2. A statement which gives a feeling of trust or inspires confidence.

as•tron•o•mer (ə-strŏn′ə-mər). A scientist who studies the universe, especially the position, motion, size and composition of the stars, planets, and other heavenly bodies.

a•tro•cious (ə-trō′shəs). 1. Extremely cruel, savage, or brutal. 2. Extremely bad.

au•di•to•ri•um (ô′də-tôr′ē-əm, -tōr′ē-əm). A building or a large hall in a school, theater, or other building in which an audience can assemble.

B

bal•ance (băl′əns). 1. An instrument for weighing, such as a scale. 2. An equality between two sides or parts. 3. A steady position; firmness. 4. Anything that remains or is left over. 5. To hold steady or to keep an object steady.

bal•sam (bôl′səm). 1. An oily or gummy substance obtained from certain trees or shrubs and used as a base for cough syrups and perfumes. 2. Any tree from which balsam is obtained: *the balsam fir*.

ban•ner (băn′ər). A flag.

ban•yan (băn′yən). A large East Indian tree whose roots grow out of the branches down into the ground to form new trunks.

bark•er (bär′kər). A person who stands outside a show, as in a circus, and tries to attract people into the show with loud, colorful sales talk.

bark•er (bär′kər). 1. A workman who removes bark from trees. 2. A machine that removes the bark from logs.

bar•ley•corn (bär′lē-kôrn′). The seed or grain of barley.

bar•ri•cade (băr′ə-kād′, băr′ə-kād′). A barrier, such as a wall or fence, made for protection against attack or for blocking the way.

ba•salt (bə-sôlt′, bā′sôlt′). A hard, dark, volcanic rock.

beak•er (bē′kər). A glass with a wide mouth and usually with a spout or lip for pouring.

beam (bēm). Any long, heavy piece of metal or timber used as a support in a building or ship.

beast of burden. Any animal used for carrying heavy loads.

beck•on (bĕk′ən). 1. To signal another person by a motion of the hand. 2. To attract as if with gestures; to have a strong attraction.

be•drag•gle (bĭ-drăg′əl). To make wet and limp.

bel•low (bĕl′ō). 1. To roar, as a bull. 2. To shout in a deep voice.

bent (bĕnt). 1. Crooked. 2. On a fixed course of action; determined: *He was bent on refusing my help.* 3. Headed toward; on the way to.

berth (bûrth). 1. A built-in bed or bunk in a ship or train. 2. A place at a wharf for a ship to anchor. 3. A job or a position of employment, especially on a ship.

bid•ding (bĭd′ĭng). 1. An invitation; command; a demand that something be done. 2. An offer of a price, as at an auction.

bill•ing (bĭl′ĭng). The order of importance of performers as shown by the position and type size in which their names are listed on programs or advertisements.

block•ade (blŏ-kād′). 1. The closing off of a city, coast, or harbor to traffic by enemy ships or forces. 2. To set up a blockade against.

blub•ber (blŭb′ər). The thick layer of fat between the skin and muscle layers of whales and other sea mammals.

blun•der•buss (blŭn′dər-bŭs′). A type of short gun with a wide muzzle, once used to shoot at close distances without taking careful aim.

boar (bôr, bōr). A wild hog or pig; a male hog or pig.

bo•ni•to (bə-nē′tō). A salt-water fish related to tuna or mackerel.

bound (bound). 1. A leap or jump. 2. A bounce. 3. To leap forward or upward; to spring.

bound (bound). 1. A boundary; limit. 2. To provide a limit to. 3. To border on another state, country, or place.

bow (bou). The forward part of a ship, boat, or airship.

bow (bou). 1. A forward bend of the head or body. 2. To bend or curve downward; stoop.

bowl•er (bō′lər). A man's hat that has a narrow, rounded brim and a round-shaped top.

brand (brănd). 1. A mark made with a hot iron to show ownership. 2. A trademark identifying a product or manufacturer.

brawn (brôn). Firm, strong muscles; muscular power.

breach (brēch). 1. A hole or opening. 2. A breaking of a law or promise. 3. The leaping of a whale from the water. 4. To make a hole in; break

ă pat/ ā pay/ âr care/ ä father/ ĕ pet/ ē be/ ĭ pit/ ī pie/ îr fierce/ ŏ pot/ ō toe/ ô paw, for/ oi noise/ ou out/ o͝o took/ o͞o boot/ th thin/ *th* this/ ŭ cut/ ûr turn/ yo͞o use/ ə about/ zh pleasure

through. 5. To leap from the water. Used in describing a whale.

breech • es (brĭch′ĭz). Trousers or pants that gather just below the knee.

brogue (brōg). Speech, characteristic especially of the Irish or Scotch in the pronunciation of English.

brow (brou). 1. The forehead. 2. The top edge of any steep slope.

brute (brōot). 1. Any animal other than man. 2. Of or having to do with beasts. 3. Without reason or intelligence. 4. Savage; cruel.

bulk (bŭlk). 1. Great size or mass. 2. The greater part of something.

bun • ker (bŭng′kər). A large storage bin, as for storing coal on a ship.

Bun • sen burn • er (bŭn′sən bûr′nər). A type of burner in which gas and air are mixed and burned at the end of a short metal tube. It produces a very hot flame.

bu • reau (byŏŏr′ō). 1. A chest of drawers, usually having a mirror. 2. A government department.

bur • lap (bûr′lăp′). A rough, coarse material, usually made from hemp or jute, used in making bags or coverings.

bur • ro (bûr′ō, bŏŏr′ō). A small donkey used as a pack animal.

C

cal • cu • late (kăl′kyə-lāt′). 1. To figure out by mathematics. 2. To make an estimate of.

cal • cu • la • tion (kăl′kyə-lā′shən). 1. The art of figuring out by mathematics. 2. The answer arrived at by calculating.

ca • per (kā′pər). 1. A playful leap or hop; a skip. 2. To leap or frisk about; frolic.

cap • size (kăp′sīz′, kăp-sīz′). To overturn; upset; turn bottom side up.

car • pet • bag (kär′pĭt-băg′). An old-fashioned suitcase made out of carpet material.

cav • i • ty (kăv′ə-tē). A hole or a hollow place.

ce • leb • ri • ty (sə-lĕb′rə-tē). A famous person.

cen • tu • ry (sĕn′chə-rē). 1. A period of 100 years. 2. A group of 100 things.

cham • ber (chām′bər). 1. A room, especially a bedroom. 2. A hall where an assembly or council meets; the assembly itself.

cham • ber • lain (chām′bər-lĭn). The person who is responsible for managing the household of a nobleman or king.

charg • er (chär′jər). A horse trained for battle.

chef (shĕf). A cook.

chis • el (chĭz′əl). 1. A metal tool with a sharp edge used to cut and shape stone, wood or metal. 2. To shape or cut with a chisel.

chuck wag • on (chŭk wăg′ən). A wagon carrying food and equipped with a stove for cooking.

clam • ber (klăm′ər, klăm′bər). To climb with difficulty using both hands and feet; scramble.

clam • or (klăm′ər). A loud uproar; confused shouting; a great outcry of voices.

clip • per (klĭp′ər). A fast sailing vessel having a large sail area and tall masts.

cock • pit (kŏk′pĭt′). An area toward the rear part of a boat, lower than the rest of the deck, from which the boat is steered.

col • lide (kə-līd′). To bump into; come against another object with full force.

colo • nel (kûr′nəl). A rank in the military; a military officer ranking just below brigadier general.

com • bus • tion (kəm-bŭs′chən). A process of burning.

com • mem • o • rate (kə-mĕm′ə-rāt′). To honor the memory of.

com • mis • sion (kə-mĭsh′ən). To give a person or persons the authority to act for someone else.

com • pact (kəm-păkt′, kŏm-, kŏm′păkt′). 1. Arranged closely together; firm or solid. 2. Not very wordy; brief.

com • pre • hend (kŏm′prĭ-hĕnd′). 1. To understand. 2. To include or take in.

con • sole (kən-sōl′). To comfort; cheer in time of grief, defeat, or trouble.

con • sul • ta • tion (kŏn′səl-tā′shən). 1. The act of consulting, or seeking advice and information. 2. A conference to discuss or share opinions.

con • ta • gious (kən-tā′jəs). 1. Catching; spreading. 2. Passing from one person to another. 3. Carrying or capable of carrying disease.

con • tempt (kən-tĕmpt′). Scorn; disgust; the feeling that an act or a person is mean or low.

cop • pice (kŏp′ĭs). A thicket; a grove of young or small trees.

cor • al (kôr′əl, kŏr′əl). 1. The stone-like skeleton of a very tiny animal usually found in warm seas and oceans. Coral may be red, pink, white, or even black. 2. The hard, rocklike structure formed by such animals.

cor • ral (kə-răl′). A pen in which horses or cattle are kept.

cor • re • spond (kôr′ə-spŏnd′, kŏr′-). 1. To be equal to something else in amount or use; to be in agreement with; equal. 2. To be similar.

court • i • er (kôr′tē-ər, kōr′-, -tyər). A person who is often present or in attendance at the court of a king or ruler.

crev • ice (krĕv′ĭs). A narrow crack or opening.

cri • sis (krī′sĭs). A time of danger or anxiety.

crit • i • cize (krĭt′ə-sīz′). 1. To judge; present an opinion about. 2. To find fault with.

cudg • el (kŭj′əl). A club or short, thick stick used as a weapon.

cu • li • nar • y (kyōō′lə-nĕr′ē, kŭl′ə-). Of or having to do with the art of cooking or the kitchen.

cul • ture (kŭl′chər). 1. The customs and religious ideas of a particular people; their way of life. 2. Knowledge and good taste gained through training.

cu • ri • os • i • ty (kyŏŏr′ē-ŏs′ə-tē). 1. A desire to know or learn, especially about something new or strange. 2. Something strange, rare, or unusual.

curt (kûrt). Rudely brief or abrupt, as in speech or manner.

cur • vi • lin • e • ar (kûr′və-lĭn′ē-ər). Formed of or bordered by curved lines.

cut • purse (kŭt′pûrs′). A person who steals from pockets.

D

da • ta (dā′tə, dăt′ə, dä′tə). Information; facts.

ă pat/ ā pay/ âr care/ ä father/ ĕ pet/ ē be/ ĭ pit/ ī pie/ îr fierce/ ŏ pot/ ō toe/ ô paw, for/
oi noise/ ou out/ ŏŏ took/ ōō boot/ th thin/ *th* this/ ŭ cut/ ûr turn/ yōō use/ ə about/
zh pleasure

de • bate (dǐ-bāt′). 1. To consider both sides or opposing points; discuss; take part in a formal discussion of a question. 2. To dispute or argue about.

de • cep • tive (dǐ-sĕp′tǐv). Misleading; that which misleads or is meant to mislead.

de • ci • pher (dǐ-sī′fər). To decode; make out or find the meaning of.

de • fraud (dǐ-frôd′). To cheat someone out of something; to swindle.

deft (dĕft). Skillful and quick.

de • fy (dǐ-fī′). 1. To challenge or dare. 2. To disregard or openly oppose. 3. To withstand.

de • ject • ed (dǐ-jĕk′tǐd). Unhappy; sad; depressed.

de • lir • i • ous (dǐ-lîr′ē-əs). 1. Wild; raving; temporarily out of one's mind, often as the result of a high fever. 2. Excited; wildly happy.

des • o • late (dĕs′ə-lǐt). 1. Lonely; deserted. 2. Dismal; gloomy.

de • spair (dǐ-spâr′). 1. Complete lack of hope. 2. To lose all hope.

des • per • ate (dĕs′pər-ǐt). 1. Reckless or violent because all hope seems gone. 2. Nearly hopeless; driven to take any risk.

des • per • a • tion (dĕs′pə-rā′shən). A feeling of hopelessness that often leads to a reckless act: *In desperation he tried to rob the store.*

des • pi • ca • ble (dĕs′pǐ-kə-bəl, dǐ-spǐk′-). Mean; despised; deserving of hatred.

di • ag • no • sis (dī′əg-nō′sǐs). The identification and naming of a disease by its signs.

dip • lo • mat (dǐp′lə-măt′). 1. A person who is skillful in dealing with other people; a person with tact. 2. A person skilled in conducting affairs between nations.

dis • mal (dǐz′məl). Dark; dreary; miserable or gloomy; causing gloom.

dis • may (dǐs-mā′). 1. A sudden or complete loss of courage in the face of trouble or danger. 2. To make anxious or afraid; fill with dread. 3. To discourage or trouble greatly.

dis • pos • al (dǐs-pō′zəl). 1. A way of getting rid of something as by selling it or throwing it away. 2. A device for getting rid of or disposing of something, as garbage.

dis • pute (dǐs-pyo͞ot′). 1. To argue against; object to; debate. 2. To question the truth of; to doubt.

dis • rep • u • ta • ble (dǐs-rĕp′yə-tə-bəl). Not honorable; not respectable in character or appearance; having a bad reputation.

dis • tend (dǐs-tĕnd′). To stretch; enlarge; swell. 2. To cause to expand.

dis • tin • guished (dǐs-tǐng′gwǐsht). Outstanding; notable; well-known.

dis • tress (dǐs-trĕs′). 1. Suffering; sorrow; unhappiness. 2. To cause suffering to; to worry or upset.

do • min • ion (də-mǐn′yən). 1. The power to rule or govern; highest authority. 2. An area governed by an individual.

don (dŏn). To dress in; to put on.

dor • sal (dôr′səl). 1. Of, toward, on, in, or near the back. 2. Having to do with the main fin on the back of a fish or sea mammal.

dou • bloon (dŭ-blo͞on′). A gold coin issued and used by the Spanish many years ago.

draw (drô). 1. To pull something toward or after one. 2. To cause to flow forth: *a pump drawing water.* 3. To take in (air): *the chimney draws well.* 4. To make a picture of (with lines). 5. To describe.

drow • sy (drou′zē). Sleepy.

dry-shod (drī′shŏd′). With dry shoes or feet.

duff (dŭf). A flour pudding boiled in a cloth bag or steamed: *plum duff.*

duff (dŭf). Decaying leaves and branches covering a forest floor.

dun • geon (dŭn′jən). A small, dark room in a jail, usually underground.

E

eaves (ēvz). That part of a roof that overhangs the side of a building.

ebb tide (ĕb tīd). The period of a tide between high water and the following low water.

ec • sta • sy (ĕk′stə-sē). A state of extreme happiness; joy; bliss.

ef • fec • tive (ĭ-fĕk′tĭv). Producing or able to produce a desired result.

E • gypt (ē′jĭpt). A country in northeast Africa.

e • la • tion (ĭ-lā′shən). A feeling of happiness, joy, or triumph.

eld • er (ĕl′dər). 1. An older person. 2. A person who occupies an important position of authority in certain churches.

el • e • ment (ĕl′ə-mənt). The simplest part of which something is made up; a simple substance.

el • e • men • ta • ry (ĕl′ə-mĕn′tə-rē, -trē). Having to do with simple, beginning rules or first stages of anything.

e • merge (ĭ-mûrj′). 1. To come out; appear; rise up. 2. To become obvious. 3. To come into existence.

em • i • nent (ĕm′ə-nənt). Well-known; important; respected; of high rank or position.

e • mo • tion (ĭ-mō′shən). Any strong feeling, such as joy, anger, happiness, or sorrow.

en • list (ĕn-lĭst′, ĭn-). To join or enroll; especially, to join a branch of the military voluntarily.

en • snarl (ĕn-snärl′). 1. To become involved in a tangled situation. 2. To become tangled or confused.

en • try (ĕn′trē). 1. A place through which to enter; an entrance way. 2. The inclusion of an item in a diary, list, or other record. 3. An item that has been entered.

en • vi • ous (ĕn′vē-əs). Having a feeling of discontent at another's good fortune which one wishes for himself.

e • ra (îr′ə, ĕr′ə). 1. A period in history that dates from some particular event or discovery. 2. A period of time noted for its new or different characteristics or events.

er • mine (ûr′mĭn). 1. White fur of an animal. 2. A weasel whose fur becomes white during the winter months.

er • rant (ĕr′ənt). 1. Roving, especially in search of adventure; wandering. 2. Mistaken; wrong; straying from the right course.

er • rat • ic (ĭ-răt′ĭk). 1. Unusual or irregular in growth or progress; odd. 2. Without a fixed or regular course; wandering.

es • cort (ĕs′kôrt′). 1. A person who accompanies another out of honor, courtesy, or for protection. 2. (ĕs-kôrt′). To accompany as an escort.

ă pat/ ā pay/ âr care/ ä father/ ĕ pet/ ē be/ ĭ pit/ ī pie/ îr fierce/ ŏ pot/ ō toe/ ô paw, for/ oi noise/ ou out/ ŏŏ took/ o͞o boot/ th thin/ *th* this/ ŭ cut/ ûr turn/ yo͞o use/ ə about/ zh pleasure

es•teem (ĕ-stēm′, ĭ-stēm′). 1. Respect. 2. To value very highly; have a high opinion of.

et•i•quette (ĕt′ə-kĕt′, -kĭt). The set of rules established for behavior in society or public life.

e•vac•u•ate (ĭ-văk′yōō-āt′). To withdraw from; move out of; leave empty.

ewe (yōō). A female sheep.

ex•cep•tion (ĕk-sĕp′shən, ĭk-). 1. A leaving out; omission. 2. An objection or criticism.

ex•cur•sion (ĕk-skûr′zhən, ĭk-). 1. A trip, usually for pleasure. 2. The party of people who take a trip.

ex•ert (ĕg-zûrt′, ĭg-). 1. To put forth or use; use one's strength. 2. To put (oneself) into great effort. 3. To bring to bear; exercise.

ex•ile (ĕg′zīl′, ĕk′sīl′). 1. One who is or has been separated from his country. 2. To expel or banish someone from his own native country.

ex•pe•di•tion (ĕk′spə-dĭsh′ən). 1. A journey for a purpose, such as discovery. 2. The group of people or ships making such a journey.

ex•ploit (ĕks′ploit′). 1. A daring act; brave deed. 2. (ĕk-sploit′). To use to the greatest possible advantage.

ex•port (ĕks′pôrt′, -pōrt′). 1. A product sent out of a country for trade or sale. 2. The act of sending goods out of a country.

F

fa•cil•i•ty (fə-sĭl′ə-tē). 1. Skill; ease; freedom from difficulty. 2. *Usually plural.* Something that makes some action or work easier: *the facilities of*

a library. 3. *Usually plural.* A place used by or serving people, as a school or restaurant.

fal•ter (fôl′tər). 1. To hesitate; waver. 2. To stumble; move unsteadily.

fash•ion (făsh′ən). 1. Custom or style, as of a dress. 2. A manner or way: *Do it in this fashion.* 3. To give shape or form to something.

fa•tigue (fə-tēg′). Exhaustion; weariness.

fe•ro•cious (fə-rō′shəs). Savage; cruel; fierce.

fer•ry (fĕr′ē). A kind of boat for carrying cars, people, and goods across a small or narrow body of water.

fig•ment (fĭg′mənt). An imaginary or unreal creation of the mind.

fig•u•rine (fĭg′yə-rēn′). A small figure or statue that has been carved or formed from wood, glass, or metal.

fil•a•ment (fĭl′ə-mənt). 1. A slender thread. 2. The very thin wire that becomes heated and gives off light in a light bulb.

fin•ish (fĭn′ĭsh). 1. The end or conclusion. 2. The material used in surfacing or finishing something: *a wax finish.* 3. To bring to an end; complete.

firm (fûrm). 1. Solid. 2. Not easily moved. 3. Definite; fixed: *a firm bargain.*

firm (fûrm). A business company.

flask (flăsk, fläsk). A bottle with a narrow neck, often having a broad, flat body.

fledg•ling (flĕj′lĭng). 1. A young bird that is just learning to fly. 2. A young, inexperienced person.

fleet (flēt). A group of warships operating together under one command.

fleet (flēt). Quick; fast; rapid.

flog (flŏg). To beat or whip severely.

floun•der (floun′dər). 1. To struggle without much success. 2. To move clumsily, as to regain balance.

flour • ish (flûr′ĭsh). 1. An act of waving. 2. A bold and sweeping gesture; a dramatic action; showy display. 3. A decorative stroke in handwriting. 4. To grow well. 5. To succeed. 6. To wave vigorously.

flu • ent (flōō′ənt). 1. Having ease or skill in the use of a language: *a fluent speaker*. 2. Effortless; flowing easily. 3. Flowing smoothly.

fluke (flōōk). One of the two parts of a whale's tail.

fore • bear (fôr′bâr′, fōr′-). 1. To keep oneself from. 2. To be tolerant or patient.

for • bear • ance (fôr-bâr′əns). 1. Patience; self-control; holding back. 2. The act of refraining from something.

fore • cas • tle (fōk′səl, fôr′kăs′əl, -käs′əl, fōr′-). 1. The part of a vessel located at the bow, in front of the foremast. 2. The forward part of a vessel in which the sailors live.

fore • man (fôr′mən, fōr′-). A man who has charge of a group of workers, as at a factory or ranch.

forge (fôrj, fōrj). 1. A furnace where metals are heated. 2. To shape metal by heating and hammering.

for • mal (fôr′məl). 1. Done with ceremony; with regard to social customs; stiff. 2. Stiffly or strictly following fixed rules or patterns.

for • mi • da • ble (fôr′mə-də-bəl). 1. Arousing fear or alarm: *He has a formidable look on his face.* 2. Difficult to defeat or undertake.

frag • ile (frăj′əl, -īl′). Frail; delicate; easily broken.

frank • ly (frăngk′lē). Honestly; speaking plainly; in an open manner.

fray (frā). 1. A fight; commotion; noisy quarrel. 2. A heated dispute or contest.

fray (frā). To unravel; wear away.

fre • quen • cy (frē′kwən-sē). 1. The repeated occurrence of an event. 2. The rate of occurrence, as of an electric current or radio wave.

fret (frĕt). 1. To cause to be uneasy. 2. To be troubled; to worry.

frig • ate (frĭg′ĭt). A square-rigged sailing warship of medium size with three masts.

frock coat (frŏk kōt). A man's double breasted jacket that reaches almost to the knees.

frol • ic (frŏl′ĭk). 1. Gaiety; merriment. 2. To romp or play about in a frisky way; romp.

frus • trate (frŭs′trāt′). To prevent from carrying out a task; defeat or block.

fu • gi • tive (fyōō′jə-tĭv). A person who is fleeing some place or some situation; a runaway.

fur • row (fûr′ō). 1. A long, narrow, shallow trench made in the ground by a plow or other tool. 2. Any rut or groove similar to this.

G

Gael • ic (gā′lĭk). Of or relating to the Celts (of Scotland or Ireland) or their languages.

gait (gāt). A manner of running or walking.

gal • le • on (găl′ē-ən). A large, sailing ship often having three masts and two

---

ă pat/ ā pay/ âr care/ ä father/ ĕ pet/ ē be/ ĭ pit/ ī pie/ îr fierce/ ŏ pot/ ō toe/ ô paw, for/ oi noise/ ou out/ ŏŏ took/ ōō boot/ th thin/ *th* this/ ŭ cut/ ûr turn/ yōō use/ ə about/ zh pleasure

or more decks, used during the 15th and 16th centuries by Spain and other countries.

gal • va • nize (găl′və-nīz′). To coat with a layer of zinc for protection: *galvanized iron.*

gang • ly (găng′glē). Tall, thin, and ungraceful; awkwardly built.

garb (gärb). Style of clothing or dress; fashion; clothing.

gar • land (gär′lənd). A wreath made of flowers or leaves.

gaunt (gônt). 1. Thin; bony. 2. Gloomy and desolate.

ges • ture (jĕs′chər). 1. A motion of some part of the body, such as hands or head, that expresses a feeling or idea. 2. To make gestures.

gin • ger • ly (jĭn′jər-lē). Cautiously; very carefully.

glare (glâr). 1. A fixed, angry stare. 2. To stare fiercely or angrily. 3. To give off a brilliant, dazzling light.

glee (glē). Joy; happiness.

glen (glĕn). A small valley.

gloat (glōt). To regard or think about something with mean pleasure or evil delight: *to gloat over one's test results.*

gnash (năsh). To grind the teeth together.

gob • bet (gŏb′ĭt). A portion or piece, usually of raw meat.

Gold • en Fleece (gōl′dən flēs). In Greek mythology, a fleece (or animal hide) of gold guarded by a dragon.

gorge (gôrj). A deep, narrow ravine or passage between two mountains; a canyon.

gout (gout). A painful inflammation or swelling in the joints of the body.

grat • i • tude (grăt′ə-tōōd′, -tyōōd′). Appreciation; thankfulness.

gris • ly (grĭz′lē). Horrible; gruesome.

grouse (grous). A game bird with feathered legs.

H

har • poon (här-pōōn′). A spear with a pointed or barbed end, used for hunting large fish or whales.

haugh • ty (hô′tē). Proud and vain; self-satisfied and scornful of others.

haunch (hônch). The part of the body in man and animals around the hips.

hear • say (hîr′sā′). Information heard from another.

heath • er (hĕ*th*′ər). A low evergreen shrub with small pinkish flowers, found in Europe and Asia.

hid • e • ous (hĭd′ē-əs). Horrible; very ugly.

hi • me • ne (hē′mə-nā). 1. A gathering place for men in a Polynesian village. 2. a native song or hymn of Polynesia.

hin • drance (hĭn′drəns). 1. The act of holding back, slowing down, or delaying. 2. Someone or something that holds back or delays; an obstruction.

hoax (hōks). A joke or trick, often meant to fool the public.

hold (hōld). 1. To grasp. 2. To support; keep up. 3. To delay: *Try to hold him until the police arrive.* 4. To believe.

hold (hōld). The inside of a ship below the deck where the cargo is stored.

hol • low (hŏl′ō). 1. A valley. 2. A gap or space within something. 3. Having nothing inside; not solid: *a hollow wall.*

horde (hôrd, hōrd). A crowd; multitude; swarm, as of people, animals or insects.

how • dah (hou′də). A seat, usually with a covering above, which is placed on an elephant's back for people to ride on.

hum•ble (hŭm′bəl). Meek; not proud; modest.

hum•mock (hŭm′ək). 1. A small rounded hill. 2. A piece of land rising above the level of a neighboring marsh.

husk•y (hŭs′kē). Rugged and strong.

hus•ky (hŭs′kē). A large, strong dog with thick fur, used by Eskimos to pull sleds.

I

i•dler (īd′lər). One who is lazy; not active.

il•le•gal (ĭ-lē′gəl). Not legal; forbidden by law.

im•bue (ĭm-byoo′). 1. To fill, or inspire, as with ideals or emotions. 2. To saturate or fill, as with color or dye.

im•mac•u•late (ĭ-măk′yə-lĭt). Pure; without blemish or stain; clean.

im•pend•ing (ĭm-pĕn′dĭng). Likely or due to happen soon.

im•per•a•tive (ĭm-pĕr′ə-tĭv). Unavoidable; urgently necessary.

im•pe•ri•al (ĭm-pîr′ē-əl). Concerning, or having to do with, an emperor or an empire; royal.

im•pos•tor (ĭm-pŏs′tər). A deceiver; one who takes the identity of someone else.

im•promp•tu (ĭm-prŏmp′too, -tyoo). On the spur of the moment; without any preparation or rehearsal.

im•pul•sive (ĭm-pŭl′sĭv). Hasty; acting on the spur of the moment without careful thought.

in•ci•dent (ĭn′sə-dənt). A happening; event; an occurrence.

in•cli•na•tion (ĭn′klə-nā′shən). 1. A personal preference or liking: *an inclination for sports.* 2. A tendency: *the inclination of wages to rise.* 3. A slope or slant: *the inclination of the earth's axis.* 4. A nod; bow: *an inclination of the head.*

in•cred•i•ble (ĭn-krĕd′ə-bəl). Unbelievable.

in•dex fin•ger (ĭn′dĕks′ fĭng′gər). The finger next to the thumb.

in•dif•fer•ence (ĭn-dĭf′ər-əns). Unconcern; lack of interest for; not caring one way or another.

in•dulge (ĭn-dŭlj′). To yield or give in to one's own or another's desire or desires.

in•fe•ri•or (ĭn-fîr′ē-ər). 1. Lower in importance or rank. 2. Not of good quality. 3. Located under or beneath.

in•fer•nal (ĭn-fûr′nəl). Horrible; terrible.

in•or•di•nate (ĭn-ôrd′n-ĭt). Excessive; too great; going beyond reasonable limits.

in•sig•nif•i•cant (ĭn′sĭg-nĭf′ĭ-kənt). 1. Not important. 2. Small. 3. Meaningless.

in•spect (ĭn-spĕkt′). To look at carefully; examine.

in•stal•la•tion (ĭn′stə-lā′shən). 1. The act of setting in position and connecting or adjusting for use. 2. A military base or camp.

in•stinc•tive (ĭn-stĭngk′tĭv). Of or having to do with a natural tendency or impulse that leads a person or an animal to behave in a certain way.

ă pat/ ā pay/ âr care/ ä father/ ĕ pet/ ē be/ ĭ pit/ ī pie/ îr fierce/ ŏ pot/ ō toe/ ô paw, for/ oi noise/ ou out/ oŏ took/ oo boot/ th thin/ *th* this/ ŭ cut/ ûr turn/ yoo use/ ə about/ zh pleasure

532

in • tel • li • gence (ĭn-tĕl′ə-jəns). 1. Superior powers of mind. 2. The ability to acquire and use knowledge. 3. Secret information; especially, such information about an enemy. 4. The work of gathering such information. 5. An office or staff employed in such work.

in • ter • pret • er (ĭn-tûr′prə-tər). One who translates orally from one language into another.

in • ter • val (ĭn′tər-vəl). 1. The period or space between events. 2. The distance or space between two objects or points.

in • tox • i • cate (ĭn-tŏk′sĭ-kāt′). 1. To make drunk. 2. To make extremely excited.

in • tri • cate (ĭn′trĭ-kĭt). Having many involved parts; complicated.

in • val • u • a • ble (ĭn-văl′yōō-ə-bəl). Precious; priceless; too valuable to have a price.

is • let (ī′lĭt). A very small island.

J

jack • al (jăk′əl, -ôl′). A kind of wild dog that supposedly hunts animals for lions and tigers, and then eats what they leave.

jeer (jîr). To mock; scoff; make fun of with insulting words.

jeop • ard • ize (jĕp′ər-dīz′). To place or put in danger.

jib (jĭb). A small triangular sail extending forward from the foremast of a boat.

jut (jŭt). To project; stick out.

K

keel (kēl). The main support timber or steel bar running lengthwise along the center of a ship's bottom.

L

lad • en (lād′n). Burdened; loaded down; heavy.

lady-in-waiting. A lady of a court who is appointed to serve a queen or princess.

la • goon (lə-gōōn′). A shallow body of water, usually separated from the sea by sandbars or coral reefs.

landing-stage. A dock; a pier.

lank • y (lăng′kē). Tall, thin, and awkwardly ungraceful.

lat • i • tude (lăt′ə-tōōd′). Distance north or south of the equator, measured in degrees.

leaf (lēf). 1. One of the flat, thin, usually green parts that grow from the stem or roots of a plant or tree. 2. One of the sheets of paper in a book or magazine, each side of which is a page. 3. A very thin sheet of metal: *gold leaf.*

lee (lē). 1. The side or part protected from the wind; the side of a ship away from the wind. 2. Any place sheltered from the wind.

let (lĕt). 1. To allow. 2. To rent or lease: *let a room to the lady.*

let (lĕt). An obstacle or obstruction.

li • an • a (lē-ăn′ə, -ä′nə). A climbing plant that roots in the ground and is characteristic of both temperate and tropical rain forest climates.

lithe (lī*th*). Able to bend easily; flexible.

loft • y (lôf′tē). 1. Very high; towering. 2. Proud; thinking too well of oneself.

loot (lōōt). Booty; spoils; plunder; stolen goods.

lope (lōp). To run or ride with a steady, easy gait or pace.

lore (lôr). Facts or knowledge about a particular subject.

low (lō). 1. Not tall. 2. Below normal height. 3. Of small value. 4. In a low position, level, or space.

low (lō). The sound uttered by cattle; a moo.

lunge (lŭnj). 1. Any sudden forward movement or plunge. 2. To plunge forward quickly. 3. To make a thrust or pass, as with a sword.

lurch (lûrch). 1. A sudden roll to one side. 2. To stagger. 3. To roll or pitch suddenly, as a ship during a storm.

M

mag • pie (măg′pī). A bird having a long tail, and black, blue, or green coloring with white markings, noted for its chattering call.

ma • lar • i • a (mə-lâr′ē-ə). A disease marked by attacks of chills, fever, and sweating and spread by the bite of a certain kind of mosquito.

mal • let (măl′ĭt). A short-handled hammer usually with a wooden head used for driving other tools.

mane (mān). The long, thick hair growing about the necks of animals such as horses and lions.

man • tel (măn′təl). A shelf above a fireplace.

man • u • script (măn′yə-skrĭpt′). A book, article, or other composition which is written by hand or typewritten.

mar • ble (mär′bəl). 1. A kind of limestone used for building or sculpture. 2. A ball of glass used by children in a game. 3. To color or streak in imitation of marble.

mast (măst, mäst). A long pole rising from the deck of a ship that supports the sails and rigging.

mast • head (măst′hĕd′, mäst′-). The top of a ship's mast.

max • im (măk′sĭm). A proverb; a rule of conduct expressed in a few words, as: *Don't count your chickens before they hatch.*

me • nag • er • ie (mə-năj′ə-rē, mə-năzh′-). A collection of live wild animals on exhibition.

me • sa (mā′sə). A hill with a flat top and steeply sloping sides.

mes • quite (mĕs-kēt′, mə-skēt′). A spiny shrub generally found in Mexico and the southwestern part of the United States.

mess (mĕs). 1. Disorder; state of confusion. 2. A group of people who usually take their meals together. 3. The place where such meals are served. 4. A meal eaten there.

mill (mĭl). 1. A building that has machinery for grinding grain into flour or meal. 2. To grind or break down into smaller pieces in a mill. 3. To move about in a disorderly fashion.

mill • er (mĭl′ər). 1. One who owns, runs, or works in a mill for grinding grain. 2. A moth whose wings look as though they might be covered with flour or dust.

mill • race (mĭl′rās′). The current of water that drives a mill wheel.

min • ute (mĭn′ĭt). A unit of time equal to 60 seconds.

mi • nute (mī-nōōt′, -nyōōt′, mĭ-). 1. Tiny. 2. Very careful in small details: *minute examination.*

mis • sion • ar • y (mĭsh′ə-nĕr′ē). A person

ă pat/ ā pay/ âr care/ ä father/ ĕ pet/ ē be/ ĭ pit/ ī pie/ îr fierce/ ŏ pot/ ō toe/ ô paw, for/ oi noise/ ou out/ ŏŏ took/ ōō boot/ th thin/ *th* this/ ŭ cut/ ûr turn/ yōō use/ ə about/ zh pleasure

who is sent out to do religious or charitable work in some foreign country.

mite (mīt). One of the group of tiny spider-
like animals that often live on plants
or other animals.

mite (mīt). 1. A very small amount of
money. 2. Any very small thing.

mock (mŏk). 1. To make fun of; laugh
at. 2. Not real, but made to look so:
a mock battle.

mod•est (mŏd′ĭst). 1. Not bold. 2. Having a low or moderate opinion of oneself or one's talents or abilities. 3. Shy;
reserved. 4. Quiet and humble in appearance.

mon•arch (mŏn′ərk). A supreme ruler;
a king, queen, or emperor.

mor•tar (môr′tər). A bowl made of a
hard material in which substances are
crushed with a pestle.

mount (mount). 1. To get up on; to place
oneself upon. 2. To rise or ascend.

mount (mount). A mountain or hill.

mul•ti•tude (mŭl′tə-tōod′, -tyōod′). A
great crowd; many persons or things;
a great number.

muz•zle (mŭz′əl). 1. The nose, jaw,
and mouth region of an animal. 2. A
covering for an animal's head to keep
it from biting. 3. The forward end of
a gun.

N

naught (nôt). Nothing; zero; the figure
0.

nav•i•gate (năv′ə-gāt′). To travel on,
across, or through.

nec•tar (nĕk′tər). 1. A delicious drink;
in Greek myths, a sweet drink of the
gods. 2. A sweet liquid present in many
flowers.

neigh (nā). 1. The cry made by a horse.
2. To utter the cry of a horse.

neu•tral (nōo′trəl, nyōo′-). 1. Not leaning toward or actively taking either
side in a dispute. 2. Belonging to neither
side nor party: *on neutral ground.* 3.
Occupying a middle position; not one
thing or the other.

nine•pins (nīn′pĭnz′). A game, somewhat like bowling, using nine large
wooden pins.

non•cha•lant (nŏn′shə-länt′). 1. Without self-consciousness or embarrass-
ment. 2. Not concerned or excited;
appearing casual or indifferent.

non•de•script (nŏn′dĭ-skrĭpt′). Of no
particular kind or type; hard to describe.

nov•el (nŏv′əl). A fictitious story usually
of book length, often about imaginary
people and events.

numb (nŭm). Without feeling or sensation. 2. Stunned, as from shock or strong
emotion.

O

o•blige (ə-blīj′). 1. To cause to do or
stop from doing something. 2. To satisfy
the wishes of. 3. To make grateful:
They were obliged to him for his help.
4. To do a service or favor.

of•fi•cial (ə-fĭsh′əl). 1. One who holds
an office or position. 2. Of or having
to do with an office or post of authority.

om•i•nous (ŏm′ə-nəs). 1. Seeming to
threaten evil, like an evil omen or sign.
2. Menacing; threatening.

op•po•nent (ə-pō′nənt). A rival; a foe;
someone who opposes another or others
in a battle or contest.

or•a•tor (ôr′ə-tər, ŏr′-). A person who
speaks in public. 2. Any skillful public
speaker.

or•deal (ôr-dēl′). A very terrible or
trying experience; a severe test.

or • der • ly (ôr′dər-lē). 1. A male worker in a hospital who helps the doctors and nurses. 2. Neat; in order; well-organized; well-behaved.

Or • lon (ôr′lŏn′). A synthetic, or man-made fiber, used for clothing or sails.

out • rig • ger (out′rĭg′ər). A canoe with a supporting float attached to the side to keep it from tipping over.

out • wit (out-wĭt′). To get the better of someone by cleverness; fool; exceed in cleverness or cunning.

o • ver • se • er (ō′vər-sē′ər). 1. One who keeps watch over and directs the work of others, especially laborers. 2. A supervisor or superintendent.

o • zone (ō′zōn′). 1. An unstable form of oxygen, present in the air in small quantities. 2. Fresh, pure air.

P

pact (păkt). An agreement; a treaty.

page (pāj). 1. A boy who carries messages, as in a hotel. 2. A boy in training to become a knight, who served as an attendant to a knight or a master. 3. A boy who attends or serves a person of rank. 4. To summon or call a person by name.

page (pāj). One side of a leaf of a book, letter, newspaper, or magazine.

paint • er (pān′tər). A person who paints.

pain • ter (pān′tər). A rope fastened to the forward part of a boat for tying it to a dock.

pal • lor (păl′ər). Lack of color; paleness of face.

pan • da • nus (păn-dā′nəs, -dăn′əs). A palmlike tree and shrub of southeastern Asia having large roots and narrow leaves.

pan • o • ram • a (păn′ə-răm′ə, -rä′mə). 1. A complete view in all directions over a wide area. 2. A scene that unrolls little by little as it is being looked at.

pan • ta • loons (păn′tə-lōōnz′). Trousers; tight pants with straps under the foot, worn in former times.

pan • to • mime (păn′tə-mīm′). 1. A play in which the actors use no words. 2. To act out or express oneself in gestures alone, without speaking.

par • a • pet (păr′ə-pĭt, -pĕt′). A low wall of stone at the edge of a roof, built as a defense.

pa • re • u (pä′rā-ōō′). A piece of cloth worn in Polynesia that wraps around the body, like a skirt or loincloth.

pas • sé (pă-sā′). Old-fashioned; out-of-date.

pas • tor (păs′tər, päs′-). 1. A minister or priest in charge of a church or a parish. 2. *Rare.* A shepherd.

pel • i • can (pĕl′ĭ-kən). A water bird; a fish-eater with webbed feet and a large bill under which is a pouch for holding fish.

pen • e • trate (pĕn′ə-trāt′). 1. To get into or to get through. 2. To enter or force a way into.

pen • sion (pĕn′shən). An allowance or sum of money paid to a person who has retired from work after many years.

pen • sive (pĕn′sĭv). Seriously thoughtful; dreamily thoughtful.

per • il (pĕr′əl). Risk; danger; exposure to injury or destruction.

ă pat/ ā pay/ âr care/ ä father/ ĕ pet/ ē be/ ĭ pit/ ī pie/ îr fierce/ ŏ pot/ ō toe/ ô paw, for/ oi noise/ ou out/ o͝o took/ o͞o boot/ th thin/ *th* this/ ŭ cut/ ûr turn/ yo͞o use/ ə about/ zh pleasure

per‧pet‧u‧al (pər-pĕch′ōō-əl). 1. Eternal; everlasting. 2. Continuing without interruption.

pes‧tle (pĕs′əl, pĕs′təl). A pounding instrument with a blunt end that druggists use to crush substances to a powder.

pe‧yo‧te (pā-ō′tē). A kind of American cactus.

phan‧tom (făn′təm). 1. Something apparently seen, heard, or sensed, but having no physical reality; a ghost. 2. Something that appears only in the mind.

pike (pīk). A long spear once used by the infantry.

pike (pīk). A long, fresh-water fish with a large mouth and a long, narrow, pointed head.

pitch (pĭch). 1. The level of a sound's highness or lowness. 2. To set at a certain pitch. 3. To throw; toss. 4. To stumble around. 5. To slope downward. 6. To fix the level of.

pit‧i‧ful (pĭt′ĭ-fəl). Arousing sympathy or pity.

pol‧i‧ti‧cian (pŏl′ə-tĭsh′ən). 1. A person skilled in or involved in the management of government affairs. 2. One who holds or seeks a political office.

pol‧len (pŏl′ən). The yellowish, powder-like grains found in seed plants and used to fertilize the seeds of a plant.

po‧made (pə-mād′, -mäd′, pō-). A perfumed ointment for the hair or scalp.

pon‧der (pŏn′dər). To think carefully.

por‧ce‧lain (pôrs′lĭn, pōrs′-, pôr′sə-lĭn, pōr′sə-). A hard, white material, thin enough to allow light to pass through.

pos‧ses‧sion (pə-zĕsh′ən). 1. Something which is owned or possessed by someone. 2. Foreign territory under a nation's control.

pot‧ter (pŏt′ər). To keep busy in a useless way.

pre‧car‧i‧ous (prĭ-kâr′ē-əs). Risky; dangerous; uncertain.

prec‧i‧pice (prĕs′ə-pĭs). A very steep or overhanging mass of rock, such as a crag or the face of a cliff.

pre‧dic‧a‧ment (prĭ-dĭk′ə-mənt). An unpleasant, dangerous, or embarrassing situation.

pre‧scrip‧tion (prĭ-skrĭp′shən). An order; a doctor's direction for the preparation and use of a certain medicine.

pre‧sum‧a‧ble (prĭ-zōō′mə-bəl). Likely; probable; quite likely to happen.

pre‧sume (prĭ-zōōm′). 1. To take for granted. 2. To suppose. 3. To undertake without permission; dare.

pre‧vi‧ous (prē′vē-əs). Earlier; taking place before.

prim‧i‧tive (prĭm′ə-tĭv). Belonging to or coming from very early times; original; first. 2. Simple or crude.

proc‧ess (prŏs′ĕs′, prō′sĕs′). 1. A series of operations in the production of something. 2. To prepare or treat by a special method or procedure.

pro‧file (prō′fīl′). 1. A side view of an object, especially of a human head. 2. A short biographical sketch. 3. A table or graph showing the results of a test, as for example an aptitude test.

prompt (prŏmpt′). 1. To move a person to action. 2. To inspire or to suggest. 3. To give a cue to (someone who has forgotten his lines).

pro‧pel‧lant (prə-pĕl′ənt). The fuel plus the oxygen that is used to move or propel a rocket.

pros‧per (prŏs′pər). To be successful; flourish; thrive.

pros‧trate (prŏs′trāt′). 1. To make oneself bow or kneel down. 2. Lying face downward; flat on the ground.

pro‧test (prə-tĕst′, prō-tĕst′, prō′tĕst′). To object strongly: *I will protest to the* *mayor about the closing of the play-ground.*

prov•en•der (prŏv′ən-dər). 1. Dry food (such as corn or hay) used for feeding animals. 2. *Informal.* Any food.

pul•let (po͝ol′ĭt). A young hen, usually less than one year old.

punt (pŭnt). 1. An open boat with a flat bottom, used in shallow waters. 2. To propel a boat with a long pole.

Q

Quak•er (kwā′kər). A member of a religious group called the Society of Friends.

ques•tion•naire (kwĕs′chə-nâr′). A printed form containing a set of questions used for gathering information.

quiv•er (kwĭv′ər). To shake; tremble.

R

ra•di•us (rā′dē-əs). 1. A straight line that joins the center of a circle with any point on its circumference. 2. An area that has certain limits.

rang•y (rān′jē). Having slender, long limbs.

rank (răngk). 1. A class; position; standing. 2. A position determined by merit or attainment.

ran•som (răn′səm). 1. Payment asked or paid for setting someone free. 2. Payment demanded or paid for the return of something valuable. 3. To pay a ransom.

rap•ture (răp′chər). A very strong feeling of joy, pleasure, or delight.

rat•line (răt′lĭn). One of many small ropes fastened across the shrouds of a ship serving as the steps of a rope ladder.

re•ac•tion (rē-ăk′shən). An action, attitude, or feeling caused by some happening.

realm (rĕlm). 1. A kingdom. 2. Any region, area or field: *the realm of science.*

re•cep•ta•cle (rĭ-sĕp′tə-kəl). A container; something that holds or contains.

reck•on (rĕk′ən). 1. To count; find the number or value of. 2. To rely or depend. 3. To think.

re•cov•er (rē-kŭv′ər). 1. To get back; obtain again after losing. 2. To regain a former state, as of health, after sickness or misfortune.

red tape. Too much attention to small details and rules resulting in a great waste of time.

reed (rēd). A kind of grass, having a hollow stem, that grows in wet places.

reef (rēf). A strip of rocks, sand, or coral that rises to or near the surface of a body of water.

re•flec•tive (rĭ-flĕk′tĭv). Thoughtful.

re•fuse (rĭ-fyo͞oz′). To decline to do, accept, give, or allow.

ref•use (rĕf′yo͞os). Trash; rubbish.

rel•ish (rĕl′ĭsh). 1. To enjoy; take pleasure in. 2. To like the flavor of.

re•luc•tant (rĭ-lŭk′tənt). Unwilling; hesitant: *reluctant to help.*

re•mote (rĭ-mōt′). Distant; far off; not close.

ren•dez•vous (rän′dā-vo͞o′, rän′də-). A meeting at a fixed place or time; a meeting by agreement.

ren•e•gade (rĕn′ə-gād′). 1. One who

ă pat/ ā pay/ âr care/ ä father/ ĕ pet/ ē be/ ĭ pit/ ī pie/ îr fierce/ ŏ pot/ ō toe/ ô paw, for/
oi noise/ ou out/ o͝o took/ o͞o boot/ th thin/ *th* this/ ŭ cut/ ûr turn/ yo͞o use/ ə about/
zh pleasure

gives up his religion, principles, cause, or group for another; a traitor. 2. An outlaw.

re·plen·ish (rǐ-plěn′ǐsh). To fill again; replace.

re·port (rǐ-pôrt′). 1. An account of something. 2. Rumor or gossip. 3. An explosive noise: *the rifle's report.* 4. To make or present an account of something. 5. To tell about.

rep·ri·mand (rěp′rə-mǎnd′, -mänd′). To scold sharply.

re·pul·sive (rǐ-pǔl′sǐv). Offensive; disgusting.

re·search (rǐ-sûrch′, rē′sûrch). 1. Careful study and investigation. 2. To study thoroughly.

re·sent·ment (rǐ-zěnt′mənt). A feeling of anger or ill will, usually arising from some personal injury, insult, or neglect.

re·serve (rǐ-zûrv′). 1. Something kept back, saved, or set aside for future use or special purpose. 2. To keep back or save for future use.

re·strain (rǐ-strān′). To hold back; to keep from doing something; to control.

ret·i·nue (rět′n-ōō′, rět′n-yōō′). A group of people who serve a person of rank or position.

rev·e·la·tion (rěv′ə-lā′shən). 1. Something that is revealed or made known. 2. The act of making something known.

rev·e·nue (rěv′ə-nōō, -nyōō). The income that a government receives from taxes, duties, and other sources.

re·vive (rǐ-vīv′). 1. To bring back to life. 2. To make fresh; restore.

ridge (rǐj). 1. Any raised strip, as in cloth. 2. A long hill or range of hills or mountains. 3. The long, narrow, upper section of something: *ridge of a wave.*

rid·i·cule (rǐd′ə-kyōōl). To make fun of.

ri·dic·u·lous (rǐ-dǐk′yə-ləs). Silly; deserving of laughter.

rig·ging (rǐg′ǐng). The ropes and chains that support and move the masts and sails of a ship.

ri·val (rī′vəl). A person who wants the same thing as someone else; an opponent or competitor.

role (rōl). 1. A part played by an actor in a play. 2. The character a person plays in real life: *the role of father.*

rouse (rouz). 1. To awaken from sleep. 2. To stir up or excite.

rou·tine (rōō-tēn′). 1. A fixed, regular way of doing something. 2. Regular; habitual. 3. Dull; lacking in interest or originality.

S

sab·o·tage (săb′ə-täzh′). 1. The destruction of the property of an employer by dissatisfied employees. 2. In time of war, the damaging or destroying of property by the enemy.

sa·loon (sə-lōōn′). 1. A bar; a place where liquors are sold or drunk. 2. A large room or hall for receptions or public entertainment.

sal·vage (săl′vǐj). 1. The rescue of a ship or its crew or cargo from fire or shipwreck. 2. The act of saving any property from loss. 3. To save (a ship, or its cargo, for example) from loss or destruction.

sap (săp). The watery liquid that flows through a plant.

sap (săp). 1. To destroy by digging under. 2. To weaken gradually.

sar·cas·tic (sär-kăs′tǐk). Sneering; unkind or mocking.

saun·ter (sôn′tər). To walk in a slow, casual way; to ramble; to stroll.

sa·vor·y (sā′vər-ē). Pleasing to the taste or smell.

scan·dal·ous (skăn′də-ləs). Shocking;

disgraceful; giving a bad example; outrageous.

scant (skănt). 1. Not quite enough; meager: *scant supplies.* 2. Being just short of the measure needed or mentioned: *a scant three miles.*

scheme (skēm). 1. A plan; skillful plot. 2. An arrangement of something according to a plan or design.

scim•i•tar (sĭm′ə-tər, -tär′). A short Oriental sword with a curved blade.

scoun•drel (skoun′drəl). A mean or dishonest person.

scow (skou). A large boat with a flat bottom.

scram•ble (skrăm′bəl). 1. To move or climb hurriedly, especially on the hands and knees. 2. To mix or throw together in a confused away.

scraw•ny (skrô′nē). Skinny; lean; thin; bony.

scruff (skrŭf). The back part of the neck; the loose skin on the back of the neck.

scull (skŭl). 1. A long oar that is twisted from side to side over the stern of a boat to propel it. 2. To move a boat with a scull or sculls.

scul•ler•y (skŭl′ə-rē). A room off the kitchen where dishwashing and other kitchen chores are done.

sculp•tor (skŭlp′tər). A person who sculptures; especially an artist who works in stone or metal.

sculp•ture (skŭlp′chər). 1. The art of making figures or shapes as by carving wood, chiseling marble, modeling clay, or casting in metal. 2. A work of art created in this manner. 3. To form by shaping or carving.

sea ur•chin (sē ûr′chĭn). A small, sea animal whose body is covered by a spiny shell and who lives on the ocean bottom.

sec•tor (sĕk′tər, -tôr′). 1. A part of a circle shaped somewhat like a piece of pie. 2. A part or a division of something.

self-im•posed (sĕlf′ ĭm-pōzd′). Something put upon oneself; something voluntarily assumed.

sen•nit (sĕn′ĭt). A braided cord or a fabric made of braided rope yarns.

se•rene (sĭ-rēn′). Calm; quiet; peaceful; dignified.

set (sĕt). 1. To place. 2. To mount. 3. To cause to sit. 4. To arrange tableware upon a table. 5. To disappear below the horizon.

set (sĕt). 1. A group of persons or things connected by or collected for their similar appearance or interest: *a chess set.* 2. The scenery that is created for a program or show of some kind.

shear (shîr). To shave; cut the hair, fleece, or wool from: *to shear a sheep.*

ship (shĭp). To travel on a ship; to transport, whether by ship, train, or truck, goods from one place to another.

shroud (shroud). 1. One of the ropes which help to support a mast of a ship. 2. A cloth used to wrap a body for burial.

shun (shŭn). To avoid; keep away from.

side-wheel•er (sīd′ hwēl′ər). A steamboat that has a paddle wheel on either side.

sig•nif•i•cant (sĭg-nĭf′ĭ-kənt). 1. Having or expressing a meaning; meaningful. 2. Having or expressing a hidden meaning; suggestive: *a significant glance.* 3. Important; valuable; notable.

ă pat/ ā pay/ âr care/ ä father/ ĕ pet/ ē be/ ĭ pit/ ī pie/ îr fierce/ ŏ pot/ ō toe/ ô paw, for/ oi noise/ ou out/ o͝o took/ o͞o boot/ th thin/ *th* this/ ŭ cut/ ûr turn/ yo͞o use/ ə about/ zh pleasure

silt (sĭlt). Fine particles of soil or earth carried in water or deposited by water, such as a river.

si • mul • ta • ne • ous (sī′məl-tā′nē-əs). At the same time.

singe (sĭnj). To burn the edge or outside of; to burn slightly; scorch.

skep • ti • cal (skĕp′tĭ-kəl). Doubting; questioning; disbelieving.

slime (slīm). Soft, moist, slippery mud; muck.

smart (smärt). 1. A sharp, stinging sensation; pain. 2. To cause a sharp, stinging pain.

smol • der (smōl′dər). To burn with little smoke and no flame.

smug • gle (smŭg′əl). To bring things in or take things out of a country illegally without paying lawful taxes for them.

sol • emn (sŏl′əm). 1. Sober; serious; grave; *a solemn expression.* 2. Done with full ceremony.

sore • ly (sôr′lē, sōr′-). 1. Painfully; causing distress or sadness. 2. Greatly; extremely: *His skill was sorely needed.*

sour • dough (sour′dō′). An old-time settler or prospector, especially in Alaska and northwestern Canada.

spec • ta • tor (spĕk′tā-tər). 1. A person who looks on at an event without taking part. 2. One who attends and views a show, sports event, or the like.

spec • tral (spĕk′trəl). Ghostly.

spell (spĕl). A word or words supposedly having magical power.

spell (spĕl). 1. A short time. 2. A short turn of work: *a spell at the helm.* 3. A short distance.

spell • bound (spĕl′bound′). Fascinated.

spent (spĕnt). 1. Worn out; used up; exhausted. 2. Over with; come to an end.

sphe • roid (sfîr′oid′, sfĕr′-). A globe or ball-shaped object.

spiel (spēl). To speak easily and rapidly; talk excessively or at length.

spon • ta • ne • ous (spŏn-tā′nē-əs). Done naturally; not planned; done from impulse; happening without apparent cause.

spon • ta • ne • ous com • bus • tion (kəm-bŭs′chən). The bursting into flame of a substance because of heat produced within itself through chemical action.

squad • ron (skwŏd′rən). 1. A group or unit organized in formation. 2. A group of naval vessels. 3. A group organized to do a specific task.

sta • bil • i • ty (stə-bĭl′ə-tē). 1. Solidness; steadiness. 2. Firmness of purpose. 3. Reliability; dependability.

stam • pede (stăm′pēd′). 1. A wild running away of startled animals, especially cattle or horses. 2. To run away wildly and aimlessly.

star • board (stär′bərd). The right-hand side of a ship, as one faces forward.

star • dom (stär′dəm). The standing or status of an actor or entertainer recognized as a star.

state (stāt). 1. Position; condition of mind or being. 2. The nature of a person or thing. 3. A social position or rank. 4. A very formal or grand style of living or doing something.

stat • ure (stăch′ər). The natural height or growth of a person or animal.

stern (stûrn). 1. Firm and unyielding. 2. Serious in manner or appearance.

stern (stûrn). The rear part of a boat.

stir • rup (stûr′əp). A loop hung from either side of a horse's saddle to support the rider's foot in mounting and riding.

stoat (stōt). An ermine, especially when it has its brown summer coat.

stout (stout). 1. Determined, bold, brave. 2. Strong in body. 3. Powerful; forceful.

strat • e • gy (străt′ə-jē). 1. The art and science of planning and carrying on a war. 2. Skillful planning and management.

stride (strīd). 1. A single long step. 2. To walk with long steps, especially in a hasty or vigorous way.

struc • tur • al (strŭk′chər-əl). Of or having to do with the structure or the way something is built: its arrangement and make-up.

sub • or • bit • al (sŭb′ôr′bĭt-əl). Involving less than one orbit.

sub • sis • tence (səb-sĭs′təns). 1. Method or means of keeping alive. 2. Means of support; livelihood. 3. The minimum amount of clothing, food, and other requirements necessary to stay alive.

suc • cor (sŭk′ər). Help; aid; relief.

sul • len (sŭl′ən). 1. Silent because of bad temper or resentment; lack of sociability; morose; sulky. 2. Gloomy or somber.

su • pe • ri • or (sə-pîr′ē-ər). 1. Higher in rank or authority. 2. Better; of great excellence. 3. Showing that one feels he is better than others.

surf (sûrf). 1. The waves of the sea that splash on the shore. 2. The sound or roar of these waves.

surge (sûrj). To move forward with a strong rush, as a wave: *The crowd surged ahead.*

sur • ly (sûr′lē). Bad-tempered; abrupt; rude.

sur • vey (sər-vā′, sûr′vā′). 1. To look over; examine. 2. To measure for size and shape.

sus • pend (sə-spĕnd′). 1. To hang so as to allow free movement. 2. To cause to stop for a period of time; interrupt.

sus • pend • ed an • i • ma • tion (sə-spĕn′dĭd ăn′ə-mā′shən). A sleeping condition resembling death produced by temporarily stopping the vital functions, such as the heart or breathing.

sus • tain (sə-stān′). 1. To support; hold up in position; prop up. 2. To keep from sinking or giving way. 3. To supply with necessities or nourishment; provide for.

swell (swĕl). 1. A bulge; a swollen part. 2. An unbroken wave or series of waves. 3. To expand. 4. To increase in size or number.

swill (swĭl). To eat or drink greedily.

swiv • el (swĭv′əl). 1. A device that permits anything attached to it to turn freely or rotate. 2. To turn or rotate.

sym • pho • ny (sĭm′fə-nē). 1. A large orchestra. 2. A musical composition for orchestra having several parts. 3. Harmony, especially of sound or color; a pleasing combination of things.

syn • thet • ic (sĭn-thĕt′ĭk). Artificial; man-made; not genuine.

T

tam • bou • rine (tăm′bə-rēn′). A shallow, drumlike musical instrument having one side open and jingling metal disks around the edge, played by shaking or striking with the hand.

tank • ard (tăng′kərd). A large drinking cup with a hinged lid and a handle.

ta • pa (tä′pə) 1. The inner bark of a mul-

ă pat/ ā pay/ âr care/ ä father/ ĕ pet/ ē be/ ĭ pit/ ī pie/ îr fierce/ ŏ pot/ ō toe/ ô paw, for/
oi noise/ ou out/ ŏŏ took/ ōō boot/ th thin/ *th* this/ ŭ cut/ ûr turn/ yōō use/ ə about/
zh pleasure

berry tree. 2. A coarse cloth made from the bark of this tree, often decorated with colorful designs.

taunt (tônt). 1. A bitter or insulting remark; a jeer. 2. To mock.

tech • nique (tĕk-nēk′). 1. Skill in or method of handling tools or materials. 2. The skills one needs to learn in order to practice a certain activity.

ten • don (tĕn′dən). A band of tough tissue that connects a muscle with a bone.

thatch (thăch). 1. Plant stalks or leaves used for roofing. 2. To cover with or as if to cover with thatch.

thrive (thrīv). 1. To improve steadily; to prosper. 2. To grow well; flourish.

throng (thrŏng). 1. A large group of people gathered or crowded closely together. 2. To crowd into.

thwart (thwôrt). A seat across a boat on which the rower sits.

tights (tīts). A tight-fitting garment covering the legs and lower body, worn by performers such as dancers.

top • gal • lant (tə-găl′ənt, tŏp-). One of the sails on a sailing vessel; the mast above the topmast.

tor • rid (tôr′ĭd, tŏr′-). Very hot; burning.

tou • can (tōō′kăn′, -kän′). A fruit-eating tropical bird that is brightly colored and has a very large beak.

trans • fer (trăns-fûr′). 1. To shift from one person or place to another. 2. To convey a drawing, mural, or design from one surface to another.

trap • pings (trăp′ĭngz). 1. The decorative covering or harness once used on horses for ornamentation. 2. Articles of dress.

trawl • er (trô′lər). A boat used for fishing by means of dragging nets along the ocean floor.

tri • umph (trī′əmf). 1. Victory; success. 2. Joy over victory. 3. To win; be successful.

troup • er (trōō′pər). A member of a company of performers or actors.

trove (trōv). A find; a treasure; something of value discovered or found.

tum • ble-down (tŭm′bəl-doun′). Shaky; about to fall down.

tun • dra (tŭn′drə). A flat plain without trees, found in very cold countries.

tur • ret (tûr′ĭt). 1. A small tower, often at the corner of a building. 2. A low, heavily armored, rotating tower containing mounted guns and their crew, as on a warship or tank.

tus • sock (tŭs′ək). A clump of growing grass.

U

ul • cer • ate (ŭl′sə-rāt′). To become affected with a sore which opens and discharges pus.

un • daunt • ed (ŭn′dôn′tĭd, -dän′tĭd). Fearless; not discouraged or fearful.

un • in • hab • it • ed (ŭn′ĭn-hăb′ə-tĭd). Not lived in by anyone; having no permanent residents.

un • mo • lest • ed (ŭn′mə-lĕs′tĭd). Not disturbed or annoyed.

ur • chin (ûr′chĭn). A very poor, usually ragged child.

ur • gent (ûr′jənt). Needing immediate attention or action.

V

vague (vāg). 1. Not clear. 2. Not stating ideas clearly or precisely. 3. Not thinking clearly.

vain (vān). 1. Useless; unsuccessful. 2. Showing too much pride in one's appearance or accomplishments.

val • iant (văl′yənt). Brave; courageous.

va • por (vā′pər). Fine particles of moisture or matter floating in the air, as steam, fog, or smoke.

ven • ture (vĕn′chər). 1. To undertake something without being sure of its success; to dare. 2. To run the risk of. 3. To say or express at the risk of criticism or denial.

ves • try (vĕs′trē). A room in a church where vestments, robes, and other sacred objects are stored.

vet (vĕt). A veterinarian.

vet • er • i • nar • i • an (vĕt′ər-ə-nâr′ē-ən, vĕt′rə-). A person who is trained to treat the diseases and injuries of animals.

vex (vĕks). 1. To annoy; bother; provoke. 2. To confuse; puzzle.

vi • al (vī′əl). A small glass bottle or container for liquids.

vis • u • al • ize (vĭzh′o͞o-ə-līz). To form a mental image or picture of something.

vix • en (vĭk′sən). 1. A female fox. 2. A bad-tempered woman.

vol • ume (vŏl′yo͞om). 1. A book. 2. A large quantity or mass. 3. The size or extent of a three-dimensional object.

W

wa • ger-boat (wā′jər-bōt′). A light, racing, sculling boat used in contests between single scullers.

wail (wāl). To cry out; grieve over.

ward (wôrd). 1. A person, especially a child, under guardianship of the court or another person. 2. A large room in a hospital usually holding six or more patients. 3. One of the divisions of a city or town.

war • y (wâr′ē). Cautious; careful; watchful.

wash (wŏsh, wôsh). 1. A disturbance of water caused by the movement of a boat or a storm. 2. Material such as silt or mud which is carried and deposited by water.

weir (wîr). A small dam placed across a river or canal.

wel • ter (wĕl′tər). 1. A rolling movement. 2. A confused state of affairs. 3. A confused mass; a jumble.

whale (hwāl). A sea animal that looks like a huge fish.

whale (hwāl). To attack or strike.

witch • craft (wĭch′krăft′, -kräft′). Sorcery; black magic; the supernatural powers of a witch.

with • ers (wĭth′ərz). The high part of a horse's or other animal's back which is just behind the neck and above the shoulders.

woe • ful (wō′fəl). 1. Sad; sorrowful; full of grief. 2. Pitiful.

work (wûrk). 1. Any physical or mental effort that is intended to accomplish something. 2. Something made or done: *an author's latest work.* 3. To have a job or position. 4. To operate or cause to function. 5. To solve.

ă pat/ ā pay/ âr care/ ä father/ ĕ pet/ ē be/ ĭ pit/ ī pie/ îr fierce/ ŏ pot/ ō toe/ ô paw, for/ oi noise/ ou out/ o͝o took/ o͞o boot/ th thin/ *th* this/ ŭ cut/ ûr turn/ yo͞o use/ ə about/ zh pleasure